# Sedum of the Trans-Mexican Volcanic Belt:

## AN EXPOSITION OF TAXONOMIC METHODS

# *SEDUM* OF THE TRANS-MEXICAN VOLCANIC BELT:

## An Exposition of Taxonomic Methods

\*

### *BY* ROBERT T. CLAUSEN

*Cornell University*

*DRAWINGS BY* ELFRIEDE ABBE

*Comstock Publishing Associates*

*A Division of* CORNELL UNIVERSITY PRESS

*Ithaca, New York, 1959*

*First published 1959*

PRINTED IN THE UNITED STATES OF AMERICA

BY CAYUGA PRESS, INC.

# Preface

THE information in this book has accumulated over a period of twenty-four years. In that time, many people have helped this study of *Sedum*. In 1935, Herbert Hice Whetzel, Professor of Plant Pathology at Cornell University, had in his garden at Ithaca, N.Y., a large collection of hardy species of *Sedum*. In addition, he had in the conservatory of the Department of Floriculture another collection of tender species, mostly Mexican, which had been assembled by C. Lansing Seymour, amateur grower of *Sedum*. Many of the plants, both in the garden and in the conservatory, were labeled with the names under which they had been received from nurseries or other growers. Some of these names were correct, others were not. My first assignment when I went to work in the herbarium of Dr. Liberty Hyde Bailey in 1935 was to identify correctly and to clarify generally the nomenclature of the cultivated plants of *Sedum*, especially those in the collections at Ithaca. This practical interest in identification and nomenclature has continued throughout the study, but gradually the realization has come that *Sedum* is an excellent group of plants for studying fundamental biological problems. The easy propagation of the plants from small pieces of stems or even from single leaves makes possible the multiplication of individuals with the same genetic structure. These vegetative offshoots may then be grown simultaneously under diverse environmental conditions. From experimental studies comes a better understanding of variation and relationships. If universal principles exist concerning the organization and evolution of the organic world, they must apply to *Sedum* as well as to all other groups of plants and animals. Work on *Sedum* should lead toward a philosophy of classification, a technique of study, and the discovery of modes of evolution.

The study of *Sedum* in the Trans-Mexican Volcanic Belt is part of a more comprehensive investigation of all species of the genus. An immediate objective of the study in the volcanic belt is to learn the reason or reasons for the diversity of species there. I have had three opportunities to visit this interesting region. In 1943 I was in Mexico and northern Central America under the auspices of the Office of Experiment Stations of the United States Department of Agriculture for the purpose of studying yam beans (*Pachyrrhizus*). Although little time was available either for *Sedum* or for exploration in the volcanic belt, some preliminary observations were made. In 1949, with the aid of grants from the Penrose Fund of the American Philosophical Society and the Mary S. Andrews Research Fund of the Torrey Botanical Club, I studied *Sedum* in the Sierra Madre Oriental of Mexico. In order to clarify relationships of certain species, I spent a little time in the volcanic region. My longest period in the Trans-Mexican Volcanic Belt was in 1955-1956 when I had a John Simon Guggenheim Memorial Foundation fellowship. I am grateful to the Guggenheim Foundation, the American Philosophical Society, and the Torrey Botanical Club for their generous financial support.

Officials of the Mexican government have aided my studies in their country by granting necessary permits and by extending various courtesies. Especially I wish to express appreciation to Ing. Ricardo Acosta V., Ing. Esteban Uranga, Ing. José Rodríguez G., and Lic. Silvestre Aguilar, of the Secretaría de Agricultura y Ganadería, and to Agr. Celerino Escalante E., President of the Comité Nacional de Combate y Control de la Mosca Prieta de los Cítricos. Professors Maximino Martínez and Faustino Miranda, of the Instituto de Biología, have always been helpful and have permitted me to consult freely specimens in the herbarium of the Instituto. On my trips in the field many men and boys have accompanied and helped me. To all, I express my thanks. Particularly I am grateful to Messrs. Angel Ramírez de Arellano, J. L. Edwards, Marcelino P. López, and Carlos Palomé.

The staff of the American Embassy in the city of Mexico has given me valuable co-operation. Mr. John A. Hopkins, Agricultural Attaché at the time of my trip in 1949, and Mrs. Ana Gomez, Assistant Agricultural Attaché during my visit in 1955-1956, have both been very helpful. Likewise, Dr. W. E. Stone, in charge of the laboratory for Mexican Fruit

Fly Research, has given his time and help in problems relative to the transportation of living plants from areas infested with fruit flies. Mr. J. B. R. Leary and Mr. G. G. Becker, of the Bureau of Entomology and Plant Quarantine, have facilitated the inspection and passage of my living collections through the inspection stations at Laredo, Texas, and Hoboken, N.J.

Before my trip in 1955, Mr. E. J. Alexander, of the New York Botanical Garden, provided valuable information concerning locations for certain species of *Sedum*. Other similar information was also obtained from labels accompanying herbarium specimens. For the privilege of studying specimens under their jurisdiction I am grateful to the curators of the Britton Herbarium at the New York Botanical Garden, the herbarium of the United States National Museum, the Pringle Herbarium of the University of Vermont, and the herbarium of the Bailey Hortorium at Cornell University.

For space in the greenhouses at Ithaca and for experimental plots in the garden I am grateful to the successive chairmen of the Department of Botany, Drs. Wiegand, Knudson, and Banks, and of the Department of Floriculture, Drs. White, MacDaniels, and Seeley. The many men who have cared for the plants have made possible the experimental studies at Ithaca. Miss Elfriede Abbe has made most of the drawings and diagrams; Miss Florence Mekeel has prepared the drawings of *Sedum longipes* ssp. *longipes;* Mr. Howard Lyon has taken many photographs; Mr. W. R. Fisher took the photograph of *S. nussbaumerianum;* and Dr. Charles Uhl has provided valuable information about chromosomes. Miss Abbe has also prepared an outline map of the Trans-Mexican Volcanic Belt, using as a basis the information on the American Geographical Society's Millionth Maps of Hispanic America. I am indebted to the Society for permission to use the data on its maps. I am grateful as well to the several persons who have typed the manuscript for me, especially to Miss Arlene Walli who has done the major part of this work.

Finally, the members of my family—my wife, Edna, and children, Eric, Joanna, Thomas, and Heidi—all have made their distinctive contributions to the study of *Sedum*. Whatever is good about the work is the result of this co-operative effort. If any parts are not good, I must assume full responsibility.

ROBERT T. CLAUSEN

*Department of Botany*
*Cornell University*
*May 30, 1959*

# Contents

# *Sedum* of the Trans-Mexican Volcanic Belt:

## AN EXPOSITION OF TAXONOMIC METHODS

CHAPTER I

# Introduction

MORE species of *Sedum* are known from the Trans-Mexican Volcanic Belt than from any other geographical area in North America. Study of the species of this region is valuable for several reasons. Descriptive data about the plants and their habitats are useful to botanists and horticulturists, especially to growers of succulents. The techniques employed and the comparisons of methods of taxonomic investigation should be of interest and use to all students of classification and distribution of plants or animals. In addition, the detailed information about the species is the kind of material needed by students of evolution in attempting to comprehend how the organic world is organized today and what may have been its past history.

The underlying reason for the large number of species of *Sedum* in the Trans-Mexican Volcanic Belt has been an important incentive for the present study. The volcanic region extending transversely across Mexico, including in the east Mt. Orizaba and in the west the Nevado de Colima, is one both of great environmental diversity and of disjunction of similar habitat. It is an ideal area for appraising the relative importance of ecological adaptation, geographical isolation, and hybridization in the origin of species.

Prior to the investigation of *Sedum* in the Trans-Mexican Volcanic Belt, my views on the classification and origin of species have been influenced by studies of the Ophioglossaceae (Clausen, R. T., 1938 and 1954—for references, see Bibliography), various groups of species of *Sedum* (Clausen, R. T., 1942, and Clausen and Uhl, 1943 and 1944), *Pachyrrhizus* (Clausen, R. T., 1945), and the Pteridophyta and Spermatophyta of the Glaciated Allegheny Plateau (Clausen, R. T., 1949). In addition, my thinking has been influenced by the ideas of many other persons, among them Anderson (1949), Babcock (1947), Clausen, Jens (1951), Darwin (1865), Edwards, J. L. (many conversations), Dobzhansky (1941), Goldschmidt (1940), Huxley (1942), Mayr (1942), Mendel (1865), and Stebbins (1950).

Some of the concepts resulting from my previous experience are summarized below as ten propositions. In chapter IX, Conclusions, each will be considered and evaluated from the standpoint of the data derived from the examination of *Sedum* in the Trans-Mexican Volcanic Belt. In the conduct of my studies, these propositions have served as working hypotheses.

1. Evolution must be the philosophical basis for a sound classification. Evolution has occurred in the past and is occurring now.

2. Taxonomic groups at one rank are not inherently more natural than those at another. Phyletic lines are natural at all stages of evolution. Similar evolutionary processes occur at all stages.

3. The lower taxonomic ranks, as subspecies and species, are easier to define objectively than are the higher ones, but difficulties both in definition and in application exist at all levels.

4. Plants which occur together, have similar characteristics, and either actually or potentially interbreed comprise a local population. Such populations may grade into each other insensibly. Sharp limits may or may not be present. Local populations are important evolutionary units.

5. Populations or series of populations which differ from each other in few or several correlated characteristics (morphological, physiological, or both) and which are isolated ecologically or geographically are subspecies. These, as local populations, may intergrade insensibly, but their mean expressions may be markedly different.

6. Species may not be rigidly defined, but a threshold exists around which concepts may fluctuate. Species should differ from

each other in several correlated characteristics. These may be morphological or physiological or both. In addition, species should be effectively isolated biologically. Populations on the border line between species and subspecies will be difficult, perhaps impossible, to appraise one way or the other.

7. Gene mutations have been and are a primary cause of organic diversity. They provide the material on which natural selection works, and they also furnish the materials which, through hybridization, may be recombined in multiple ways. Further, they often are the basis for the development of genetic isolation.

8. Physiological changes, caused by gene mutations, have enabled plants to inhabit diverse environmental conditions. Single individuals or small numbers of individuals, fortuitously adapted to new conditions, may found new populations (ecotypes) ecologically isolated from the ancestral ones. This is one of the most universal and important evolutionary phenomena.

9. Isolation of populations has protected them from better-adapted types and permitted them to survive. Similarly, structural changes of chromosomes and polyploidy, both leading to differences in numbers of chromosomes, have been important in producing genetic isolation within previously interbreeding populations. Chance individuals with different numbers of chromosomes may become the nucleus for the evolution of new species.

10. Hybridization, involving the recombination of characteristics of different local populations, different subspecies, different species, or even different genera, has played an important part in evolution. Sometimes new species have resulted from such hybridization.

Besides affording an excellent opportunity for testing hypotheses, such as the ten listed above, the study of *Sedum* in the Trans-Mexican Volcanic Belt has provided a good occasion for the appraisal of different methods of taxonomic study. A valuable test of any method is whether it provides useful results. In taxonomy, methods of study are diverse. For purposes of discussion, three types of procedures are considered, but various combinations of these, supplemented by other techniques, may be employed by a taxonomist. In chapter VIII, a comparison will be made of the kinds of interpretations of the species of *Sedum* of the Trans-Mexican Volcanic Belt which would result from each of the three modes of approach to the study. The selected taxonomic methods for comparison are these:

1. A combination of study of herbarium specimens and literature.

2. Study of herbarium specimens and literature, supplemented by some experience with living cultivated plants.

3. Study of wild populations, using ecological and statistical methods, and culture of selected plants from these populations in experimental plots, supplemented by examination of herbarium specimens and literature.

The present study has been so long in process that each of these types of approach has been employed. In the initial phases of the work, many of the species were known only from herbarium specimens or the literature. A few cultivated plants of some species were available, but the sources in the wild of most of these were unknown. In 1949 a beginning was made in studying wild populations, but most of the work in the field was done in 1955–1956. Adequate experiments with plants of known characteristics in the field and selected from known populations were not possible until 1956. As a result of the way the present study has developed, it is possible to report the effect of each method on the conclusions concerning classification and interpretation of species.

The taxonomist seldom performs detailed genetic or physiological experiments. Neither does he make comprehensive investigations of the internal anatomy or embryology. Were he to do so, he would become a geneticist, physiologist, anatomist, or embryologist. The resultant data would be very useful, but would lack significance unless someone else did the work of organization which a taxonomist usually does. Rarely is an individual so gifted and his life so long that he is able to apply all techniques to a given group of plants or animals.

The conclusions on *Sedum* in the Trans-Mexican Volcanic Belt are based primarily on gross morphology and ecology. To a limited extent, genetic data, as indicated by actual or potential breeding relationships in the field, are available and utilized in attaining taxonomic interpretations. A little data about chromosomes, the results of studies by C. H. Uhl, are available. Information about chromosomes, if used to modify taxonomic conclusions, ideally should include both number and detailed morphology and

should involve experimental crosses and sometimes induced polyploidy. Scant data are available on internal anatomy, embryology,
and chemical analyses. Such data, when used to overrule conclusions based primarily on details of gross morphology and ecology,
should be based on samples sufficiently large to be of statistical
significance. Because of the incompleteness of cytological, anatomical, and other kinds of data, the taxonomic interpretation of *Sedum*
in the Trans-Mexican Volcanic Belt has needed to depend primarily on morphological and ecological data. In future years, I
will be interested to note the extent to which the conclusions
reached here are sustained or rejected by students who employ
other techniques of study.

An attempt has been made to see the available literature concerning *Sedum* in the Trans-Mexican Volcanic Belt. All names
listed in Index Kewensis which might apply to species in the area
have been investigated. Valuable data have been obtained from
the comprehensive treatments of *Sedum* by Britton and Rose (1905),
Praeger (1921), Berger (1930), and Fröderström (1930–1935).
Original descriptions of all pertinent names have been studied
carefully and the details compared with the data obtained for
populations in the field.

The data accompanying specimens in herbaria, as well as published information, were very useful in planning the program of
activity in the field. Locations of populations and the times when
plants are in flower often were learned from herbarium specimens.
Names of herbaria are abbreviated as follows, using the abbreviations as listed by Lanjouw and Stafleu (1954):

BH    Herbarium of the Bailey Hortorium, Cornell University, Ithaca,
      N.Y.
CU    Wiegand Herbarium, Cornell University, Ithaca, N.Y.
F     Herbarium of the Chicago Natural History Museum, Chicago, Ill.
GH    Gray Herbarium of Harvard University, Cambridge, Mass.
Mexu  Herbario Nacional del Instituto de Biología, Mexico, D.F.
NY    Britton Herbarium of the New York Botanical Garden, New
      York, N.Y.
UC    Herbarium of the University of California, Berkeley, Calif.
US    Herbarium of the United States National Museum, Washington,
      D.C.
Vt    Pringle Herbarium of the University of Vermont, Burlington, Vt.

Some examination of specimens has also been made in other herbaria additional to those listed above. The names of these herbaria are indicated in the accounts of the species. Likewise, photographs of some types, especially of specimens in European herbaria, have been available. These have been helpful in clarifying the typification of certain species.

I prepared herbarium specimens of plants of the populations of *Sedum* studied in the field, and I have also preserved specimens of the plants cultivated at Ithaca, N.Y. My first set of specimens will be deposited in the Wiegand Herbarium (CU). Duplicate specimens will go to Mexu, NY, US, and UC. In addition to collections of *Sedum*, I collected in the field samples of plants competing with *Sedum* in the same environmental conditions. Specimens of these competing species will be placed in the same herbaria as the specimens of *Sedum*.

Work in the field was planned with the major objectives of the study in mind, namely, to prepare full descriptions of each of the species and to acquire detailed information on their geographical distribution and ecology. Such descriptive data, valuable by themselves, are essential in any attempt to understand the relationships or evolution of the species.

At the beginning, a major decision needed to be made concerning the pattern of activity in the field. Only six months were available for work in Mexico in 1955. Time was precious and needed to be well spent. Three principal methods of procedure seemed possible:

1. To explore the volcanoes systematically. This plan was rejected because it might involve visiting mountains at times when the species were not in flower. Moreover, adjacent areas, important in understanding the status of the species on the volcanoes, might not be investigated.

2. To visit all type localities. This plan too was rejected because, if effort were concentrated in this endeavor, many important populations, from which types had not been selected, might be neglected.

3. To visit as many populations as possible when the plants might be in flower or fruit. This plan was adopted because it insured a maximum experience with *Sedum*. It also permitted the inclusion of some trips of exploration as well as visits to some type

localities. Adherence to a schedule for visiting populations resulted in at least one failure to find a species, namely, *S. nussbaumerianum*, but the advantages greatly offset the disadvantages.

The procedure adopted in the field was more in the nature of inspection than exploration, though a little of the latter was possible too. All together, 75 populations of *Sedum* were studied in the Trans-Mexican Volcanic Belt. Attention in each population was given to precise geographical location, altitudinal range, extent of area, size in number of plants, exposure, soil, drainage, pH, competing species, and climatic conditions. In collecting samples for study of variation, plants were selected from as many different environmental conditions in a population as could be detected. Likewise, populations studied were selected, as far as possible, from widely separated localities. In the first part of the period in the field, quadrats, 2 x 1 m., were used for sampling environmental conditions. Later, the use of quadrats for this purpose was abandoned and considered as unsatisfactory because definite sizes or shapes cannot be assigned to conditions of light, moisture, competition, or litter. In fixed quadrats, many plants probably are included which are of inconsequential importance to the species being studied. Moreover, even in small quadrats, environmental conditions, as light, moisture, or soil, may vary from one part of the quadrat to the other. Plants which affect the environment of a species can be neither limited exactly by area nor rated rigidly as to relative importance. Therefore, each plant of a species selected for study in the field was observed carefully, and all those other plants were listed which seemed to be affecting it by competing for nourishment or moisture, by producing litter, or by causing shade. In order that such data might be summarized, the total number of instances was determined in which each other species was associated with plants of any particular species of *Sedum*. The species with the highest score would be the commonest competitor on the basis of the sample studied.

In deciding how large a sample of a population to study, an attempt was made to find those characters of greatest discriminatory value. Usually a single well-developed plant was selected initially for detailed study of the maximum number of characters of gross morphology. Ten observations ideally were made of each character, and standard deviations were estimated using the short-cut method of computation based on table 8 b 3 of Dixon and Massey (1951). Coefficients of variability were calculated, and those characters were selected which had low coefficients. The means of these characters were then determined and compared with means of the same characters in other populations of the species or in populations of related species. Next, selection was made of confidence intervals of the means which would be necessary if the characters are of value in separating populations either of the same species or of different species. An adaptation by Cochran (1953) of Stein's (1945) two-sample test, brought to my attention by Dr. Robert Steel, was then employed to determine the number of observations needed per plant. The formula used is

$$n = \frac{t_{.05}^2 s^2}{d^2}$$

where $n$ = number of observations needed and $d^2$ = half of the confidence interval squared. Usually fewer than 10 observations per plant were sufficient for the characters chosen. The next step was to select plants from as many different environmental conditions as the population inhabited. These plants were then studied, and analyses of variance were made to determine both within and among plant variances. Again using the formula cited above and selecting a confidence interval which would be reasonable from a taxonomic standpoint if the population were different from other populations of the same species or of different species, the number of plants needed for sampling from the population was calculated. No limit was set on the number of populations studied, but sometimes no more than one could be found. In practice, as many populations were studied as could be found. Chapter VIII includes further discussion of sampling.

Those plants in each population which were selected for special study were numbered in the order in which they were chosen. Small cardboard tags were attached. Although most of these tags were fastened to the plants during the rainy season, they withstood the moisture remarkably well. Principal loss of tags was through removal by boys in places where plants were close to paths or roads. Most plants were visited twice, when they were in flower and again when in fruit. Some plants were visited more frequently, and a few only once. Parts of the numbered plants eventually were collected and sent to Ithaca for propagation. In addition, herbarium specimens were, as far as possible, prepared of other parts of these same plants. Since the plants of most species are large and propagation from cuttings is easy, it was usually possible to make this division of plants into parts for pressing and propagation, plus a part to continue growth in the field. Not all plants survived the trip to Ithaca, but most did. Air parcel post, via the Inspection House at Laredo, Texas, proved most satisfactory for shipment of cuttings. Wrappers of wax paper were superior to plastic bags. All cuttings were sent in dry condition to avoid molding and rotting.

For cultural work, 234 plants and more than 100 tubers successfully reached Ithaca in living condition in 1955–1956. With some plants available from the work in the field in 1949 and others from other collectors, a total of 264 perennial plants was available. These were arranged randomly on two benches in the greenhouse. The plants were numbered, and the positions on the benches were also numbered. Numbers were then selected from a table of random numbers, the numbers of the plants being the numbers drawn and the numbers of the positions being the numbers of the order of drawing. The only perennial species omitted from the series of 264 perennial plants was *Sedum clavifolium*. Its relationships appear clearly to be with a group of species which otherwise are biennial and have tubers. These were handled in a separate experiment, also of completely random design. The perennial plants all were placed in earthen pots with a diameter of 12.5 cm. across the top. These were arranged on the benches in the greenhouse as just described. The biennial species and *S. clavifolium* also were placed in the greenhouse, but in pots with a diameter of 10.5 cm. across the top. In addition, 96 perennial plants, parts of those in the greenhouse, were placed in a cold frame to test their responses there. These 96 plants belonged to 8 species. They too were in 12.5 cm. pots and were randomly arranged. Further, 51 plants of 10 species were tested for hardiness outdoors both in the Test Garden, Cornell University, Ithaca, N.Y., and in my garden at 1421 Slaterville Road, Ithaca. Of the species tested, *S. aoikon*, *S. frutescens*, and *S. griseum* were most susceptible to freezing, showing damage at temperatures slightly below 0° C. *Sedum clavifolium*, *S. cremnophila*, and *S. oxypetalum* were similarly sensitive in the garden. *Sedum bourgaei*, *S. dendroideum*, *S. moranense*, and *S. obcordatum*, though damaged at

—10° C., survived such treatment without protective covering. Only four plants of *S. moranense* survived the entire winter of 1956–1957, however, when the minimum temperature in the garden was —25° C. These plants were from near Acultzingo and Las Vigas, both in Vera Cruz. Likewise, in 1957–1958, when the minimum temperature was —23° C., only plants of *S. moranense* from Acultzingo and Las Vigas survived.

Observations of floral parts were made when the plants were in flower. Observations of vegetative parts were made long enough after propagation to remove the possibility that the responses being observed in cultivation may have been predetermined by environmental conditions prevailing when the buds were forming in the field. The goal in the study of the cultivated plants in Ithaca has been to compare the plants with each other on a basis of characters of shoots developed from buds formed subsequent to the time when each plant was placed in its precise location in the cultural experiments. These experiments are still in progress.

Soil used in the pots in the experiments in the greenhouse and cold frame is a combination of one-third silt loam, one-third sand, and one-third leaf mold. Sieved cinders are placed in the bottom of each pot for about an eighth of the depth. The pH of the soil mixture ranges from 7.6 to 7.8. The soil at the Test Garden is a well-drained stony silt loam with pH ranging from 6.2 to 6.6. The soil in my garden on the Slaterville Road, Ithaca, is a poorly drained clay loam with pH ranging from 6.4 to 6.8. Plants in the greenhouse and cold frame are watered uniformly, usually in the afternoon after three o'clock. In the summer, watering may be daily, except in periods of cloudy weather. In the winter, water is applied only two or three times per week. Plants in the gardens are not watered artificially. Temperatures in the greenhouse are not automatically regulated. For this reason, precise controls are impossible. In summer, temperatures may go over 40° C., and in winter, at night, as low as 5° C. When control is possible, temperature in the day is maintained at 18° C. and at night at 7° C. These data are important because they indicate the conditions of soil, moisture, and temperature under which the plants cultivated in the experiments have made the responses which will be reported.

Light has not been regulated. Except as an adjacent plant might slightly affect a neighboring one, all plants have the same potential for receiving light. Ithaca, where all cultural experiments were conducted, is at 42° 26′–27′ N.

An attempt has been made to keep pots and plots with *Sedum* free from weeds. Likewise, the plants in the greenhouse have been kept nearly clean from insect pests. They have been sprayed almost weekly with a solution of Black Leaf 40 and a detergent. This has been necessary to control various pests, especially aphids and mealy bugs. Few pests have attacked the plants grown in the cold frame or gardens. For that reason, no insecticides have been used there.

Measurements of plants in the field have been made with a steel ruler, no. 412D, made by Chesterman Sheffield, London, England. Those of height have been made to the nearest centimeter, those concerned with the length and width of leaves to the nearest millimeter. Floral parts and the thickness of leaves have been examined with a low-power binocular microscope and measured with an ocular micrometer to the nearest tenth of a millimeter. Tests of pH have been made using the following dyes as indicators: bromcresol green for range of 3.8–5.0; chlorphenol red for range of 5.0–6.0; bromthymol blue for range of 6.0–7.0; and phenol red for range of 7.0–8.2. According to Mason and Obenshain (1938), results with dyes may be accurate within .7 of a pH. More precise readings are unnecessary in the field where the method and time of collecting the samples may be greater sources of variation than the method of determination. The ease with which the dyes and color charts could be carried around in the field and the rapidity with which many tests could be made were practical factors in favor of their use. Determinations of altitudes were made with a Lufft altimeter. This was chosen because of its convenient small size and reasonable accuracy. It was set daily at places of known altitude, as indicated in the Anuario del Observatorio Astronómico Nacional de Tacubaya for the year 1955, edited by Ing. Ricardo Toscano. Sometimes it was possible to check the altimeter with known points two or three times in a day. Most determinations in the field probably are within 100 m. of accuracy, and some which were checked several times may be within 10 m. Temperatures were determined in two ways, with a bimetallic maximumminimum thermometer, Taylor no. 5320, and with a Bacharach pocket-style mercury thermometer. Thermometers were usually placed near or even supported in the plant being studied. Information about temperatures was intended to show a pattern. No claims can be made for precision, though I tried always to obtain as accurate data as my instruments permitted.

CHAPTER II

# History of the Study of *Sedum* in the Trans-Mexican Volcanic Belt

THE inhabitants of the Trans-Mexican Volcanic Belt probably were familiar with most of the species of *Sedum* which occur there long before trained botanists began to record information about these plants. A few species were used medicinally. For example, the Aztec herbal, written and possibly illustrated by Martinus de la Cruz, 1552 (Emmart, 1940), includes at least two species of *Sedum*. Tetzmitl, plate 19, is a yellow-flowered plant which might be *S. dendroideum*, but the illustration is not good enough for certain identification. Similarly, texiyotl, plate 38, could be *S. oxypetalum*, but Reko (1947) identified it as *S. bourgaei*.

Linnaeus, in Species Plantarum, 1753, did not list any species of *Sedum* from the Trans-Mexican Volcanic Belt. Formal taxonomic information about the species of this region has accumulated since his time.

In the present discussion, attention is first given to the discoverers of local populations of *Sedum*. If the inhabitants of the Trans-Mexican Volcanic Belt knew most of the species long before the advent of professional botanists, they were the true discoverers of the populations, but no records of their discoveries are available. Even the early explorers and collectors who did keep records did not write enough information to make possible the determination of the exact locations of the populations which they knew. As a result, the following list of discoverers of populations is a chronicle of the persons who first left records full enough, whether in the form of herbarium specimens or published information, to locate each population. Names of botanists are arranged chronologically according to the years when their discoveries were made. The number of populations which each botanist found is indicated after his name, as are also the names of species which each discovered.

(1787–1804  Sessé, Mociño, Castillo, and Maldonado—*S. botterii, S. bourgaei, S. ebracteatum, S. jaliscanum, S. moranense,* and *S. oxypetalum*—localities uncertain or not mentioned)

1846        Carl Heller—1—*S. napiferum*
1850–1878   Mateo Botteri—1
1853        Frederick Mueller—1—*S. hemsleyanum*
1865–1866   Eugène Bourgeau—6
1882        Manuel Villada—1
1884–1886   Comisión Geográfica Exploradora—3
1885–1888   Anonymous—7
1890        Paul Maury—3
1890–1899   Cyrus Pringle—10—*S. cremnophila, S. longipes,* and *S. minimum*
1893–1894   Edward Nelson—1—*S. obcordatum*
1903–1909   Carl Purpus—11—*S. aoikon, S. clavifolium,* and *S. nussbaumerianum*
1903–1905   Joseph Rose—1—*S. frutescens*
1903        Joseph Rose and Joseph Painter—4
1903        Edward Goldman—1
1906–1911   Gerfroy Arsène—17—*S. quevae*
?1908       Joseph Purpus—1
1913        Carl Reiche—2—*S. grandipetalum*
1927        Ynez Mexia—2
1932–1938   George Hinton—18—1 unnamed species
1932        Harald Fröderström and Eric Hultén—1
1935        Eric Walther—1—*S. lucidum*
1937        Eizi Matuda—1
1938        Edward Balls—4
1938        Otto Nagel—1
1940        Harold Moore—1
1941–1955   Faustino Miranda—3
1944        Aaron Sharp and Efraim Hernández-Xolocotzi—1
1946        Edward Alexander—6—2 unnamed species
1948        Harold Moore and Carroll Wood, Jr.—2

1949–1956   Robert Clausen—28
1949–1953   Rogers McVaugh—3
1955        George Kennedy—1

These are the people who have hiked in the land, climbed the rocks, and made the observations in the field. About 36 men have found a total of 144 populations. After Sessé, Mociño, Castillo, and Maldonado, the three persons who found the most new species were Pringle—3, Purpus—3, and Alexander—2. Pringle and Purpus were general collectors; Alexander is especially interested in Cactaceae and Crassulaceae. Besides the species listed after the names above, one native species was first described from cultivated plants, and five were discovered outside of the Trans-Mexican Volcanic Belt.

The data of the foregoing list may be organized in another way to indicate the numbers of populations and species discovered and adequately recorded by half centuries.

|           | *No. of populations discovered* | *No. of species discovered* |
|-----------|-------------------------------|---------------------------|
| 1801–1850 | 2                             | 1                         |
| 1851–1900 | 28                            | 8                         |
| 1901–1950 | 83                            | 9                         |
| 1951–1956 | 31                            | 0                         |

The period of greatest discovery, both of populations not previously recorded and of species new to science, was the first half of the present century. The botanists who found the largest number of unrecorded populations in that period were Hinton—18, Arsène—17, and Purpus—11. In the second half of the nineteenth century, Pringle found the largest number of previously unrecorded populations—10.

The list of discoverers of populations is as accurate as my data permit. Probably extensive search in old manuscripts and herbaria, especially in Europe, would effect some changes. On the other hand, more than half of the species have been found since 1851. The comparative recency of our knowledge of the species of *Sedum* of the Trans-Mexican Volcanic Belt is indicated in a list in which are compared the numbers of species known to each of several writers whose publications theoretically included all the species of *Sedum* of this region.

Linnaeus—1753—0 species
Hemsley—1879–1888—9 (+2?) species
Britton and Rose—1905—15 (+1?) species
Fröderström—1930–1935—23 species

Frequently botanists who describe species are not familiar with the plants in the field. This is well demonstrated by the experience with *Sedum* in the Trans-Mexican Volcanic Belt. In the following list are the names of all authors of species of *Sedum* known from this region. Comparison of this list with the one for discoverers of populations indicates that only five botanists (names are starred) have both discovered new populations in and described new species from the Trans-Mexican Volcanic Belt.

| Year or years | Botanists | No. of species proposed | Recognized in present study | Synonyms in present study |
|---|---|---|---|---|
| 1823 | Humboldt, Bonpland, and Kunth | 2 | 2 | 0 |
| 1828 | Augustin de Candolle | 2 | 2 | 0 |
| 1847 | Alphonse de Candolle | 1 | 0 | 1 |
| 1859 | Johann Peyritsch | 1 | 1 | 0 |
| 1878 | William Hemsley | 5 | 4 | 1 |
| 1878 | Maxwell Masters | 1 | 0 | 1 |
| 1887, 1894 | Sessé* and Mociño* | 4 | 0 | 4 |
| 1887–1890 | Sereno Watson | 2 | 1 | 1 |
| 1900 | Herman Solms-Laubach | 1 | 1 | 0 |
| 1903–1911 | Joseph Rose* | 14 | 5 (+2) | 7 |
| 1911 | Charles Thompson | 1 | 1 | 0 |
| 1914 | Raymond Hamet | 1 | 1 | 0 |
| 1917 | Robert Praeger | 2 | 1 | 1 |
| 1917 | Eberhard Ulbrich | 1 | 1 | 0 |
| 1919 | Townshend Brandegee | 2 | 0 | 2 |
| 1923 | George Bitter | 1 | 1 | 0 |
| 1935 | Marcus Jones | 1 | 0 | 1 |
| 1936 | Harald Fröderström* | 3 | 1 | 2 |
| 1941, 1951 | Robert Clausen* | 2 | 2 | 0 |

Besides the five men who both explored in this area and described new species of *Sedum*, Thompson and Jones each collected in the field in Mexico, but their activities with respect to *Sedum* were outside of the Trans-Mexican Volcanic Belt. Humboldt and Bonpland may have studied populations of *Sedum* in the volcanic belt, but the locations of these are uncertain.

Twenty-two botanists have proposed forty-seven species of *Sedum* for the Trans-Mexican Volcanic Belt. Twenty-one of the specific names proposed are synonyms. Rose, Hemsley, and Sessé and Mociño have published the largest number of species. Of species which are recognized as valid now, Rose and Hemsley published the largest number. Likewise, Rose published the largest number of species which must go into synonymy.

From the standpoint of the conduct of the present study, whether or not species have been described before has made little difference, but whether or not populations had been found and samples collected and preserved has made a great difference. In other words, my studies have been helped most by the men who have found populations in the field and provided data concerning times of flowering and fruiting. Without their information, I would never have been able to cover the ground which I did or to see plants of so many species in flower.

Before the present account, no special publication has ever been concerned with the problems of *Sedum* in the Trans-Mexican Volcanic Belt. The significance of the large number of endemic plants and animals in this region long has attracted interest, but *Sedum*, in this connection, has not received as much attention as some other genera. Heilprin (1892) discussed the general problem and indicated the anomaly of the large number of endemic species and the recent origin of the volcanoes. He suggested the possibility of the recent migration of plants from older to newer slopes, a view which, with modification, seems to be fundamentally sound.

In the preparation of this historical discussion, the data have been derived primarily from the specimens in herbaria and the publications of the men who have been concerned with *Sedum* in the Trans-Mexican Volcanic Belt. Useful information, such as the correct spelling of the full names of botanists and a few references, also has been available from the bibliography of León (1895) and the work of Hemsley (1879–1888). Botanists who find new populations in the field, provide interpretations of new material, or discover new facts about plants already known to science are increasing knowledge. Measured on this basis, those who have most advanced the understanding of *Sedum* in the Trans-Mexican Volcanic Belt were Pringle, Purpus, Hinton, Arsène, and Rose.

CHAPTER III

# Geology of the Trans-Mexican
# Volcanic Belt

THE Trans-Mexican Volcanic Belt extends transversely across Mexico from the vicinity of the Gulf of Mexico to the Pacific Coast. Most of the peaks lie between 19° and 20° N, but the Tuxtla group is between 18° and 19° N and those near Tepic are between 21° and 22° N.

Geologists have used different names for the transverse zone of volcanism in Mexico. Among recent designations have been Volcanes de la Mesa Central del Sur (Ordóñez, 1946), Sierra Volcánica Transversal (Vivo, 1949), Sierra de los Volcanes (Garfias and Chapin, 1949), Neo-Volcanic Zone (Williams, 1950), and Mexican Volcanic Axis (Foshag and González, 1956). Dr. Federico Mooser first suggested to me the name Trans-Mexican Volcanic Belt. It is descriptive and accurate. Since the volcanoes of this belt do not form a single range of mountains, nor are they the only recent ones in Mexico, a designation which does not imply either or both of these ideas is preferable to one which does the reverse.

The Trans-Mexican Volcanic Belt (fig. 1) includes that part of Mexico, between 18° and 22° N, which is composed primarily of rocks of volcanic origin. The general limits of this belt are easily stated. The precise limits can be described only after intensive geological investigation. The Trans-Mexican Volcanic Belt is situated between the Central Mexican Plateau and the Sierra Madre del Sur. The plateau to the north is a region of folded

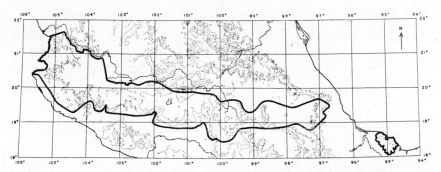

*Fig. 1.* Approximate boundaries of the Trans-Mexican Volcanic Belt; prepared from information on the Millionth Maps of Hispanic America of the American Geographical Society.

sedimentary rocks and extrusive igneous materials. The mountains to the south are deeply eroded and complex in structure, with extensive areas of ancient, crystalline rocks exposed as well as areas of Mesozoic limestones and more recent volcanic rocks. The obvious southern limit of the volcanic belt in the west is the valley of the Balsas River which cuts across the northwestern part of the Sierra Madre del Sur. In the west the volcanic belt passes out into the Pacific Ocean, and in the east it terminates at the Gulf Coastal Plain and the Gulf of Mexico.

Seven peaks of the Trans-Mexican Volcanic Belt attain a height of more than 4,000 m. above the level of the sea. These are the peak of Orizaba, 5,700 m.; Popocatepetl, 5,452 m.; Iztaccihuatl, 5,286 m.; Nevado de Toluca, 4,578 m.; Malinche (Malintzin), 4,461 m.; Nevado de Colima, 4,340 m.; and Cofre de Perote (Nauhcampatepetl), 4,282 m. Elevations are taken from the American Geographical Society's map of Hispanic America.

For convenience, the Trans-Mexican Volcanic Belt may be subdivided into eight sections or groups of volcanoes. In some cases, the volcanoes form short ranges of mountains with their axes north and south. In other cases, the arrangement of the volcanoes seems to lack pattern. Williams (1950) has discussed the alignment of the volcanoes and has emphasized their haphazard occurrence in the Michoacán section. Mooser (1956) has discussed the origins and relationships of the volcanoes in the southern part of the Valley of Mexico. In the accompanying diagram (fig. 2) are shown the highest peaks in each of the eight sections, the dis-

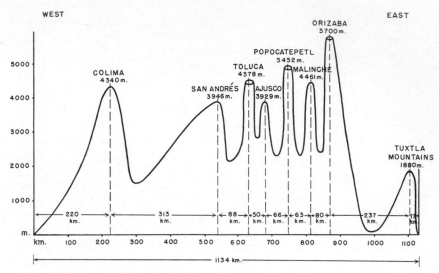

*Fig. 2.* Highest peaks in each of the eight sections of the Trans-Mexican Volcanic belt. Sections extend from valley to valley.

tances between these peaks, and the highest parts of the valleys between the various sections.

The Tuxtla Mountains, situated on the Coastal Plain southeast of Vera Cruz, are a disjunct part of the volcanic belt. According to the data of World Aeronautical Chart no. 644, ed. 6, 1953, of the U.S. Air Force, the highest peak in this group attains a height of 1,880 m. Between these mountains and the rest of the volcanic belt is a broad expanse of Coastal Plain with the valleys of the San Juan and Papaloapan Rivers.

West of the Coastal Plain is a high range of mountains of which the peak of Orizaba and the Cofre de Perote are the dominant southern and northern summits respectively. The eastern slopes of this range are deeply dissected by many streams which carry the water from the mountains to the Gulf. The lowest point on the summit ridge from the peak of Orizaba to the Cofre de Perote has an altitude of about 2,500 m. This point occurs just south of the latter peak. Ordóñez (1946) and others have included the peak of Orizaba and the Cofre de Perote in the Sierra Madre Oriental, but those mountains are very different structurally.

An extensive area of high plain lies to the west of the peak of Orizaba. This plain, in contrast with the forested slopes of the mountains to the east, is mostly treeless and broken only occasionally by isolated mountains. The northern and southern parts of the plain drain to the Gulf of Mexico, but much of the drainage is to interior basins. Oriental, located in one of these basins 43 km. southwest of Perote, has an elevation of 2,345 m. Mt. Malinche, with its associated smaller volcanic cones, is a solitary peak about 80 km. west from Mt. Orizaba. The topography west from Malinche is more dissected and plateaulike. Drainage is into the Atoyac River, a tributary of the Balsas River which flows into the Pacific Ocean. North of this area is the Sierra del Norte de Puebla, and to the west is the Sierra Nevada, dominated in the south by the two high peaks, Iztaccihuatl and Popocatepetl.

The city of Mexico, altitude 2,300 m., is situated in the broad Valley of Mexico. West of Popocatepetl, this valley is narrowest. At Amecameca, near its highest part, it attains an altitude of 2,468 m. The valley is bordered on the south and west, as well as on the east, by high mountains of which Ajusco, 13 km. southwest of Tlalpam, is the highest. Associated with Mt. Ajusco are many other volcanic peaks, and to the northwest of these are the Sierra de las Cruces and Sierra de la Marquesa. Farther to the west is the valley of the Lerma River. The divide between its headwaters and those of the Tenancingo River is at about 2,800 m. in the region between Tenango and Tenancingo. Next to the west is the Nevado de Toluca, and beyond that the mountains of Temascaltepec.

The valley of the Tuxpan River, with its northward extension through Irimbo to Tungarco in the Lerma Valley, forms a topographic break between the highlands to the east and the extensive Michoacán Volcanic Region. This region, following Foshag and González (1956), extends from the Sierra de Ozumatlán to the western side of Lake Chapala. It is a land of hundreds of volcanic peaks. The highest mountains of the region are the huge volcanoes of San Andrés, 3,946 m.; Tancítaro, 3,860 m.; Patambán, 3,750 m.; Tecolote, 3,400 m.; and El Zirate, 3,340 m.

To the west of the Michoacán Volcanic Region and east of the range which includes the Nevado de Colima and Sierra de Tapalpa is the trough in which are located Lakes Zapotlán and Sayula. This valley is a major topographic feature of the volcanic belt. West of it, the Nevado de Colima is the only peak more than

4,000 m. high. In the northwestern part of the belt, near the Pacific Ocean 12 km. southwest of Tepic, is the Cerro San Juan with an elevation of 2,391 m.

Geologists have studied in detail only portions of the area under discussion. The recent eruption of the volcano of Paricutín has attracted much attention. Many persons have investigated it. Authors of important reports on Paricutín have been Flores (1945), Ordóñez (1947), Segerstrom (1950), Williams (1950), Wilcox (1954), and Foshag and González (1956). White (1951, 1956) has reported on the late Pleistocene history of Popocatepetl and the glacial history of Iztaccihuatl. Early in the century, Ordóñez (1902, 1904, 1905) described in detail the Nevado de Toluca, the Cofre de Perote, and other peaks. He also discussed the distribution in Mexico of special classes of rocks. Waitz (1910) described briefly the peak of Orizaba and the Sierra Negra. The accumulated data of these and other geologists are the basis for the present understanding of the structure and history of the Trans-Mexican Volcanic Belt.

Areas of lava of known age are of great interest because they provide a means of determining how rapidly plants colonize new environmental conditions, which species come first, how these species interact with each other, and to what extent they vary. Likewise, an actively erupting volcano affords an opportunity to learn how populations of plants are affected, how great is the destruction, and to what extent populations may be changed in the region peripheral to the zone of maximum alteration by the eruption.

The eruptive life of Paricutín (fig. 3) began, according to Ordóñez (1947), on Feb. 20, 1943, and ended, according to Wilcox (1954), on March 4, 1952. Wilcox stated that in nine years of volcanic activity, the new lavas covered an area of 24.8 sq. km. as determined by Fries and Gutiérrez. Segerstrom (1950) reported that the maximum thickness of the new lava is 150 m. In his opinion all plants not only in the area completely covered by the lava, but also within a radius of 3 to 7 km. of the cone, were killed by the ash which buried the smaller plants, broke the tops and branches of the trees, and sealed the pores of leaves, preventing respiration and transpiration. Segerstrom determined the greatest thickness of ash, at Casita Canicjuata, within 850 m. of the base of the cone, as 1,083 cm. He considered that the vegetation was destroyed wherever the ash was more than 1 m. in depth. He found only a few oaks and a very few young pines surviving where the mantle of ash was as thick as 1 m. He described the area of semidevastation of plants as that where the ash was from .25 to 1 m. deep. This area lies within a radius of 6 to 11 km. of the cone. There the older pines were killed, but other trees survived. Small herbs were buried. The village of Angahuán lies in that area, as also does San Juan Parangaricutiro, which now is under the field of lava.

*Fig. 3.* Volcanic cone of Paricutín as seen from the site of San Juan Parangaricutiro, Sept. 27, 1955.

My own observations near Paricutín were between Angahuán and San Juan Parangaricutiro, on the lava around San Juan, on an old field of lava near San Lorenzo, 17 km. from the cone of Paricutín, and at Capacuaro, 27 km. from the cone. The pines which survived in the area between Angahuán and San Juan Parangaricutiro are of two species, *Pinus montezumae* and *P. leiophylla.* Presumably the forests destroyed by the lava were of these same two species. Pines on the leeward slope of Mt. Capatzun, toward San Juan, apparently survived the eruptions, although that low mountain, elevation 2,415 m., is within 3.7 km. of the crater and completely surrounded by the new lava. Segerstrom reported that slopes received less ash per unit of area than flat areas and also that leeward slopes received less than those facing the volcano. Probably the survival of pines on Capatzun was possible because of a diminished fall of ash on the slope away from the volcano. The circumstance is interesting because it illustrates how close to a major eruption plants may survive. Associated with the pines between Angahuán and San Juan is much *Pteridium aquilinum*, the subspecies which includes var. *feei*. Possibly the rootstocks of this fern survived under the ash and, where the mantle was not too deep or has eroded away, have continued growth and produced new leaves. Near the edge of the field of lava northeast of San Juan are two large opuntias which, to judge from their size, must have survived the eruptions. On the lava itself, close to San Juan, at an elevation of 2,270 m., I found eight kinds of ferns: *Adiantum poiretii*, *Cystopteris fragilis*, *Notholaena aurea*, *N. candida*, an *Asplenium*, a *Pellaea*, a *Polypodium*, and a *Woodsia;* there were also two mosses, identified by Professor Albert Andrews as *Pogonatum cuspidatum* and *Brachymenium barbae-montis*, and two species of *Gnaphalium*. These plants, all with air-borne disseminules, are growing in small accumulations of ash under overhanging rocks or in tiny caves where seepage occurs. The pH of ash in a crevice near San Juan was 5.8. Several species of Asteraceae and a grass, possibly an *Aristida*, grow on the lava along the path followed by visitors from Angahuán to San Juan. Perhaps these were brought in by horses which sometimes are led along this trail. I found no *Sedum* or other Crassulaceae either on the lava or in the area where the ash was more than .25 m. deep. A large population of *S. griseum* occurs on lava southwest of San Lorenzo. Lava there probably originated from one of the cones which Williams considered as not more than a few thousand years old. This site, only 17 km. from the cone of Paricutín, is the nearest to the volcano at which I have found *Sedum*. Large plants there undoubtedly antedate the recent eruptions. Still farther away, at Capacuaro, *S. tortuosum* occurs as an epiphyte on oaks. According to Williams, the eruption which produced the flow of lava on which these oaks are growing probably occurred either within the last thousand years or in the preceding millennium.

If other volcanoes have had the same effect on vegetation as Paricutín, destruction of plants in the period since the Trans-

Mexican Volcanic Belt was raised above the sea has never been complete. Many plants must have survived at sites quite close to areas of volcanic activity. From such sites, recolonization of devastated areas must have proceeded.

Ordóñez (1947, pl. 15) published a photograph of a hill near Paricutín which in one night was pushed up 30 m. above its original level by the injection of fluid lava beneath. The ash beds on the top were not disturbed and appear in horizontal strata as though nothing unusual had happened. This kind of phenomenon illustrates the problem in interpreting the history of the topography of the volcanic belt and in turn in understanding why plants grow where they do. Changes in topography may occur rapidly.

The lavas from the volcano of Xitli, covering an extensive area in the southern part of the Valley of Mexico, have an elevation almost the same as the lavas from Paricutín. The climate is similar. From the standpoint of colonization by plants, the principal difference is age. The lava from Xitli, according to information from the Copilco Museum of Modern Man, dates back to 500 B.C. Human remains, found under or in this lava, indicate that some inhabitants of the valley were overtaken by the flows. Many species of plants—mosses, ferns, and seed plants—both herbs and shrubs, now grow on this lava. *Sedum oxypetalum* occurs on low cliffs and even in the bottom of pits which may be the remains of old steam vents or fumaroles.

Popocatepetl, highest peak in the Sierra Nevada, most recently erupted in 1920–1924 according to Foshag and González (1956). White (1951) has described the complex history of this cone which has involved several periods of eruption, followed by erosion, with glaciation and alluviation superimposed. According to White, the present cone of Popocatepetl probably began to develop early in the Pleistocene on the site of the older Nexpayantla Volcano which may have been constructed at the end of the Miocene. The present Barranca de Nexpayantla and its surrounding ridges of the head wall are remnants of this older volcano. White stated that earlier in the Miocene greatest volcanic activity in the Sierra Nevada was north of the present Popocatepetl. Nexpayantla was not the oldest volcano in this range.

I have explored the cliffs of the Nexpayantla Canyon between

3,800 and 4,200 m. and also the northern slopes of Popocatepetl up to about 4,200 m. The alpine flora of Popocatepetl is disappointing. Vegetation is sparse. The species of plants appear to be a selection of those which occur farther down on the slopes. Each species seems to extend up the mountain as far as its physiological constitution permits. Only a few are able to survive the low temperatures above 4,000 m. In addition, gases emitted from the crater may have a deleterious effect. The smell of sulphur dioxide was strong at the time of my visit in August, 1956. The fact that Popocatepetl has erupted in recent time suggests that many sites

*Fig. 4.* Mt. Iztaccihuatl, view from the southwest, Dec. 18, 1955.

for plants on the upper slopes have not been available for long. The flora on Iztaccihuatl, at similar elevations, is much richer. Whereas *Sedum minimum* is common there from 3,700 to 4,150 m., I found none of that or any other *Sedum* in the same elevational range on Popocatepetl. Even the Nexpayantla Canyon lacked *Sedum*, but *Villadia batesii* and *Echeveria secunda* both were common there on cliffs and rocky slopes.

On the west side of Iztaccihuatl (fig. 4), White (1956) found evidences of five substages of glaciation, all probably Wisconsin. The earliest and lowest glaciers reached down to 3,100 m. or lower. The extent of the glaciers downward in the valleys of the mountain depended on the exposure as well as on the size of the collecting areas upward.

Ordóñez (1902) classified the Nevado de Toluca (fig. 5) with Popocatepetl and Orizaba as a volcano which had erupted many times. He believed that rarely is enough lava emitted in an eruption to cover all of an already-high cone. As a result, the layers of lava erupted at different times become stratified. Ordóñez suggested that toward the end of the Nevado's volcanic life, after a long period of inactivity, a final phase of activity followed in which were erupted products of detritus, cinders, and especially tuff

Fig. 5. Nevado de Toluca, upper slopes and Pico del Fraile, Nov. 27, 1955.

which today mantle the volcano. He attempted to appraise the age of the Nevado in comparison with some of the other peaks of the volcanic belt. As evidence he used both the degree of weathering of the crater and the mineralogical composition of the lavas. He also considered the conditions of the cones of volcanoes which had erupted in the three centuries prior to his publication, namely: Orizaba, 1687; Jorullo, 1759; Tuxtla, 1793–1805; Popocatepetl, 1804; Volcán de Colima, 1806, 1818, 1869, 1877, and 1885; and Ceboruco, 1870. The order of antiquity which Ordóñez conceived is Ajusco and Malinche among the oldest, then possibly the Nevado de Colima, later Iztaccihuatl and the Nevado de Toluca, and in more recent time Orizaba, Popocatepetl, Ceboruco, and the Volcán de Colima. He suggested that Ajusco and Malinche might have been built at the end of the Miocene, Iztaccihuatl and the Nevado de Toluca at the beginning of the Pliocene, and the four more recent volcanoes in the middle of the Pliocene.

The Cofre de Perote, according to Ordóñez (1905), resembles Iztaccihuatl, but may be a little older, possibly dating from the Miocene. It possesses no true crater at its summit. The walls of the old crater are greatly eroded. This volcano, when it was formed, must have erupted great quantities of andesitic lava which

*Fig. 6.* Peak of Orizaba as seen in the morning from Fortín de las Flores, Aug. 6, 1955.

formed an enormous dome. Because of the slight fluidity of the lava, this grew more in height than in horizontal surface. After the initial period of eruptions which produced the dome, later eruptions of basaltic lavas occurred at places on the eastern slope. The tuff on the lower slopes probably came from one or more of the nearby volcanoes, not from the Cofre de Perote itself. If the idea about the antiquity of the dome of the mountain is correct, then it has been available as a habitat for plants for an enormously long period. Possibly it is the place from which *Sedum obcordatum* has spread to the more recent peak of Orizaba.

The Sierra Negra also is older than the peak of Orizaba (fig. 6).

Both mountains, according to Waitz, have built at least two major cones, one superimposed upon the other. Since I did not spend time on the Sierra Negra, I do not know whether *Sedum obcordatum* occurs there.

The biggest area in Mexico where Pre-Cambrian rocks are exposed, according to Ordóñez (1904), is in the Sierra Madre del Sur in the state of Oaxaca. This region may have been a place from which plants spread into the Trans-Mexican Volcanic Belt when the latter area first arose above the sea. Some evidence derived from modern distributional patterns of *Sedum*, to be discussed in chapter VII, supports this idea.

Williams (1950) stated that the time of the beginning of volcanic activity in the Mexican volcanic belt is uncertain. He cited Robles as authority for the idea that the oldest lavas are of Eocene age, but suggested that doubts about the age and sequence of the Tertiary lavas will not be dispelled until the fossil floras and faunas of the interbedded tuffs have been examined. Although precise ages of Tertiary lavas are uncertain, the youthfulness, from the standpoint of geological time, of the volcanic belt seems certain. Probably the whole area was submerged under the sea in the Cretaceous. All plants and animals which occur there today must have moved in since that time.

As I have traveled around in the volcanic belt of Mexico, I have been impressed by the complexity of geological structure. Since some volcanoes have erupted many times and tremendous erosion has been occurring for millions of years, dating any particular bed of conglomerate or old flow of lava is hazardous, even by a geologist after careful study. From consideration of the degree of weathering and the development of vegetation, I think that fields of lava might be appraised in age as between that of Paricutín and that of Xitli or older than the latter, but not more closely without detailed geological information. Beds of conglomerate, particularly the older ones, are even more difficult to appraise. They may be of Miocene or Pliocene Age or much more recent. Special study of each stratum is necessary. The degree of weathering of the cones of the volcanoes, as shown by Ordóñez (1902), affords a means of appraising the relative ages of the peaks themselves. Those with well-formed cones and craters are most recent, those in which the rims of the craters are greatly eroded or even have disappeared are most ancient, and those in which the rims of the craters are somewhat eroded are intermediate.

The glacial history of many of the peaks of the Trans-Mexican Volcanic Belt still is uncertain. Whereas White (1956) reported that in the Pleistocene glaciers probably reached down to 3,100 m. on the western side of Iztaccihuatl, Williams (1950) noted no signs of glaciation on Mt. Tancítaro, a peak with an elevation of 3,860 m., which must have been in existence through much of the period of the ice ages.

The soils of the Trans-Mexican Volcanic Belt are derived primarily from volcanic ash or the weathering of volcanic rocks. Erosion of the older volcanoes has resulted in the production of many alluvial fans. In addition, sediments have accumulated from the outwash of the glaciers of the higher peaks. On the youngest lavas, only lithosols exist. Where ash or sediments are old and augmented with organic matter from successive generations of plants, there have developed latosols, gray wooded soils, or mountain meadow soils, depending on the climate. Latosols are commonest in the valleys and on the lower slopes of the mountains. Here the wet and dry seasons are most sharply defined. Higher on the slopes of the mountains, rainfall is greater and more evenly distributed throughout the year. There, in the zone of coniferous forests, especially of *Abies* and *Pinus*, gray wooded soils have developed. Finally, mountain meadow soils occur only above the limit of trees on the peak of Orizaba, Mts. Popocatepetl and Iztaccihuatl, and the Nevado de Toluca. The alpine flora occurs in these mountain meadow soils or in undifferentiated lithosols. Most of the species of *Sedum* of the Trans-Mexican Volcanic Belt occur in crevices in rocks. Although the soil in these crevices is thin, the relative organic content may be high from the decay of mosses, liverworts, or other flowering plants growing in the same sites. At least four of the species of *Sedum* occur as epiphytes in the organic matter and ash which have accumulated on the bark of trees or in crotches made by branches.

While in the Trans-Mexican Volcanic Belt from July, 1955, to January, 1956, I made 182 tests of pH of soils in which plants of *Sedum* were growing. The total range of pH was from 5.2 to 7.8, and the average was 6.7. Usually, values of pH were slightly higher in the dry than in the wet season. Of ten samples tested in both seasons, the average increase was .2 of a pH.

Probably the alternating dry and wet seasons and the rapidity of organic decay are both important in explaining the values of pH, as well as the greater amount of leaching in the wet season. In order to indicate some of the differences in amount of precipitation between the dry and wet seasons, contrasting data for nine localities are available in the following table. The data are taken from Contreras Arias (1942). Measurements are in millimeters and are averages for five or more years. Unless otherwise indicated, the four driest months are December, January, February, and March, and the four wettest months are June, July, August, and September.

| | | | Precipitation | |
| | | | Four driest | Four wettest |
| Locality | Alt. | Annual | months | months |
| | (m.) | (mm.) | (mm.) | (mm.) |
|---|---|---|---|---|
| Huatusco | 1,344 | 2,078 | 190 | 1,422 |
| Jalapa | 1,427 | 1,588 | 206 | 1,003 |
| Las Vigas | 2,421 | 1,349 | 143 | 876 |
| | | | (Dec., Feb., | (June, Aug., |
| | | | Mar., Apr.) | Sept., Oct.) |
| Tlaxacala | 2,252 | 718 | 21 | 549 |
| | | | (Nov., Dec., | |
| | | | Jan., Feb.) | |
| Tacubaya | 2,308 | 765 | 29 | 599 |
| Desierto de los Leones | 3,220 | 1,281 | 48 | 999 |
| Toluca | 2,675 | 792 | 37 | 597 |
| Tenancingo | 2,080 | 1,550 | 48 | 1,228 |
| Pátzcuaro | 2,174 | 1,109 | 45 | 899 |
| | | | (Jan., Feb., | |
| | | | Mar., Apr.) | |

Differences in length of the period when frosts may occur and in the months when extremes of temperature occur are further indicated for the same nine localities in the following table.

| | Alt. | Months with | Months of highest | Months of lowest |
| Locality | (m.) | frosts | temp. | temp. |
|---|---|---|---|---|
| Huatusco | 1,344 | 0 | Apr., May | Jan. |
| Jalapa | 1,427 | 0 | Apr., May | Feb. |
| Las Vigas | 2,421 | 11 | June | Feb. |
| Tlaxcala | 2,252 | 4 | May | Jan. |
| Tacubaya | 2,308 | 6 | May | Feb. |

| Locality | Alt. (m.) | Months with frosts | Months of highest temp. | Months of lowest temp. |
|---|---|---|---|---|
| Desierto de los Leones | 3,220 | 7 | Mar. | Mar. |
| Toluca | 2,675 | 5 | May | Feb. |
| Tenancingo | 2,080 | 6 | June | Jan. |
| Pátzcuaro | 2,174 | 5 | Mar. | Jan., Feb. |

In the alpine zone of the highest mountains, temperatures may drop below freezing every night. Temperatures are highest in the day in the dry season; the greatest diurnal changes in temperature also occur at that season. Observations in 1955 on Iztaccihuatl and the Nevado de Toluca, in the area of populations of *Sedum minimum*, indicate this situation, as in the table that follows.

| Mountain | Alt. of observations m. | Date | Time of day A.M.   P.M. | Temperature Range °C. | Temperature Average °C. |
|---|---|---|---|---|---|
| Iztaccihuatl | 3,820–4,050 | Aug. 13 | 11    −3.30 | 9–17 | 13 |
|  | 4,150 | Aug. 28 | 9:20–2 | 10–19 | 13 |
|  | 3,820–4,050 | Oct. 8 | 10:30–2:20 | 14–28 | 18 |
| Nevado de Toluca | 3,940–4,040 | Sept. 11 | 11:30–3:30 | 8–17 | 13 |
|  | 3,940–4,100 | Nov. 27 | 11    −2:43 | 5–33 | 18 |

The observations on Aug. 13 and Oct. 8 were made at the same sites on each date, and so were the observations on Sept. 11 and Nov. 27, except that a few observations on Nov. 27 were made a little above the area studied on Sept. 11.

The present climates of the Trans-Mexican Volcanic Belt determine both the kinds of plants and the kinds of soils which occur there. Similarly, past climates have affected the distribution of plants and the formation of soils. Modern conditions are the result both of contemporaneous physical factors and of historical ones.

Volcanism has been dominant in determining the physical environment of the Trans-Mexican Volcanic Belt. The high mountains, with many climatic zones from tropical to frigid, are the products of volcanic eruptions. The different ages of these mountains and the formations derived from them are important in any consideration of problems concerned with the origin, development, and extinction of species of plants.

CHAPTER IV

# The Species of *Sedum* Native in the

# Trans-Mexican Volcanic Belt

THE accounts of species in this chapter are organized according to a definite pattern. The accepted specific name appears as the heading at the beginning of each account. Then comes a paragraph devoted to diagnostic characteristics. Here are cited those features of greatest practical value in separating the species from all others in the genus. This discussion is followed by a detailed description.

Each description of a species or subspecies begins with indication of the number of plants and number of populations from which the data are derived. For each quantitative characteristic, the following are cited: $n$, the number of plants studied; $n\text{-}obs$, the number of observations of the characteristic in the whole sample; $\bar{x}$, the arithmetical mean of the sample; $s$, the standard deviation among plants of the sample; and $w$, the observed range of variation of the sample, the absolute extreme dimensions being cited. When the variation of one character is considered in relation to another, $b$, the regression coefficient per unit of the other, is indicated. As many characters as possible have been made quantitative in order to permit statistical comparisons. Although coefficients of variation are not regularly cited in the descriptions, they are easily calculated from the data available by multiplying the value for $s$ by 100 and dividing by the value for $\bar{x}$. Inclusion of $\bar{x}$ and $s$ thus makes possible an appraisal of the relative variability of samples; it also demonstrates the relationships of populations and indicates the different expressions of plants in the wild and under conditions of cultivation. The detailed quantitative data for the various samples provide an objective basis for conclusions about classification. Likewise they are a measure of the quality of the study, indicating whether evidence is strong or weak.

In order that descriptive details may be located easily, the descriptions are organized as a series of short paragraphs. The sequence of characters and paragraphs is as follows: habit, leaves, inflorescences, flowers, sepals, petals, stamens, nectaries, pistils, fruits, and seeds. To keep together information on any structure, quantitative and nonquantitative data are included side by side. This is a standard taxonomic procedure and avoids the necessity of consulting special tables for part of the data.

In the descriptions, certain data are always included unless information is lacking and a statement is made to that effect. These data are: height of the plants; length, width, and thickness of the blades of the leaves; number of flowers per inflorescence; diameter of the flowers; length and width of sepals and of petals; amount of adnation of epipetalous stamens to petals; length and diameter of anthers; length and width of nectaries; length of carpels; number of ovules per ovary; length of bodies of follicles; and length and diameter of seeds. In addition, the following details may be included: diameter of tubers or rhizomes when these are present; length of petioles when present; length of torus when present; length of cohesion of sepals, of petals, and of carpels when any of these are connate; and width of corky ridges on the margins of follicles if these are present. Unless otherwise mentioned, the following conditions may be assumed: leaves one per node, simple, and estipulate; sepals, petals, and pistils averaging five per whorl; stamens averaging ten; and placentation submarginal. Although these details have been checked for each plant studied, to save space they are not included in descriptions except when species depart from the usual condition.

All dimensions, unless otherwise stated, are of mature fresh structures. Figures for height apply to plants in flowering or fruiting condition. Data for floral parts apply to flowers at anthesis, generally with some anthers shedding pollen and others unopened.

The significance of differences among means of populations of species or between wild and cultivated plants, as determined by computing analyses of variance and by calculating variance ratios, often is indicated in the descriptions. They are further and more fully discussed in the section on variation following each formal description. When differences are designated as significant, the chances of samples being alike are between one in twenty and one in a hundred. This is the 5 per cent level of significance, indicated in tables of comparison by a single asterisk. When differences are designated as highly significant, the chance of samples being alike is less than one in a hundred. This is the 1 per cent level of significance, indicated in tables of comparison by a double asterisk. For explanation of the statistical methods employed, see Snedecor (1956).

If differences among populations are of such importance that subspecies are recognized, a key to these is provided. Such keys include subspecies occurring both within and outside the Trans-Mexican Volcanic Belt.

For species without subspecies, the various botanical names which have been applied are listed in chronological sequence, with brief discussion of each, after the detailed description and the consideration of variation. Since the names are in chronological sequence, the dates are placed at the left, before the names. Data accompanying each name include a complete bibliographical citation and designation of the type locality, location of the type, date of collection of the type, and name of the collector of the type. When names have been transferred from one status to another, reference to the previous publication is provided. When a species comprises subspecies, a synonymy, with all information just mentioned, is provided for each subspecies. Likewise, a description is provided for each subspecies.

Following the synonymy in the account of a species without subspecies, or after the description under the name of a subspecies, comes the section devoted to distribution. Here are cited the number of known populations and the general geographical distribution of these. When the number of populations is less than ten, the location of each is listed. Type populations and populations which have been studied in some detail are discussed at greater length. Ecological information is provided for these. Full discussions of populations include the precise location, date of discovery, name of discoverer, number of plants, extent of area, altitudinal range, kind of rocks and soil, and indication of drainage, pH, exposure, light, climate, commonest competitors, flowering time, and fruiting time.

In the account of each species, a discussion of relationships follows that on distribution. Here are included ideas about phylogeny and practical comparisons necessary to demonstrate the differences between related species. Finally, when persons have reported pertinent, original information, references to their publications are cited in a section at the end of each account. References to illustrations also are cited.

The accounts of species are arranged according to a system in which closely related ones are kept together and the sequence is from species with few to those with many specializations. This arrangement is discussed and evaluated in chapter VII.

Generic limits in the Crassulaceae are difficult to define. For purposes of the study in the Trans-Mexican Volcanic Belt, *Sedum* comprises species which have succulent stems and leaves, usually four- or five-merous flowers, as many pistils as petals, twice as many stamens as petals, no or slight cohesion ( <1 mm.) of petals, separate or nearly separate carpels, and simple, dry fruits, each dehiscent on the ventral suture. The following groups of species are excluded: *Villadia*, with the petals connate for >1.2 mm.; *Echeveria*, with the petals erect, thick, fleshy, and connate for >.8 mm. and with the floral stems axillary; *Graptopetalum*, also with axillary floral stems and petals connate for >1.5 mm., but these spreading from near the middle and either banded or spotted; and *Lenophyllum*, with the flowers in spikes of cymules and at least some of the leaves opposite or whorled. Problems exist with respect to the relationships of each of these genera with *Sedum*, as well as with each other. When intergeneric hybrids occur, these are discussed in the section on relationships under the appropriate species. Likewise, morphological characteristics suggesting relationship of any species of *Sedum* with other genera are discussed in the section on relationships under the species concerned. Despite the existence of some intergeneric hybrids and the sparsity of absolute morphological distinctions, the genera recognized here have practical value. This is the principal justification for maintaining them. The distinctions between the genera are further indicated in the key in chapter VI. Although that key is designed primarily for the identification of species of *Sedum*, it can also be used to identify, at least to genus, plants of other genera of Crassulaceae which might be mistaken for *Sedum*. That and the other keys to species are placed after the accounts of species in order that variation and the many problems involved in identification might first be emphasized.

My intention is to include in this publication discussion of all names applying to species of *Sedum* which occur naturally in the Trans-Mexican Volcanic Belt and also names proposed in *Sedum* for species in this area which either belong in other genera or cannot be interpreted satisfactorily. All names mentioned in the text, regardless of their status, are listed in alphabetical sequence in the index.

Certain binomials of Sessé and Mociño are of uncertain status. According to Dr. Elena Paunero, curator of the herbarium of the Instituto Botánico "Antonio José Cavanilles" in Madrid, the plants of Sessé and Mociño are at present in Chicago. John Millar, deputy director of the Chicago Natural History Museum, has reported that the following species of *Sedum* of Sessé and Mociño are not in the collection there: *S. anacampseros*, *S. arborescens*, *S. cordifolium*, *S. murale*, *S. paniculatum*, *S. reflexum*, and *S. spicatum*. But the museum has made available, at the suggestion of Dr. Rogers McVaugh, specimens illustrating *S. acre*, *S. peregrinum*, and four unpublished names. In the following text, I discuss *S. arborescens* and *S. peregrinum* under *S. oxypetalum*, *S. cordifolium* under *S. ebracteatum*, and *S. acre* under *S. bourgaei*. The identification of the remainder of the names is uncertain. The mention of entire, cuneiform leaves, decumbent stems, corymbose flowers, and flowering in July is not enough to identify *S. anacampseros*, Plantae Nouae Hispaniae, ed. 1, p. 74 (1888). That name possibly was wrongly applied to some Mexican species. *Sedum murale*, Flora Mexicana, p. 128 (1887), might apply to *S. moranense;* but without a confirming specimen or illustration, the interpretation is doubtful. The type locality is Zacatlán on the eastern escarpment of the Central Mexican Plateau. The species was growing there on the top of walls. *Sedum paniculatum*, Plantae Nouae Hispaniae, ed. 1, p. 75 (1888), with the stems three feet high and the inflorescences paniculate on peduncles arising below the leaves, is an *Echeveria*, possibly *E. gibbiflora*. *Sedum Reflexum*, Plantae Nouae Hispaniae, ed. 1, p. 75 (1888), as *S. anacampseros*, probably was wrongly applied to a Mexican species, possibly to *S. mexicanum*. An original description is not available; there are only the brief descriptions of Linnaeus and Haller, which apply to a European species. *Sedum spicatum*, Plantae Nouae Hispaniae, ed. 1, p. 75 (1888), according to Augustin de Candolle (1828) applies to *Echeveria coccinea* (Cav.) DC. An illustration of that has been cited as plate 87 in the volume of drawings Dessins des Plantes de Mociño et Sessé, prepared under the direction of de Candolle. The copies of this book at the New York Botanical Garden and at the Smithsonian Institution in Washington lack this plate, and Dr. Baehni has reported that the principal copy in Geneva similarly lacks it. The type locality is San Angel near the city of Mexico.

Lindley in 1838 described a *Sedum miserum* from plants raised in England from Mexican seeds. Hemsley (1879–1888) accepted this and provided a description apparently based on that of Lindley. Britton and Rose (1905) listed *S. miserum* among the excluded and doubtful species, unknown to them. Fröderström (1930–1935) did not mention the name. The original specimen is preserved at the University of Cambridge. Dr. S. M. Walters of the Botany School there has kindly provided a photograph of this type. It is *Villadia parviflora* (Hemsley) Rose. Since Lindley's specific epithet antedates by forty years Hemsley's *parviflora*, the name of the species must now be changed.[1] The nomenclatural type of the genus *Villadia* is this species.

Of the several species of *Sedum* proposed by Hemsley, *S. confusum* (Diag. Pl. Nov., 1: 10, 1878), described from a cultivated plant, questionably from Mexico, concerns us here because it appears to be related to *S. dendroideum*, a species occurring in the eastern portion of the Trans-Mexican Volcanic Belt, and also to *S. aoikon*. In my studies in this area, I have not found *S. confusum* either in the wild or in cultivation. Two clues concerning the location of populations of *S. confusum* are available. Walther (1935) reported that it occurs along the edges of streams and waterfalls near Pueblo Nuevo north of Pachuca. In 1949 I visited Pueblo Nuevo, but though I found *S. dendroideum* growing on rocks by a stream there, I saw no *S. confusum*. Another clue is from Fernando Schmoll. In

---

[1] *Villadia* **misera** (Lindley), comb. nov., fundata super *Sedum miserum* Lindley, Bot. Reg. 24:65 (1838).

1948 he reported that a plant of *S. confusum* which he had sent to me came from the state of Guanajuato. If this was from a wild population, possibly *S. confusum* is native on the Central Mexican Plateau. Elsewhere, I (1948) have discussed the relationships of *S. confusum*. Further data on this subject appear below in the accounts of *S. dendroideum* and *S. aoikon*.

Fröderström's *Sedum platystylum*, based on Ynez Mexia's collection no. 1594 (NY), from La Bufa, Jalisco, with petals connate for 1.2–1.6 mm., appears to be a *Villadia*.[2] Possibly it is related to *Villadia grandisepala*,[3] with petals connate for 1.6–1.8 mm., and to "*Altamiranoa galeottiana*," a species of which I have not seen specimens.

## 1. *SEDUM BOTTERII* (figs. 7–9)

Distinguishing features of *Sedum botterii* (fig. 7) are the oblanceolate or ovate, dull green leaves, large flowers, sepals as long as or longer than the petals, and the petals pale green speckled with purple or pink. The nectaries are large and red. The only plants which I have seen were epiphytes, but persons living in the region where *S. botterii* occurs have told me that it also grows on cliffs.

**Description.** Materials: 6 plants—4 from 2 trees of *Erythrina americana* and 2 from a tree of (? *Yucca elephantipes*), all from the Barranca de Cuautilla, north-northwest of Huatusco, Vera Cruz. Measurements marked cult. are of plants cultivated in the greenhouse at Ithaca, N.Y.

Plants of *Sedum botterii* are subshrubs having angulate stems with prominent ridges which extend diagonally from either side of each leaf base to adjacent sides of the next two lower leaves.

| | $n$ | $\bar{x}$ (dm.) | $s$ (dm.) | $w$ (dm.) |
|---|---|---|---|---|
| Height—cult. | 3 | .9 | .3 | .6–1.2 |

[2] *Villadia* **platystyla** (Fröderström), comb. nov., fundata super *Sedum platystylum* Fröderström, Act. Hort. Goth. 10 (App.): 38 (1936).

[3] *Villadia* **grandisepala** (Clausen), comb. nov., fundata super *Sedum grandisepalum* Clausen, Cact. Succ. Jour. 21: 149 (1949).

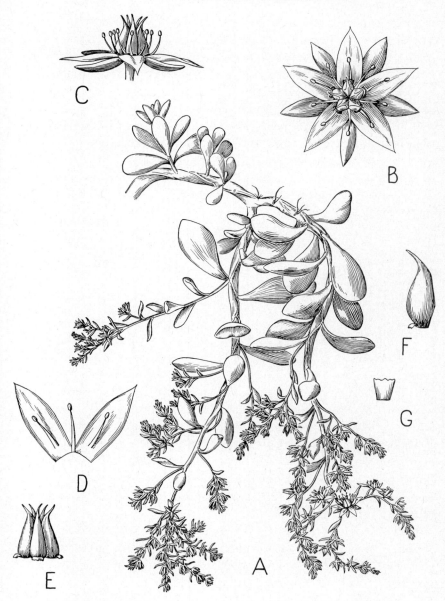

*Fig. 7.* Plant of *Sedum botterii* from the Barranca de Cuautilla, Vera Cruz, cultivated in the greenhouse at Ithaca, N.Y.   A. Habit sketch (x .4).   B. Flower from
above (x 2).   C. Flower from side (x 2).   D. Petal and stamens (x 2.4).   E. Pistils
(x 2.4).   F. Single pistil (x 3.2).   G. Nectary (x 4).

Leaves are oblanceolate or obovate, petiolate, rounded or slightly emarginate, dull green. Leaves attain maximum size when plants are in flower. Differences in dimensions of leaves between plants in the field and those in the greenhouse are not significant.

| | $n$ | $n$-obs. | $\bar{x}$ (mm.) | $s$ (mm.) | $w$ (mm.) |
|---|---|---|---|---|---|
| Length—wild | 6 | 15 | 39 | 9.7 | 14 −50 |
| —cult. | 3 | 14 | 51 | 6.9 | 42 −71 |
| Width—wild | 6 | 15 | 17 | 5.1 | 6 −22 |
| —cult. | 3 | 14 | 23 | 2 | 18 −31 |
| Thickness—wild | 6 | 15 | 2.5 | .4 | 2 − 4 |
| —cult. | 2 | 6 | 3.5 | .1 | 2.5− 4 |

Fifteen leaves, measured when fresh and 13 months later, after having been dried as herbarium specimens, shrank in all dimensions, but not significantly except in thickness, which difference was highly significant.

| | $\bar{x}$ (mm.) | $s$ (mm.) | $w$ (mm.) |
|---|---|---|---|
| Length—fresh | 38.8 | 9.9 | 14 −50 |
| —dried | 35.4 | 8.9 | 13 −46 |
| Width—fresh | 17 | 4.9 | 6 −22 |
| —dried | 14 | 4.1 | 6 −20 |
| Thickness—fresh | 2.5 | .6 | 2 − 4 |
| —dried | .1 | .03 | .1− .2 |

Inflorescences terminate main stems and branches; cymes are pendulous, of 1–10 cincinni; after flowering, the ends of the floral stems usually die and further growth is from lateral shoots arising from the lower portions of the stems.

| | $n$ | $n$-obs. | $\bar{x}$ | $w$ |
|---|---|---|---|---|
| No. of flowers per cyme—cult. | 3 | 9 | 38 | 7–114 |

Flowers (fig. 8) are pedicellate. Pistils can be separated from the torus without damaging the walls of the ovaries.

| | $n$ | $n$-obs. | $\bar{x}$ (mm.) | $s$ (mm.) | $w$ (mm.) |
|---|---|---|---|---|---|
| Pedicels—length—cult. | 2 | 16 | 3.1 | .9 | 1 − 5.6 |
| Flowers—diameter—cult. | 3 | 19 | 17.6 | 1.5 | 14 −19 |
| Torus—length—cult. | 2 | 15 | 1.5 | 0 | .8− 1.8 |

*Fig. 8.* Flowers of plant of *Sedum botterii* from the Barranca de Cuautilla, Vera Cruz, cultivated in the greenhouse, Ithaca, N.Y., March 21, 1956 (x 3.3).

Sepals are elliptic-oblong or oblanceolate-elliptical, green speckled with purple, unequal. Dimensions apply to longest sepal of each flower.

|  | $n$ | $n$-*obs.* | $\bar{x}$ (*mm.*) | $s$ (*mm.*) | $w$ (*mm.*) |
|---|---|---|---|---|---|
| Length—cult. | 3 | 19 | 7.7 | 2.7 | 4.4–12.4 |
| Width—cult. | 2 | 16 | 2 | .5 | 1.4– 2.9 |

Petals are lanceolate, acute, mucronate-appendaged, pale green speckled with purple or pink.

| | n | n-obs. | $\bar{x}$ (mm.) | s (mm.) | w (mm.) |
|---|---|---|---|---|---|
| Length—cult. | 3 | 19 | 8 | .2 | 6.8–8.9 |
| Width—cult. | 3 | 18 | 2.9 | .5 | 2.2–3.6 |

Eight petals, measured when fresh and again after drying, had shrunk significantly in width, but not in length.

| | $\bar{x}$ (mm.) | s (mm.) | w (mm.) |
|---|---|---|---|
| Length—fresh | 7.9 | .1 | 7.4–8.6 |
| —dried | 7.6 | .4 | 6.6–8.6 |
| Width—fresh | 3.1 | .1 | 2.6–3.6 |
| —dried | 2.4 | .05 | 2.1–2.8 |

Stamens have yellow anthers.

| | n | n-obs. | $\bar{x}$ (mm.) | s (mm.) | w (mm.) |
|---|---|---|---|---|---|
| Adnation of epipetalous filaments—cult. | 3 | 19 | 1.1 | 0 | .5–1.6 |
| Anthers—length—cult. | 2 | 16 | 1.2 | .1 | 1 –1.3 |
| —diameter—cult. | 2 | 16 | .6 | .01 | .5– .7 |

Nectaries are obovately subquadrate, erose, dark red or pink spotted with red.

| | n | n-obs. | $\bar{x}$ (mm.) | s (mm.) | w (mm.) |
|---|---|---|---|---|---|
| Length—cult. | 3 | 19 | 1.3 | .2 | 1 –1.7 |
| Width—cult. | 3 | 19 | 1 | .1 | .7–1.4 |

Pistils are erect; ovules linear, pendulous from the submarginal placentas.

| | n | n-obs. | $\bar{x}$ | s | w |
|---|---|---|---|---|---|
| Length—wild | 3 | 19 | 5.3mm. | .8mm | 4.1– 7mm. |
| No. of ovules per ovary—cult. | 3 | 19 | 28 | — | 16 –38 |

Follicles are divergent or erect.

| | n | n-obs. | $\bar{x}$ (mm.) | s (mm.) | w (mm.) |
|---|---|---|---|---|---|
| Length—wild | 2 | 10 | 3.3 | .4 | 2.4–4 |
| —cult. | 1 | 2 | 4.1 | — | 3.9–4.4 |

Seeds are linear, caudate at both ends, glabrous, yellow-brown.

|                 | $n$ | $n$-obs. | $\bar{x}$ (mm.) | $w$ (mm.) |
|-----------------|-----|----------|-----------------|-----------|
| Length—cult.    | 1   | 5        | 1.4             | 1.3–1.6   |
| Diameter—cult.  | 1   | 5        | .2              | .2        |

**Variation.** Although the plants of my sample were growing within 6 m. of each other, they differed in length and width of leaves, as well as in length of follicles. In the greenhouse, the three plants which survived after shipment from Mexico differed in length of leaves, length of pedicels, diameter of flowers, length and width of sepals, width of petals, length of anthers, length and width of nectaries, and length of pistils. These differences are interesting, especially because of the small size of the sample and of the population from which it came. Since no other *Sedum* occurs in association with *S. botterii*, the easiest explanation for this variability, if it is genetic, is mutation.

The average length of 13 petals of 4 dried plants from the Sierra de Chiapas is only 5.3 mm., but this is not significantly different from the length of petals of plants which flowered in the greenhouse at Ithaca. Similarly, the average length of 19 leaves of these same 4 dried plants, plus 1 other from the Sierra de Chiapas, is 24 mm., also not significantly different from the average length of 35 mm. of 15 dried leaves from the Barranca de Cuautilla. Although present data do not indicate significant differences between plants from the eastern base of Mt. Orizaba and those from the Sierra de Chiapas, some distinctions may exist. Until adequate numbers of plants from both regions have been grown together under similar conditions, this problem may remain unsettled.

Measurements of leaves and floral parts cited by Fröderström (1935), based on dried specimens, are smaller than those cited by me. Particularly striking is the difference in length of sepals. The average length of 19 sepals of the 3 plants in the greenhouse at Ithaca was 7.7 mm., whereas the range cited by Fröderström is 2.2–4 mm. Since the sepals shrink more than the petals in drying, they appear relatively longer with respect to the petals in fresh than in dried specimens.

**Nomenclature.** *Sedum botteri* Hemsley, Diag. Pl. Nov. 1: 10 (1878). The type locality is Orizaba. According to Hemsley, the type, collected by Botteri sometime between 1850 and 1878, is in the herbarium at Kew. I have studied an isotype (US). A collection of Sessé, Mociño, Castillo, and Maldonado (Bot. Gard., Madrid), available through the courtesy of the Chicago Natural History Museum, indicates that one of these collectors found the species between 1787 and 1804. The unpublished specific epithet on the label, under *Cotyledon*, probably antedates Hemsley's binomial.

**Distribution.** Besides the type population at Orizaba which, if extant, I have not rediscovered, I know about 8 populations of *Sedum botterii:* 2 at the eastern base of Mt. Orizaba—Barranca de Cuautilla in the municipality of Axocuapan and Córdoba; and 6 in the Sierra de Chiapas—between Tapalapa and Blanca Rosa (Santa Mónica), between Rincón Chamula and San Bartolo Rayón, Santa Cruz between Pueblo Nuevo Solistahuacán and Rincón Chamula (at an elevation of about 1,830 m.), Mapastepec, Siltepec, and Mt. Ovando. The maximum extent of the range of the species northeast and southwest is about 630 km. The distance between the populations at Córdoba and Santa Mónica is about 450 km.

Carl Purpus collected *Sedum botterii* at Axocuapan in 1909. I found 37 plants, including seedlings, in an area 6 x 4 m., on Aug. 8, 1955, in the Barranca de Cuautilla, municipality of Axocuapan, about 10 km. north-northwest of Huatusco, at an altitude of about 1,225 m. The plants were growing as epiphytes in moss, *Brachymenium systylium* (identified by Professor Albert Andrews) and other species, on the trunks of two trees of *Erythrina americana* and one of (? *Yucca elephantipes*). The drainage of the organic matter in which the plants were rooted was moderate, pH 5.4, and exposure north, northeast, and northwest. Commonest competitors were *Peperomia quadrifolia* and *Polypodium polypodioides*, the subspecies including var. *aciculare*. Two plants had follicles, but all seeds had been shed. Although I walked 14 km. each way on trails from Totutla to Ohuapa and the Barranca de Cuautilla, I found *S. botterii* at only one place. I was unable to confirm the statement of men in Ohuapa that this species is common on rocks in the Barranca de Tlilapa. Plants from the Barranca de Cuautilla, in the greenhouse at Ithaca, N.Y., have had flowers in anthesis in January, February, March, April, and July.

Bourgeau collected *Sedum botterii* at Córdoba in 1866. Matuda obtained it at Mapastepec in 1938, at Siltepec in 1936, and on

Mt. Ovando in 1939. T. MacDougall found it in 1951 at Santa Mónica, Rayón, and Santa Cruz.

**Relationships.** *Sedum botterii* appears to be closely related to *S. tortuosum.* It is one of the least specialized species in the Trans-Mexican Volcanic Belt. Possibly it is most like the ancestral stock from which various other groups of species have evolved. *Sedum dendroideum, S. oxypetalum, S. obcordatum,* and *S. longipes,* all relatively unspecialized in the groups to which they belong, each possess some features in common with *S. botterii. Sedum rhodocarpum* of the Sierra Madre Oriental has some similarities. Of species elsewhere in the world, perhaps *S. epidendrum* of the Ethiopian Plateau of Africa is most similar. Although plants of *S. hultenii* have sometimes been identified as *S. botterii,* that species possibly is not as closely related as some of the others just mentioned.

*Sedum botterii* and *S. tortuosum* both are epiphytes with flat leaves broadest above the middle. Both are relatively unspecialized in floral structure, without cohesion of parts. *Sedum tortuosum* has the longest seeds of any species of *Sedum* in the world. *Sedum botterii,* of the species of the Trans-Mexican Volcanic Belt, has the second longest seeds. In both *S. botterii* and *S. tortuosum,* the submarginal placentas extend only part of the length of the ovary. In *S. tortuosum* the placentas are subbasal, in *S. botterii* median. The two species differ in the color of the petals, those of *S. botterii* being pale green speckled with purple or pink, those of *S. tortuosum* white. Further, *S. botterii* differs from *S. tortuosum* in a highly significant degree in the average length of the largest leaves, 51 mm. versus 20 mm., and in the average width of the largest leaves, 23 mm. versus 6 mm., and in a significant degree in the average length of the sepals, 7.7 mm. versus 3 mm., and in the average width of the nectaries, 1 mm. versus .7 mm. The tests of significance are based on 3 plants of *S. botterii* and 5 plants of *S. tortuosum,* all cultivated under similar conditions in the greenhouse.

Small plants of *Sedum dendroideum* appear similar to those of *S. botterii.* Usually *S. dendroideum* is larger, with longer stems, shiny leaves, and yellow flowers. In addition, it differs from *S. botterii* in its smaller, yellow or white nectaries and smaller seeds. Further consideration of these differences appears in the discussion of relationships in the account of *S. dendroideum.*

Although the large, shrubby *Sedum oxypetalum* appears unlike *S.*

*botterii*, its floral structure also is relatively unspecialized. None of its floral parts cohere. Its petals are greenish or yellowish streaked with pink, similar to those of *S. botterii*. The principal specializations of *S. oxypetalum* are in vegetative parts, namely, deciduous leaves and branchlets, and the ability to withstand frost. Other differences from *S. botterii* are the following: stout trunks with bark peeling in papery layers; smaller, emarginate leaves; smaller flowers with shorter sepals and petals; and narrower, oblong, yellow nectaries.

Plants of *Sedum longipes* are trailing herbs with small, elliptical leaves. Its flowers are smaller than those of *S. botterii*. Its petals are pale green speckled with red, and its nectaries are large and dark red. In the color of petals and nectaries, as well as in the size of the latter, plus the lack of any cohesion of floral parts, flowers of *S. longipes* and *S. botterii* are remarkably similar. That *S. longipes* is derived from the same ancestral stock as *S. botterii* seems more reasonable than that it might be more closely related to some species in another part of the world.

*Sedum rhodocarpum* of the Sierra Madre Oriental of Mexico differs from *S. botterii* in the arrangement of its leaves in whorls of three, as well as in its decumbent habit, smaller nectaries, and shorter seeds. Its leaves, however, resemble in shape and size those of *S. botterii*; its stems also are angulate; and its petals are white becoming magenta-rose below the middle. It may be derived from the same ancestral stock as *S. botterii*.

Possibly *Sedum epidendrum* of the Ethiopian Plateau is also distantly related to *S. botterii*. Unfortunately, I have not had plants of that for study. According to Fröderström (1930–1935), its leaves are shorter than those of *S. botterii* (20–27 mm.), its sepals are very short (2 mm.), its petals cohere (.5–.7 mm.), and its seeds are long and winged (2–3 mm.). It and related species in the highlands of tropical Africa might be derived from the same ancestral group of species which in previous ages may have ranged widely in tropical forests. Today, these species, as *S. botterii* and related species in tropical America and *S. epidendrum* and its relatives in tropical Africa, may be isolated remnants of such a group.

Highly significant differences in the average lengths and widths of petals exist between *Sedum botterii* and *S. hultenii* of the eastern escarpment of the Central Mexican Plateau: 8.1 versus 4.7 mm.

and 2.9 versus 1.8 mm. In addition, plants of the two species, cultivated under uniform conditions, differ significantly in the average width of the leaves: 25 versus 15 mm. The margins of the leaves of *S. botterii* are entire; those of *S. hultenii* are obscurely crenate. Further, the petals of the two species differ in color, those of *S. botterii* being pale green speckled with purple or pink and those of *S. hultenii* yellow. When grown side by side, plants of these two species (fig. 9) appear quite different. Morphologically, *S. hultenii* resembles *S. dendroideum* more than it does *S. botterii.*

*Fig. 9. Sedum hultenii* (left) from near Huauchinango, Puebla, and *S. botterii* (right) from the Barranca de Cuautilla, Vera Cruz, as they appeared in the greenhouse, Ithaca, N.Y., March 26, 1956 (x .2).

## 2. *SEDUM TORTUOSUM* (figs. 10–14)

The very long, slender seeds of *Sedum tortuosum* and their attachment to nearly basal, submarginal placentas distinguish this species from all others. In addition, it differs from the other epiphytic species in the Trans-Mexican Volcanic Belt in having flowers with white petals and pale yellow nectaries.

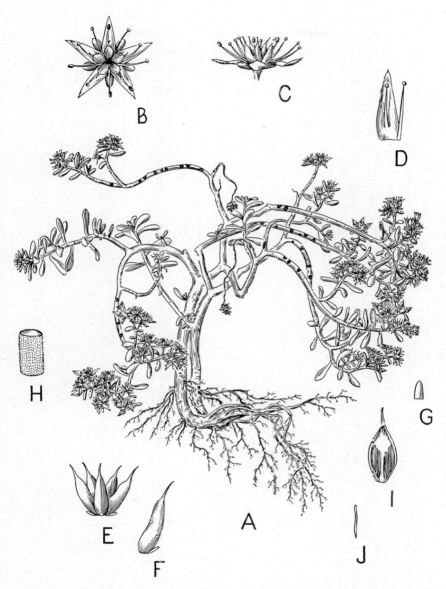

*Fig. 10.* Plant of *Sedum tortuosum* from the Nevado de Colima, cultivated in the greenhouse, Ithaca, N.Y.  A. Habit sketch (x .4).  B. Flower from above (x 1.6). C. Flower from side (x 1.6).  D. Petal and stamens (x 2.4).  E. Pistils (x 2.4). F. Single pistil (x 3.2).  G. Nectary (x 4).  H. Portion of stem (x 2.4).  I. Pistil spread open showing ovules (x 3.2).  J. Single ovule (x 4).

**Description.** Materials: 32 plants—1 from the ravine of the Tiscalatengo River 4 km. west of Tenancingo, Mexico; 10 from Capacuaro, northeast of Mt. Tancítaro, Michoacán; and 21 from the northwestern slope of the Nevado de Colima, Jalisco. Measurements marked cult. are of plants cultivated in the greenhouse at Ithaca, N.Y.

Plants of *Sedum tortuosum* are subshrubs (fig. 10), usually epiphytic, much branched, either erect, spreading, or pendulous; stems are gray-brown, reddish brown upward, finely papillose, with papillae .02–.1 mm. long.

| | $n$ | $n$-obs. | $\bar{x}$ (dm.) | $s$ (dm.) | $w$ (dm.) |
|---|---|---|---|---|---|
| Height | | | | | |
| Capacuaro—cult. | 1 | 1 | 1.4 | — | 1.4 |
| Nevado de Colima—cult. | 7 | 7 | 1.1 | .1 | 1 –1.5 |
| Length of floral stems | | | | | |
| Tiscalatengo Ravine | 1 | 3 | 2.2 | — | 2.1–2.3 |
| Nevado de Colima | 20 | 34 | 2 | .4 | 1.1–3.5 |

Leaves are mostly deciduous, oblanceolate or elliptic-spatulate, minutely spurred, obtuse, rarely slightly emarginate, finely papillose at apex, green or suffused with red.

| | $n$ | $n$-obs. | $\bar{x}$ (mm.) | $s$ (mm.) | $w$ (mm.) |
|---|---|---|---|---|---|
| Length | | | | | |
| Tiscalatengo Ravine | 1 | 4 | 24 | — | 23 –26 |
| Capacuaro | 10 | 20 | 19 | 4.8 | 9 –27 |
| Nevado de Colima | 19 | 45 | 24 | 5.4 | 15 –41 |
| Capacuaro—cult. | 1 | 6 | 18 | — | 15 –23 |
| Nevado de Colima—cult. | 6 | 24 | 20 | 2 | 15 –28 |
| Width | | | | | |
| Tiscalatengo Ravine | 1 | 4 | 8 | — | 7 – 9 |
| Capacuaro | 10 | 20 | 7.7 | 1.8 | 4 –11 |
| Nevado de Colima | 19 | 45 | 6.4 | 1 | 4 –10 |
| Capacuaro—cult. | 1 | 6 | 6 | — | 6 – 7 |
| Nevado de Colima—cult. | 6 | 24 | 5.8 | .8 | 4 – 9 |
| Thickness | | | | | |
| Tiscalatengo Ravine | 1 | 3 | 1.1 | — | 1.1 |
| Capacuaro | 10 | 20 | 1 | .2 | .6– 1.5 |
| Nevado de Colima | 12 | 27 | 1.2 | .2 | .7– 1.8 |
| Nevado de Colima—cult. | 6 | 24 | 1.7 | .3 | 1.1– 2.4 |

Inflorescences are terminal on primary and secondary axes, and are compound dichasial cymes.

|  | n | n-obs. | $\bar{x}$ | w |
|---|---|---|---|---|
| No. of flowers per cyme |  |  |  |  |
| Tiscalatengo Ravine | 1 | 3 | 5 | 3– 8 |
| Capacuaro | 7 | 7 | 6 | 1–12 |
| Nevado de Colima | 20 | 47 | 7 | 2–15 |
| Capacuaro—cult. | 1 | 6 | 4 | 1– 6 |
| Nevado de Colima—cult. | 6 | 19 | 8 | 1–31 |

Flowers are on papillose pedicels.

|  | n | n-obs. | $\bar{x}$ (mm.) | s (mm.) | w (mm.) |
|---|---|---|---|---|---|
| Pedicels—length |  |  |  |  |  |
| Capacuaro | 3 | 5 | 3.3 | 1.3 | 2.4– 4.8 |
| Flowers—diameter |  |  |  |  |  |
| Tiscalatengo Ravine | 1 | 5 | 10.8 | — | 9 –13 |
| Capacuaro | 3 | 4 | 13.5 | 0 | 12 –15 |
| Nevado de Colima | 11 | 33 | 14.7 | 2.3 | 11 –19 |
| Capacuaro—cult. | 1 | 12 | 14.7 | — | 12 –17 |
| Nevado de Colima—cult. | 2 | 3 | 14 | 2.1 | 13 –16 |
| Torus—length |  |  |  |  |  |
| Nevado de Colima—cult. | 5 | 18 | .8 | .2 | .4– 1 |

Sepals are oblong, oblong-elliptical, lanceolate, or ovate, minutely spurred, obtuse or acute, green, sometimes speckled with red, very unequal. Dimensions are of the longest sepals of each flower.

|  | n | n-obs. | $\bar{x}$ (mm.) | s (mm.) | w (mm.) |
|---|---|---|---|---|---|
| Length |  |  |  |  |  |
| Tiscalatengo Ravine | 1 | 5 | 2.5 | — | 2.2–3.1 |
| Capacuaro | 3 | 5 | 3.4 | .1 | 2.8–4 |
| Nevado de Colima | 11 | 34 | 3.4 | 1.1 | 2.1–5.8 |
| Capacuaro—cult. | 1 | 12 | 2.5 | — | 1.7–3.4 |
| Nevado de Colima—cult. | 6 | 20 | 3.6 | .6 | 1.7–7.7 |
| Width |  |  |  |  |  |
| Tiscalatengo Ravine | 1 | 5 | 1.2 | — | 1.1–1.3 |
| Capacuaro | 3 | 5 | 1.6 | .2 | 1.4–1.8 |
| Nevado de Colima | 11 | 34 | 1.3 | .3 | .8–1.9 |
| Nevado de Colima—cult. | 1 | 1 | 2.4 | — | 2.4 |

Petals are lanceolate, acute, mucronate-appendaged, white, green on dorsal keel, sometimes streaked with pink at apex or on dorsal surface.

|  | n | n-obs. | x̄ (mm.) | s (mm.) | w (mm.) |
|---|---|---|---|---|---|
| **Length** | | | | | |
| Tiscalatengo Ravine | 1 | 5 | 5.9 | — | 5.1– 6.7 |
| Capacuaro | 3 | 5 | 7.9 | 1 | 6.9– 9 |
| Nevado de Colima | 11 | 34 | 7.5 | 1.2 | 5.2–10.1 |
| Capacuaro—cult. | 1 | 12 | 7.4 | — | 6.0– 8.6 |
| Nevado de Colima—cult. | 6 | 19 | 6.9 | .3 | 5.8– 7.8 |
| **Width** | | | | | |
| Tiscalatengo Ravine | 1 | 5 | 2 | — | 1.6– 2.3 |
| Capacuaro | 3 | 5 | 2.3 | .1 | 2.2– 2.5 |
| Nevado de Colima | 11 | 34 | 2.2 | .3 | 1.5– 2.8 |
| Capacuaro—cult. | 1 | 12 | 2.2 | — | 1.6– 2.9 |
| Nevado de Colima—cult. | 6 | 19 | 2.1 | .1 | 1.8– 2.4 |

Stamens have the anthers yellow suffused with red, sometimes yellow or red.

|  | n | n-obs. | x̄ (mm.) | s (mm.) | w (mm.) |
|---|---|---|---|---|---|
| **Adnation of epipetalous filaments** | | | | | |
| Tiscalatengo Ravine | 1 | 5 | 1.3 | — | 1.0–1.9 |
| Capacuaro | 3 | 5 | 1.6 | .1 | 1.4–1.9 |
| Nevado de Colima | 11 | 34 | 1.3 | .2 | .8–2 |
| Nevado de Colima—cult. | 6 | 19 | .9 | .2 | .4–1.6 |
| **Anthers—length** | | | | | |
| Tiscalatengo Ravine | 1 | 3 | .9 | — | .9 |
| Capacuaro | 3 | 5 | 1 | .1 | .9–1 |
| Nevado de Colima | 4 | 12 | .8 | .01 | .8–1 |
| Capacuaro—cult. | 1 | 9 | .8 | — | .7–1.1 |
| Nevado de Colima—cult. | 5 | 10 | .8 | .1 | .6–1 |
| **Anthers—diameter** | | | | | |
| Capacuaro—cult. | 1 | 9 | .6 | — | .5– .8 |
| Nevado de Colima—cult. | 6 | 12 | .6 | 0 | .5– .6 |

Nectaries are subquadrate or reniform, pale yellow or creamy white.

|  | n | n-obs. | x̄ (mm.) | s (mm.) | w (mm.) |
|---|---|---|---|---|---|
| **Length** | | | | | |
| Tiscalatengo Ravine | 1 | 5 | .8 | — | .6– .9 |
| Capacuaro | 3 | 5 | .8 | 0 | .7– .9 |
| Nevado de Colima | 11 | 34 | 1 | .1 | .7–1.3 |
| Capacuaro—cult. | 1 | 12 | .8 | — | .6–1 |
| Nevado de Colima—cult. | 6 | 19 | 1.1 | .1 | .7–1.3 |

| | n | n-obs. | x̄ (mm.) | s (mm.) | w (mm.) |
|---|---|---|---|---|---|
| Width | | | | | |
| Tiscalatengo Ravine | 1 | 5 | .8 | — | .7– .9 |
| Capacuaro | 3 | 5 | .9 | 0 | .8–1 |
| Nevado de Colima | 11 | 34 | .8 | .1 | .6–1 |
| Capacuaro—cult. | 1 | 12 | .9 | — | .6–1.2 |
| Nevado de Colima—cult. | 6 | 19 | .8 | .1 | .4–1.1 |

Pistils (fig. 11) have ovules linear and erect on submarginal placentas near bases of ovaries.

| | n | n-obs. | x̄ | s | w |
|---|---|---|---|---|---|
| Length | | | | | |
| Nevado de Colima—cult. | 6 | 19 | 5.2 mm. | .4 mm. | 3.8– 6.4 mm. |
| No. of ovules per ovary | | | | | |
| Nevado de Colima—cult. | 6 | 19 | 11 | — | 4 –17 |

Follicles are brown, widely spreading at maturity, with corky lips about .3 mm. wide toward bases on ventral margins.

| | n | n-obs. | x̄ (mm.) | s (mm.) | w (mm.) |
|---|---|---|---|---|---|
| Length | | | | | |
| Nevado de Colima—cult. | 4 | 8 | 4.4 | .1 | 3.4–5 |

Seeds are brown, glabrous, winged at both ends, appearing linear.

| | n | n-obs. | x̄ (mm.) | s (mm.) | w (mm.) |
|---|---|---|---|---|---|
| Length | | | | | |
| Nevado de Colima—cult. | 4 | 8 | 2.3 | .3 | 1.9–2.8 |
| Diameter | | | | | |
| Nevado de Colima—cult. | 4 | 8 | .2 | .1 | .2– .4 |

**Variation.** On the basis of study of plants in the field, differences among the three populations of *Sedum tortuosum* in the Trans-Mexican Volcanic Belt are not significant except for the length of the nectaries, which are significantly shorter in the plants from the ravine of the Tiscalatengo River and Capacuaro. Only one plant from Capacuaro flowered in the greenhouse. That had shorter nectaries (av. .8 mm.) than those (av. 1.1 mm.) of plants from the Nevado de Colima, and the plant was taller. Otherwise, in the greenhouse this plant and the ones from the Nevado de Colima were similar.

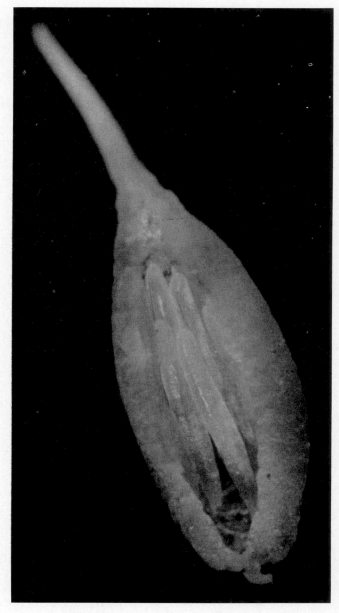

*Fig. 11.* Pistil of *Sedum tortuosum*, opened on the ventral suture with ovules exposed, Dec. 19, 1956 (x 27).

In the field, plants in the same population differed in the following characters: length of longest floral stems, length, width, and thickness of leaves, length of pedicels, diameter of flowers, length and width of sepals, length and width of petals, length of adnation of stamens, and length and width of nectaries. In the greenhouse, plants differed in the width and thickness of leaves, length of torus, width of petals, length of adnation of the epipetalous stamens, length and width of nectaries, and length of

Fig. 12. *Sedum tortuosum* from Nevado de Colima, in the greenhouse, Ithaca, N.Y., Dec. 5, 1956 (x 4.3).

seeds. Otherwise, differences noted in the field were not present among plants in the greenhouse, but length of floral stems, length of pedicels, and width of sepals were not studied for the plants grown at Ithaca.

Plants of *Sedum tortuosum* do not thrive in cultivation (fig. 12). Those growing in the greenhouse had shorter, narrower leaves than they did in the field. These differences in foliage are highly significant.

Plants from the Sierra Madre del Sur resemble those from the Trans-Mexican Volcanic Belt. The range of variation of most characters is similar for plants from the two regions.

Flowers vary greatly in size depending upon their positions in the cymes. Central flowers are largest, and those on peripheral branches the shortest. The two flowers shown in fig. 13 are from the same cyme. One flower of a cultivated plant was 6-merous.

*Fig. 13.* Large and small flowers from a plant of *Sedum tortuosum* from Capacuaro, Michoacán, cultivated in the greenhouse, Ithaca, N.Y., Jan. 2, 1957 (x 4.8).

**Nomenclature.** *Sedum tortuosum* Hemsley. Diag. Pl. Nov. 1: 10 (1878). Type locality: Mexico, without more specific location. John Parkinson, English consul in Mexico from 1838 to 1840, collected the type which is preserved in the herbarium at Kew. I have studied a photograph of the type. This is a portion of a plant with some leaves and a packet of which I have not seen the contents. The identity of the specimen seems certain. This is confirmed by additional information of Hemsley (1879–1888) that the seeds are linear and almost 3 mm. ("sesquilineam") long. No other species of *Sedum* in Mexico has seeds that long. Were subspecies to be recognized, a problem might exist concerning the subspecific status of Parkinson's specimen, but fortunately such a difficulty has not arisen.

Synonyms are:

1903. *Sedum Nelsoni* Rose, Bull. N.Y. Bot. Gard. 3: 43. Type locality: in the Sierra Madre del Sur, on the road between Ayusinapa and Petatlán, Guerrero. Type: E. W. Nelson, no. 2,191 (US 48,382), Dec. 14, 1894.

1936. *Sedum lignicaule* Fröderström, Act. Hort. Goth. 10 (App.): 36–37 (1935). Type locality: in the western portion of the Trans-Mexican Volcanic Belt, rocky, precipitous slope, alt. 2,500 m., La Bufa, Real Alto, Jalisco. Type: Ynez Mexia, no. 1,600 (NY), Jan. 30, 1927.

**Distribution.** (fig. 14). The main area of occurrence of *Sedum tortuosum* appears to be in the Sierra Madre del Sur. T. MacDougall collected plants at five localities in Oaxaca, and Nelson obtained it in Guerrero between Ayusinapa and Petatlán and near Chilpancingo. The species appears to have invaded the Trans-Mexican Volcanic Belt from the south. I have studied three populations in

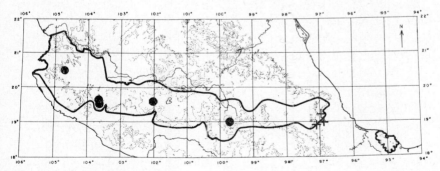

*Fig. 14.* Known distribution of *Sedum tortuosum* (•) and *S. botterii* (+) in the Trans-Mexican Volcanic Belt and adjacent regions.

this belt. In addition, George Kennedy collected plants on the slope of the Volcán de Colima, at an altitude of 1,372 m. Samples of this collection have reached me from Paul Hutchison of the University of California.

On Jan. 1, 1956, I found a plant in flower in the ravine of the Tiscalatengo River 4 km. west of Tenancingo, Mexico. Carlos Palomé, who accompanied me, saw additional plants, but none in bloom. The flowering plant was on a cliff of andesite, facing northwest, at an elevation of 2,320 m. It was about 5 m. above the bed of the river.

The plants at Capacuaro, northeast of Mt. Tancítaro, Michoacán, are epiphytic on three trees of *Quercus* on the east side of the village and 20 m. east of the highway, at an altitude of 2,350 m. I found this population on Sept. 29, 1955, and studied it again on Dec. 5, 1955. The plants had small floral buds on Sept. 29. These were larger, but still not expanded on Dec. 5. The oaks were only 5 m. apart. The maximum number of plants of *Sedum* seen was 18. These were in semishade, exposed to the west and north, rooted in organic matter and volcanic ash on the bark of the oaks. The pH ranged from 5.8 to 6.6. Drainage was moderate. Commonest competitors were mosses, lichens, and ferns. The lava on which the oaks were growing, according to the data of Williams (1950), is not more than 2,000 years old. One of the oaks is *Quercus reticulata* H. et B.; the other two possibly are *Q. microphylla* Née, though some of the leaves of these trees are nearly twice as long as is usual for that species. In the greenhouse at Ithaca, a plant of *S. tortuosum* from Capacuaro flowered in January.

Drs. Rogers McVaugh and R. L. Wilbur, on March 28, 1949, found *Sedum tortuosum* on the northwestern slope of the Nevado de Colima, above Jazmín and about a kilometer above El Isote. The plants were past flowering at that time and had fruits or immature fruits. On Dec. 10, 1955, I visited this locality and found about 350 plants of *S. tortuosum* in two ravines, one about 2 km. eastsoutheast of El Isote and the other about 2 km. southeast of El Isote. The area of occurrence is 5–6 km. southeast of Jazmín, at an elevation of 2,490–2,510 m., in a region where oaks and firs, *Abies religiosa*, grow together in the forest. The total area in which these two local populations occur is about 2,250 sq. m. The plants are epiphytic on trees, mostly *Quercus*, and rooted in organic matter and moss with pH ranging from 6.5 to 7.2. They are in partial shade, exposed to the northeast, east, east-southeast, and south-southwest. Commonest competitors are mosses, lichens, ferns, and a species of *Peperomia*. Professor Andrews has identified one of the mosses as *Brachythecium flexiventrosum* (C.M.) Jaeg. On Dec. 10, 1955, *S. tortuosum* was at the height of bloom, but some buds were still unopened, and other flowers were past anthesis. At Ithaca, plants from the Nevado de Colima have flowered in November, December, January, and April.

In December, 1913, Carl Reiche collected a *Sedum* epiphytic on trees on the Nevado de Colima. Specimens are preserved in the herbarium of the Instituto de Biología, Mexico. They may be *S. tortuosum*, but are peculiar in several respects: very large flowers with sepals 7–9 mm. long and petals 10–13 mm. long, presence of what appears to be a tuber 7 mm. in diameter, and undeveloped ovules only 1.1 mm. long. Some of the shoots appear etiolated, suggesting that the plants may have been left for a long time after collecting, before pressing. My opinion is that Reiche's specimens probably are *S. tortuosum*, but etiolated, with remarkably large flowers, undeveloped ovules, and a tuber.

The localities in the Sierra Madre del Sur in Oaxaca where MacDougall has found *Sedum tortuosum* are Santo Domingo Lachivitó, Santo Domingo Chontecomatlán, Santo Tomás Téipan, Cerro Madreña between Quiechapa and Lachivía, and the Tlaxiaco Region. Plants at some of these places appear to be more vigorous than those in the volcanic belt. For example, MacDougall reported seeing plants with stems 9 dm. high on the Cerro Madreña.

**Relationships.** Of the species in the Trans-Mexican Volcanic Belt, *Sedum tortuosum* is most closely related to *S. botterii*. The distinctions between these have already been discussed under the latter species. Possibly even more closely related is *S. guatemalense* of the volcanic mountains of central and western Guatemala. That also is an epiphyte with long, narrow seeds, caudate at either end, 2–3 mm. long. It differs from *S. tortuosum* in its narrower, subterete leaves, 2–4 mm. wide; in shorter, pink petals, 4–6 mm. long; and in longer pedicels, 3–8 mm. long. *Sedum millspaughii*, including *S. salvadorense*, another species of the Central American Volcanic Upland, also appears related, but the seeds of that are unknown. It differs from *S. tortuosum* especially in having the petals connate basally and the stamens very short, about 2 mm. long. Another possible relative is *S. epidendrum* of the Ethiopian Plateau. According to Fröderström (1930–1935), that has long, winged seeds as does *S. tortuosum*, but it differs in having the petals connate for .5–.7 mm. and the pedicels 5–7 mm. long. Other species described as having the placentas near the bases of the ovaries are *S. przewalskii* and *S. purdomii*, both of the eastern part of the Tibetan Highlands in Asia. Plants of these species are tiny inhabitants of alpine regions, possibly annual or biennial, in appearance very unlike *S. tortuosum*. Probably their phylogenetic history has been different. If this idea is correct, then reduction of the placentas to the basal parts of the ovaries has occurred independently at least twice in *Sedum*.

## 3. *SEDUM DENDROIDEUM* (figs. 15–20)

Bright green, spatulate leaves and paniculate cymes of yellow flowers on axillary branches distinguish *Sedum dendroideum* from most other species of *Sedum* in the Trans-Mexican Volcanic Belt. The plants are shrubby, usually pendent from cliffs or epiphytic. The stems surpass in length those of all other species which I have studied. Sometimes they are 5 m. long. The leaves arise spirally. The leaves of *S. obcordatum* and *S. stahlii* are opposite. Larger vegetative and floral parts separate *S. dendroideum* from *S. confusum, S. luteoviride*, and other yellow-flowered species. *S. aoikon*, with leaves similar in size to *S. dendroideum*, has shorter sepals.

Several authors have reported that *Sedum dendroideum* (including *S. praealtum*) has medicinal properties. Tetzmitl, crudely illustrated in the Badianus manuscript, the Aztec herbal of 1552 (Emmart, 1940), very likely is this species. Its medicinal value probably was known long before the Spanish conquest. In the Badianus manuscript, the stems are mentioned as being used in a lotion for swollen eyes, fevers, swellings about bruised veins, and burns. According to the edition of Hernández, 1651, by Ximénez (1888, p. 135), Tetzmitl de Tonalla possesses similar properties, as well as additional ones, but the description of the leaves as long and narrow is inappropriate for *S. dendroideum*. The reported distribution in the warm regions of the lower Mixteca needs to be confirmed, though that is a reasonable possibility. Standley (1922) stated that the juice of *S. dendroideum* is astringent and is used for hardening the gums and for hemorrhoids, chilblains, and dysentery. He also reported the belief that if applied to the forehead, it stops nosebleed. Martínez (1944) cited the use of the crushed plant for burns, for washing the gums, and for scurvy. In addition, he mentioned that the juice of the leaves, applied to the eyes, cures irritation. Likewise, Standley and Steyermark (1946) stated that about Cobán, in Guatemala, the juice of the leaves is employed for treating inflammation of the eyes and mouth. Palarea (1954) has reported the complete recession of cataracts in the eyes of three dogs and of three women after application of the juice from leaves of plants from Guatemala which he called "*S. praealtum*." According to Thomas and Ranson (1954), metabolism in plants which they listed as "*S. praealtum*" is of the acid type characteristic of other Crassulaceae, in which respiratory $CO_2$ is consumed in acid synthesis in the hours of darkness.

**Description.** Materials: 19 plants—3 from Río Blanco, Vera Cruz; 1 from Maltrata, Vera Cruz; 8 from Malinche; 4 from Iztaccihuatl; 1 from Popocatepetl; 1 from San José Chiltepec, Oaxaca; and 1 of unknown origin in the wild. Plants marked below as cult. were grown in the greenhouse at Ithaca, N.Y. Measurements marked pr. are from flowers preserved in alcohol. Those marked cf. are of plants cultivated in an experiment in a cold frame at Ithaca.

Plants of *Sedum dendroideum* are shrubs with stems erect, pendulous, or prostrate, .6–5 m. long, with bark of older portions brown or gray-brown. In the greenhouse, the stems are erect. Occasionally stems are cristate. The following heights apply to nonflowering plants after a year of cultivation. Differences among populations are not significant.

| | $n$ | $\bar{x}$ (dm.) | $s$ (dm.) | $w$ (dm.) |
|---|---|---|---|---|
| Río Blanco—cult. | 3 | 3 | .6 | 2.5–3.9 |
| Maltrata—cult. | 1 | 3.1 | — | 3.1 |
| Malinche—cult. | 8 | 2.7 | .3 | 2 –3.1 |
| Iztaccihuatl—cult. | 4 | 2.8 | .6 | 1.9–3.4 |
| San José Chiltepec—cult. | 1 | 3 | — | 3 |

Leaves are elliptic-oblanceolate, spatulate, or obovate, sessile or petiolate, rounded, obtuse, or apiculate, lustrous, sometimes either red or dotted with red on margins. Marginal glands, either red or dark green, occur only on the leaves of plants from Maltrata and San José Chiltepec.

Differences in length of leaves among populations in the wild are not significant, but in cultivation highly significant differences exist between plants from Río Blanco and Malinche and between plants from Malinche and Iztaccihuatl. The difference between dried and fresh leaves is significant.

| | $n$ | $n$-obs. | $\bar{x}$ (mm.) | $s$ (mm.) | $w$ (mm.) |
|---|---|---|---|---|---|
| Length | | | | | |
| Río Blanco | 2 | 18 | 56 | 15 | 36–76 |
| Maltrata | 1 | 7 | 41 | — | 37–45 |
| Malinche | 3 | 13 | 47 | 4.6 | 33–61 |
| Iztaccihuatl | 3 | 16 | 70 | 12.8 | 56–94 |
| Popocatepetl | 1 | 2 | 33 | — | 15–51 |
| Río Blanco—cult. | 3 | 9 | 59 | 3.1 | 55–64 |
| Maltrata—cult. | 1 | 3 | 46 | — | 40–54 |
| Malinche—cult. | 8 | 24 | 41 | 3.9 | 31–48 |
| Iztaccihuatl—cult. | 4 | 12 | 52 | 4 | 36–80 |
| San José Chiltepec—cult. | 1 | 3 | 36 | — | 31–39 |
| Iztaccihuatl—fresh lvs. | 1 | 10 | 66 | (7.8) | 56–76 |
| —dried lvs. | 1 | 10 | 58 | (9.1) | 42–69 |

Differences in width of leaves among populations in the wild are insignificant, but in cultivation the differences between plants from Río Blanco and Malinche and between plants from Malinche and Iztaccihuatl are highly significant. The difference between fresh and dried leaves is highly significant.

| | $n$ | $n$-obs. | $\bar{x}$ (mm.) | $s$ (mm.) | $w$ (mm.) |
|---|---|---|---|---|---|
| Width | | | | | |
| Río Blanco | 2 | 18 | 18.8 | 4.1 | 13–24 |
| Maltrata | 1 | 7 | 17.5 | — | 15–19 |
| Malinche | 3 | 13 | 17.2 | .3 | 14–20 |
| Iztaccihuatl | 3 | 16 | 25.3 | 3.1 | 20–37 |
| Popocatepetl | 1 | 2 | 13.5 | — | 7–20 |
| Río Blanco—cult. | 3 | 9 | 20 | 1 | 19–25 |
| Maltrata—cult. | 1 | 3 | 17 | — | 16–18 |
| Malinche—cult. | 8 | 24 | 15 | 1.7 | 12–19 |

| | n | n-obs. | $\bar{x}$ (mm.) | s (mm.) | w (mm.) |
|---|---|---|---|---|---|
| Iztaccihuatl—cult. | 4 | 12 | 20 | 0 | 18–25 |
| San José Chiltepec—cult. | 1 | 3 | 17.3 | — | 16–19 |
| Iztaccihuatl—fresh lvs. | 1 | 10 | 23 | (1.6) | 20–26 |
| —dried lvs. | 1 | 10 | 19 | (3.3) | 12–24 |

Differences in regression of length per millimeter of width of leaves among populations and between fresh and dried leaves are not significant.

| | n | n-obs. | b (mm.) |
|---|---|---|---|
| Regression of length per mm. of width | | | |
| Río Blanco—cult. | 3 | 9 | .8 |
| Malinche—cult. | 8 | 24 | 1.5 |
| Iztaccihuatl—cult. | 4 | 12 | 4.3 |
| —fresh lvs. | 1 | 10 | (.04) |
| —dried lvs. | 1 | 10 | (1.7) |

Differences in thickness of leaves among populations in the wild are not significant, but in cultivation the difference is highly significant between plants from Río Blanco and Malinche. Also highly significant is the difference between fresh and dried leaves. The plants from Maltrata and San José Chiltepec have the thickest leaves.

| | n | n-obs. | $\bar{x}$ (mm.) | s (mm.) | w (mm.) |
|---|---|---|---|---|---|
| Thickness | | | | | |
| Río Blanco | 2 | 18 | 2.7 | .1 | 2 –4 |
| Maltrata | 1 | 7 | 4 | — | 4 |
| Malinche | 3 | 13 | 2.6 | .1 | 2 –3 |
| Iztaccihuatl | 3 | 16 | 2.9 | .3 | 2.4 –4 |
| Popocatepetl | 1 | 2 | 2 | — | 1.5 –2.5 |
| Río Blanco—cult. | 3 | 9 | 2 | .2 | 2 –4 |
| Maltrata—cult. | 1 | 3 | 4 | — | 4 |
| Malinche—cult. | 8 | 24 | 2 | .1 | 1 –3 |
| Iztaccihuatl—cult. | 4 | 12 | 2 | 0 | 2 –3 |
| San José Chiltepec—cult. | 1 | 3 | 4.4 | — | 4 –5 |
| Iztaccihuatl—fresh lvs. | 1 | 10 | 2 | (.1) | 3 –4 |
| —dried lvs. | 1 | 10 | .02 | (.007) | .01– .03 |

Inflorescences are paniculate cymes of 7–38 cincinni at apices of axillary branches.

| | n | n-obs. | x̄ | w |
|---|---|---|---|---|
| No. of flowers per cyme | | | | |
| Malinche | 1 | 1 | 162 | 162 |
| Iztaccihuatl | 2 | 6 | 126 | 83–178 |
| Popocatepetl | 1 | 2 | 146 | 44–249 |
| San José Chiltepec—cult. | 1 | 3 | 68 | 55– 82 |

Flowers are sessile or on very short pedicels, rarely 4- or 6-merous; one flower of a plant on Iztaccihuatl had 7 petals and 10 pistils.

| | n | n-obs. | x̄ (mm.) | s (mm.) | w (mm.) |
|---|---|---|---|---|---|
| Flowers—diameter | | | | | |
| Malinche | 1 | 4 | 17 | — | 15–18 |
| Iztaccihuatl | 2 | 6 | 15 | 1 | 13–18 |
| Popocatepetl | 1 | 2 | 11 | — | 9–14 |
| Río Blanco—cf. | 2 | 14 | 13 | .7 | 11–15 |
| San José Chiltepec—cult. | 1 | 3 | 16 | — | 16 |
| Torus—length | | | | | |
| Iztaccihuatl—pr. | 1 | 3 | 1 | — | .7–1.2 |
| San José Chiltepec—cult. | 1 | 3 | .7 | — | .6– .8 |
| Origin unknown—cult., pr. | 1 | 3 | .7 | — | .6– .8 |

Sepals are ovate, lanceolate, or elliptic-oblong, sometimes minutely spurred, obtuse, green, unequal, usually separate, but connate for .2–.3 mm. in preserved flowers of a cultivated plant of unknown origin. The plant with connate sepals is similar vegetatively to plants from Río Blanco. Dimensions are of the longest sepals of each flower.

| | n | n-obs. | x̄ (mm.) | s (mm.) | w (mm.) |
|---|---|---|---|---|---|
| Length | | | | | |
| Malinche | 1 | 4 | 3 | — | 2.4–3.7 |
| Iztaccihuatl | 2 | 6 | 8.1 | 0 | 6.4–9.6 |
| Popocatepetl | 1 | 2 | 3.5 | — | 3 –4 |
| Río Blanco—cf. | 2 | 14 | 4.5 | 1 | 3.1–6.1 |
| San José Chiltepec—cult. | 1 | 3 | 2.5 | — | 1.8–3 |
| Origin unknown—cult., pr. | 1 | 2 | 1.7 | — | 1.5–2.1 |
| Width | | | | | |
| Malinche | 1 | 4 | 1.8 | — | 1.7–1.9 |
| Iztaccihuatl | 2 | 6 | 2.5 | 0 | 1.9–3.2 |
| Popocatepetl | 1 | 2 | 1.2 | — | 1 –1.5 |
| Río Blanco—cf. | 1 | 7 | 1.7 | — | 1.6–1.9 |
| San José Chiltepec—cult. | 1 | 3 | 1.7 | — | 1.6–1.7 |
| Origin unknown—cult., pr. | 1 | 2 | 1.4 | — | 1.2–1.6 |

Petals are lanceolate, acute or obtuse, mucronate-appendaged, yellow, green on dorsal keel above middle.

| | $n$ | $n$-obs. | $\bar{x}$ (mm.) | $s$ (mm.) | $w$ (mm.) |
|---|---|---|---|---|---|
| Length | | | | | |
| Malinche | 1 | 4 | 8.4 | — | 7.3–9 |
| Iztaccihuatl | 2 | 6 | 8.5 | 0 | 7.5–9.5 |
| Popocatepetl | 1 | 2 | 6.2 | — | 5.5–7 |
| Río Blanco—cf. | 2 | 10 | 6.4 | .5 | 5.4–7 |
| San José Chiltepec—cult. | 1 | 3 | 7.8 | — | 7.5–8.1 |
| Origin unknown—cult., pr. | 1 | 2 | 6.6 | — | 6.6–6.7 |
| Width | | | | | |
| Malinche | 1 | 4 | 3.3 | — | 3 –3.6 |
| Iztaccihuatl | 2 | 6 | 3.3 | .2 | 3 –4 |
| Popocatepetl | 1 | 1 | 2.5 | — | 2.5 |
| Río Blanco—cf. | 2 | 14 | 2.1 | .1 | 1.9–2.5 |
| San José Chiltepec—cult. | 1 | 3 | 3.2 | — | 3.1–3.2 |
| Origin unknown—cult., pr. | 1 | 2 | 1.6 | — | 1.3–1.9 |

Stamens have yellow anthers.

| | $n$ | $n$-obs. | $\bar{x}$ (mm.) | $s$ (mm ) | $w$ (mm.) |
|---|---|---|---|---|---|
| Adnation of epipetalous filaments | | | | | |
| Iztaccihuatl | 2 | 6 | .9 | 0 | .8–1 |
| Popocatepetl | 1 | 1 | .5 | — | .5 |
| San José Chiltepec—cult. | 1 | 3 | 1.1 | — | .8–1.3 |
| Origin unknown—cult., pr. | 1 | 2 | 1.1 | — | 1.1–1.2 |
| Anthers—length | | | | | |
| Malinche | 1 | 2 | 1.1 | — | .9–1.3 |
| Iztaccihuatl | 1 | 1 | 1.2 | — | 1.2 |
| San José Chiltepec—cult. | 1 | 3 | 1.6 | — | 1.5–1.6 |
| Origin unknown—cult., pr. | 1 | 2 | 1 | — | 1 |
| Anthers—diameter | | | | | |
| Iztaccihuatl—pr. | 1 | 3 | .9 | — | .9 |
| San José Chiltepec—cult. | 1 | 3 | .8 | — | .7– .9 |
| Origin unknown—cult., pr. | 1 | 2 | .4 | — | .4– .5 |

Nectaries are subquadrate or reniform, truncate, broadly rounded or emarginate, pale yellow, yellowish white, cr translucent.

| | $n$ | $n$-obs. | $\bar{x}$ (mm.) | $s$ (mm.) | $w$ (mm.) |
|---|---|---|---|---|---|
| Length | | | | | |
| Malinche | 1 | 4 | .6 | — | .5– .7 |
| Iztaccihuatl | 2 | 6 | .7 | .04 | .6– .9 |

| | n | n-obs. | x̄ (mm.) | s (mm.) | w (mm.) |
|---|---|---|---|---|---|
| Popocatepetl | 1 | 1 | .5 | — | .5 |
| Río Blanco—cf. | 1 | 7 | .4 | — | .3–.6 |
| San José Chiltepec—cult. | 1 | 3 | .4 | — | .3–.5 |
| Origin unknown—cult., pr. | 1 | 2 | .3 | — | .3 |
| Width | | | | | |
| Malinche | 1 | 4 | .7 | — | .6–.8 |
| Iztaccihuatl | 2 | 6 | .8 | .09 | .5–.9 |
| Popocatepetl | 1 | 1 | .5 | — | .5 |
| San José Chiltepec—cult. | 1 | 3 | .6 | — | .5–.7 |
| Origin unknown—cult., pr. | 1 | 2 | .4 | — | .4–.5 |

Pistils are erect or divergent and are yellow.

| | n | n-obs. | x̄ | w |
|---|---|---|---|---|
| Length | | | | |
| Malinche | 1 | 1 | 4.5 mm. | 4.5 mm. |
| Popocatepetl | 1 | 1 | 4.5 mm. | 4.5 mm. |
| San José Chiltepec—cult. | 1 | 3 | 5.8 mm. | 5.6–5.9 mm. |
| Origin unknown—cult., pr. | 1 | 2 | 5 mm. | 5 mm. |
| No. of ovules per ovary | | | | |
| Iztaccihuatl—pr. | 1 | 3 | 59 | 48–71 |
| Río Blanco—cf. | 2 | 14 | 26 | 18–32 |
| San José Chiltepec—cult. | 1 | 3 | 65 | 60–68 |
| Origin unknown—cult., pr. | 1 | 2 | 43 | 39–48 |

Follicles are brown, widely divergent, with lips of ventral margins .1–.2 mm. wide.

| | n | n-obs. | x̄ (mm.) | s (mm.) | w (mm.) |
|---|---|---|---|---|---|
| Length | | | | | |
| Malinche | 3 | 13 | 3.2 | .4 | 2.5–3.6 |
| Iztaccihuatl | 1 | 10 | 4.6 | — | 3.9–5.5 |
| Popocatepetl | 1 | 2 | 4.2 | — | 3.5–5 |

Seeds are brown, elliptic-pyriform, finely verrucose.

| | n | n-obs. | x̄ (mm.) | s (mm.) | w (mm.) |
|---|---|---|---|---|---|
| Length | | | | | |
| Malinche | 3 | 9 | .6 | .05 | .6–.8 |
| Diameter | | | | | |
| Malinche | 3 | 9 | .3 | 0 | .2–.3 |

**Variation.** Visits to populations of *Sedum dendroideum* in 1955 were mostly at the wrong season for flowers. Further, only two plants from the Trans-Mexican Volcanic Belt, propagated at Ithaca, have flowered. As a result, data for an appraisal of variation are sparse. Although the four populations studied in 1955 differ from each other in some respects, testing 15 characters of plants under natural conditions does not reveal significant differences. In the greenhouse, differences among samples from these same populations are highly significant in length, width, and thickness of leaves. Within populations, plants differed in the field in length and width of leaves and length of follicles and in cultivation in length and width of leaves, diameter of flowers, and length of both sepals and petals.

On the basis of the shrinkage, noted in the preceding tables, of ten leaves collected from a plant on the western slope of Iztaccihuatl, measured when fresh on Sept. 7, 1955, and again in dried condition on April 21, 1957, herbarium specimens are unreliable for information about the dimensions of leaves.

The four populations studied in the field in 1955 differ ecologically. Some of the differences are indicated in the following table:

| Location | n-plants | Area | Alt. range | pH | Drainage |
|---|---|---|---|---|---|
| Río Blanco | 130 | .5 x .5 km. | 1,330–1,370 m. | — | moderate |
| Maltrata | 3 | 5 x 2 m. | 1,779–1,780 m. | 7.4 | excessive |
| Malinche | >2,000 | 2 x 2 km. | 3,390–3,600 m. | 6.6–7.2 | moderate |
| Iztaccihuatl | >1,300 | 2 x 1 km. | 2,910–3,450 m. | 6.2–6.8 | poor to moderate |

The plants at Río Blanco are in the humid, tropical zone. They are shaded for part of the day. Those at Maltrata are exposed to the sun through most of the day. The plants on Malinche and Iztaccihuatl are in the zone of firs, *Abies religiosa*, where frosts are of frequent occurrence. Since different specific names are available for three of these populations and since the fourth is as different from the others as these are from each other and also since differences in length, width, and thickness of leaves are highly significant when plants from these populations are grown under similar conditions, some taxonomic recognition is reasonable. The populations are too much alike to be different species, but too dissimilar to belong to the same subspecies. Accordingly, they are included in four different subspecies which are isolated geographically and ecologically.

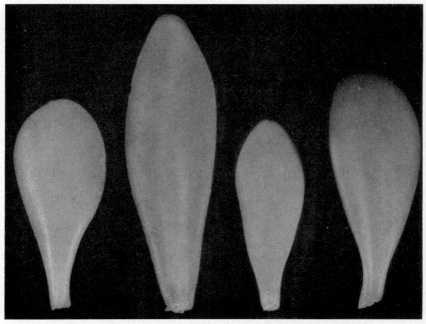

*Fig. 15.* Leaves of four subspecies of *Sedum dendroideum* from plants cultivated in the greenhouse, Ithaca, N.Y. From left to right: ssp. *dendroideum* from Maltrata, ssp. *praealtum* from Río Blanco, ssp. *parvifolium* from Malinche, and ssp. *monticola* from Iztaccihuatl, April 22, 1957 (ca. x 1.4).

## KEY TO SUBSPECIES

A. Leaves spatulate, broadly rounded at apex, cuneate and petiolate basally, averaging 4 mm. thick, 41 mm. long, and 17 mm. wide, with margins having subepidermal glands which appear as reddish or dark green dots.......................ssp. *dendroideum*, p. 69

AA. Leaves oblanceolate and obscurely petiolate or oblong-elliptical and sessile, averaging 2–3 mm. thick, 40–91 mm. long, and 16–30 mm. wide, with margins lacking subepidermal glands...........B

   B. Leaves oblong-elliptical and sessile, averaging 46–67 mm. long and 16–22 mm. wide; petals averaging 2–2.2 mm. wide.......
    ....................................ssp. *praealtum*, p. 70

   BB. Leaves oblanceolate and obscurely petiolate, averaging 40–91 mm. long and 17–30 mm. wide; petals averaging 2.5–3.6 mm. wide..............................................C

      C. Leaves averaging 40–52 mm. long and 17–18 mm. wide; sepals averaging 3 mm. long.........ssp. *parvifolium*, p. 72

      CC. Leaves averaging 65–91 mm. long and 24–30 mm. wide; sepals averaging 8 mm. long.........ssp. *monticola*, p. 73

*Sedum dendroideum* ssp. *dendroideum*

**Nomenclature.** *Sedum dendroideum* A.P. DC., Mém. Fam. Crass., p. 37, pl. 9 (1828). The brief, original description is based on drawings, reproduced as plate 9, taken from Mociño's unpublished Flora of Mexico. The distinctive shape of the leaves, mentioned in the description as obovate-cuneate and shown in the illustration, makes reasonably certain the application of this name. Whether or not the plant was preserved from which the drawings were made is uncertain. Neither is the locality known from which this plant was originally collected. In the absence of a type, de Candolle's plate 9 should serve for typification.

The distinctive features of ssp. *dendroideum* are the thick, spatulate leaves with the margins having subepidermal glands which may appear as reddish or dark green dots. No other subspecies of *Sedum dendroideum* has this condition. Plants belonging to ssp. *dendroideum*, included in the above description, are from Maltrata and San José Chiltepec. The plant from San José Chiltepec flowered in the greenhouse in Ithaca in December, 1956.

**Distribution.** Subspecies *dendroideum* occurs in the Central American Volcanic Upland of Guatemala and in the Sierra Madre del Sur of Mexico. It occurs at least as far north as the southeastern base of Mt. Orizaba at Maltrata, Vera Cruz. The description of *Sedum praealtum* by Standley and Steyermark (1946, p. 413) indicates that plants which they had seen are *S. dendroideum* ssp. *dendroideum*. Further, herbarium specimens collected by them and by E. W. Nelson from five localities in Guatemala are this

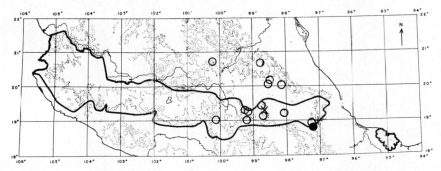

*Fig. 16.* Known distribution in the Trans-Mexican Volcanic Belt and adjacent regions of the subspecies of *Sedum dendroideum:* ssp. *dendroideum* (•), ssp. *praealtum* (+), ssp. *parvifolium* (o), and ssp. *monticola* (x).

subspecies. In Mexico, it is known from Maltrata and from Tlaxiaco and San José Chiltepec in Oaxaca, the two latter populations discovered by T. MacDougall.

At Maltrata, I found only three plants on Nov. 6, 1955. These were in an area of 10 sq. m., at an altitude of 1,780 m., in the midst of populations of *Sedum lucidum* and *S. stahlii*. The plants were on a slope facing southeast and, except in the late afternoon, were exposed to the full amount of sunlight. The largest plant was 7.5 dm. high, with a trunk 3 cm. in diameter. The rocks at the site were limestone; drainage was excessive; and pH was 7.2. Besides the other two species of *Sedum*, commonest competitors were composites, mints, a species of grass, and a *Tillandsia*. At the time of my visit, the *S. dendroideum* had tiny floral buds. Although stems with buds were sent to Ithaca, transplanting was too hard on the cuttings and no flowers developed. In the garden at Ithaca, a plant from Maltrata was more sensitive to freezing than were plants of the other subspecies, although it did survive the first, light frosts.

## *Sedum dendroideum* ssp. *praealtum*

**Nomenclature.** *Sedum dendroideum* ssp. **praealtum** (A. DC.), comb. nov., fundatum super *Sedum praealtum* Alphonse de Candolle, Mém. Soc. Phys. et Hist. Nat. Genève 11: 445–447 (1847–1848). The type was a cultivated plant, which was received from an amateur and which flowered at Geneva, Switzerland, in May, 1847. The locality of origin, date of collection in the wild, and collector all are unknown. De Candolle did not indicate in his description whether or not he preserved a herbarium specimen of the type. He was uncertain about the taxonomic status of his plant and remarked that, except for the leaves, it was the same as the plant illustrated in A. P. de Candolle's Mémoire sur la Famille des Crassulacées, plate 9. He suggested that either the drawing of the leaves in plate 9 is not exact or else his plant, *S. praealtum*, is a distinct species or variety. He described the leaves as oblong-obovate, sessile, obtuse, 15–24 lines long, and 6–8 lines wide.

The diagnostic characters of ssp. *praealtum* are the elliptic-oblanceolate, sessile leaves which are both longer and thinner than those of ssp. *dendroideum*, the large cymes with many cincinni, and the narrow petals less than 2.5 mm. wide. In the description of

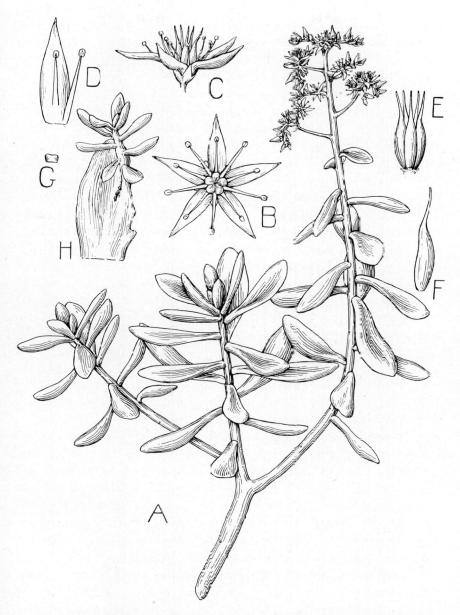

*Fig. 17.* Plant of *Sedum dendroideum* ssp. *praealtum* of unknown origin, cultivated in the greenhouse, Ithaca, N.Y. A. Habit sketch (x .5). B. Flower from above (x 2.5). C. Flower from side (x 2.5). D. Petal and stamens (x 4). E. Pistils (x 4). F. Single pistil (x 5). G. Nectary (x 7.5). H. Fasciated portion of stem (x .8).

the species, the data for the plants from Río Blanco and for the plant of unknown origin apply to ssp. *praealtum*.

**Distribution.** The only place where I have seen ssp. *praealtum* growing in the wild is at Río Blanco, Vera Cruz. It could have been introduced there, but is just as likely native. Pérez Arbeláez and Cuatrecasas, no. 8,179A (US), have collected it at an altitude of 2,750 m. near Arcabuco in the Department of Boyacá, Colombia. Whether or not it is native there is unknown. Since ssp. *praealtum* commonly is cultivated, the possibility of naturalization anywhere in tropical America is great.

At Río Blanco, about 130 plants occurred in an area about .5 km. long, on limestone on the south side of the river, from 1,330 to 1,370 m. above sea level. The plants were in partial shade, exposed to the west. Small plants may have been seedlings, but they also could have developed from broken parts of stems or leaves which had rooted. The soil in which they were growing was a moderately drained, sandy loam. On Nov. 9, 1955, plants had neither flowers nor buds. *Kalanchoe pinnata*, surely naturalized, was a common competitor, as also was *Epidendrum ibaguense*. The only other competing species of Crassulaceae was *Echeveria nuda*.

## *Sedum dendroideum* ssp. **parvifolium**

Subspecies nova *Sedi dendroidei* cum foliis 47 ± 12.4 mm. longis, 17.2 ± 1.9 mm. latis et 2.6 ± .5 mm. crassis; mutatio longitudinis per mm. latitudinis foliorum 1.5 mm.; sepal separata, circiter 3 mm. longa. Typus in Herbario Wiegand, Universitatis Cornellianae, de Malinche, in declivitate inter septentriones et orientem spectante, 50 m. sub cavo sub fonte, Manantiales de la Concha, collectio Roberti Clausenii, planta una, 1955, Oct. 16, est.

The small, relatively thin leaves distinguish ssp. *parvifolium* from the other subspecies. The shorter sepals, averaging 3 mm. long, separate it from ssp. *monticola*. All data in the preceding description for plants from Malinche apply to ssp. *parvifolium*.

**Distribution.** Subspecies *parvifolium* occurs in the eastern part of the Trans-Mexican Volcanic Belt and in the adjacent Central Mexican Plateau to the north. Mostly it is found on rocks in the zone where *Abies religiosa* is common. Populations in the Trans-Mexican Volcanic Belt and discoverers of each are: Sierra Negra, Edward Balls (US); Manantiales de la Concha, Malinche, Edward

Balls (US); Texcoco, Eugène Bourgeau (photo published by Fröderström, 1930–1935); Popocatepetl, Edward Balls (US); near
San Angel, Valley of Mexico, Joseph Rose and Joseph Painter
(US); Río Hondo Canyon, Cyrus Pringle (NY, US); Montes Las
Tres Marías, Harald Fröderström and Eric Hultén (NY); and Tel-
pintla, District of Temascaltepec, George Hinton (US). Specimens of the Mexican Geographical Exploring Commission, labeled
as from Jalapa and Puebla, may be this subspecies. Possibly the
specimens originated in mountains near these cities. A single, nonflowering plant, found by my daughter Joanna, on the lava southeast of Las Vigas, northeast of the Cofre de Perote, might also be
ssp. *parvifolium*.

At the time of my visit to the northeastern slope of Malinche on
Oct. 16, 1955, plants of ssp. *parvifolium* were mostly in bud. Only
a few flowers were in anthesis. The plants occurred there in the
Cañada de San Juan, on banks of breccia and on cliffs facing in
all directions. Small plants appeared to be seedlings. The only
species of Crassulaceae occurring with the *Sedum dendroideum* was
*Villadia batesii*. I saw no evidence there of hybridization between
these two species. *Acaena elongata* was a vigorous competitor of the
*S. dendroideum*, as also were several species of mosses.

### *Sedum dendroideum* ssp. *monticola*

**Nomenclature.** *Sedum dendroideum* ssp. **monticola** (T. S. Bran-
deg.), comb. nov., fundatum super *Sedum monticola* T. S. Brandegee,
Univ. Calif. Pub. Bot. 6: 498 (1919).

Brandegee's description of *Sedum monticola* is inadequate. It is
based on fragmented, dried specimens obtained by Carl Purpus,
no. 7,690 (UC 115,361), on Iztaccihuatl. Except for the reported
color of the flowers, which might be Brandegee's appraisal derived
from the dried specimens, the fragments of the type, which I examined in 1940, could be *S. dendroideum*. The oblong sepals, described by Brandegee as about 4 mm. long, are longer than those
of the other subspecies. On a basis of the length of these, plus the
locality, but with considerable hesitation, I base on Brandegee's
species the subspecies common in the large ravine tributary to
the Milpulco Valley on Iztaccihuatl. Regarding the color of the
flowers, the petals of some of my dried specimens have faded to
pale yellow or white. Further, the leaves have become significantly

shorter and narrower in drying. If Purpus collected specimens with small leaves, the kind of discrepancies existing between the dimensions cited by Brandegee and my own are to be expected. Fröderström (1930–1935, pl. 14) published a photograph of the type collection.

The diagnostic characters of ssp. *monticola* appear to be the large sepals, in my sample averaging 8.1 mm. long and 2.5 mm. wide, and the long leaves which are significantly longer and broader than those of ssp. *parvifolium*, averaging 70 mm. long and 25 mm. wide.

**Distribution.** Subspecies *monticola* is known only from the western slope of Iztaccihuatl. The population there appears to be disjunct from that of ssp. *parvifolium* on Popocatepetl.

In the big ravine tributary to the Milpulco Valley, ssp. *monticola* occurs both on cliffs of basalt and of conglomerate and as a pendulous epiphyte on *Quercus*. On Sept. 4, 1955, plants had tiny, green buds. On Dec. 18, 1955, these plants had buds, flowers in anthesis, and some immature fruits. Although small plants occur, they could be developed from broken parts of stems or even from leaves. *Villadia batesii*, the only other species of Crassulaceae in the vicinity, grows on the same cliffs with the *Sedum dendroideum*. At one place, plants occur which are morphologically intermediate between the two species. These plants appear to be sterile. They are what Praeger called *S. amecamecanum* and are discussed in detail below. The population of ssp. *monticola* occurs on Iztaccihuatl near the upper limits of the distribution of *Quercus* and in the zone of *Abies religiosa*. It does not extend into the alpine zone.

**Relationships.** The species most closely related to *Sedum dendroideum* are *S. aoikon*, *S. confusum*, and *S. cremnophila*. These all appear to be more specialized than *S. dendroideum*. *Sedum cremnophila* is native in the Trans-Mexican Volcanic Belt, *S. aoikon* may be native, but *S. confusum* is known only from cultivation.

*Sedum aoikon* is similar to ssp. *praealtum* of *S. dendroideum* in the narrowness of its petals, but differs in dimensions of leaves and sepals. My samples of both are too small for a satisfactory comparison. On the basis of two plants of *S. aoikon* and three plants of *S. dendroideum* ssp. *praealtum* cultivated in the greenhouse, differences in average width and thickness of leaves are significant, respectively 14 mm. and 1.8 mm. in *S. aoikon* and 20 mm. and 3 mm. in *S. dendroideum* ssp. *praealtum*. Likewise, *S. aoikon* resembles *S. dendroideum* ssp. *parvifolium* in length of sepals and in width and thickness of leaves, but in each of these characteristics is smaller.

*Sedum confusum* appears like a small edition of *S. dendroideum*. It is easily separated from ssp. *parvifolium*, the subspecies which it most resembles, by the following differences in dimensions of leaves, which are based on plants cultivated under similar conditions:

| | S. dendroideum ssp. parvifolium | | | | S. confusum | | | |
|---|---|---|---|---|---|---|---|---|
| | n | n-obs. | $\bar{x}$ | s | n | n-obs. | $\bar{x}$ | s |
| | | | (mm.) | (mm.) | | | (mm.) | (mm.) |
| Length** | 8 | 24 | 41 | 3.9 | 4 | 11 | 20 | 0 |
| Width* | 8 | 24 | 15 | 1.7 | 4 | 11 | 11.7 | 0 |

In addition, the petals of *Sedum confusum* are significantly shorter than those of *S. dendroideum*, and the inflorescences have fewer flowers ($\bar{x} = 24$).

*Sedum cremnophila* obviously differs from *S. dendroideum* in its thick, dark green leaves, long, narrow inflorescences, and smaller flowers. Of the subspecies of *S. dendroideum*, ssp. *monticola* appears most similar to *S. cremnophila*. Both have long sepals, large leaves, and large nectaries, but they are easily distinguished by the following differences:

| | S. dendroideum ssp. monticola | | | | S. cremnophila | | | |
|---|---|---|---|---|---|---|---|---|
| | n | n-obs. | $\bar{x}$ | s | n | n-obs. | $\bar{x}$ | s |
| | | | (mm.) | (mm.) | | | (mm.) | (mm.) |
| Leaves—width* | 4 | 12 | 20 | 0 | 4 | 32 | 38 | 7 |
| —thickness** | 4 | 12 | 2 | 0 | 4 | 32 | 12.4 | 1.2 |
| Petals—length** | 2 | 6 | 8.5 | 0 | 9 | 36 | 6 | .7 |
| —width* | 2 | 6 | 3.3 | .2 | 9 | 36 | 2.8 | .3 |

The data for leaves are from plants cultivated under similar conditions in the greenhouse. The data for petals are from plants in the wild.

*Sedum aoikon*, *S. confusum*, and *S. cremnophila* all differ from *S. dendroideum* in having smaller flowers. *Sedum aoikon* and *S. confusum* also have shorter anthers than do either *S. dendroideum* or *S. cremnophila*. Further, the sepals of *S. aoikon* are minutely connate as in some flowers of *S. dendroideum* ssp. *praealtum*, to which it appears closely related, and its inflorescences appear condensed. The leaves of *S. confusum* are much smaller than those of *S. dendroideum*, but the leaves of the other two species are as large or larger. In considering these four species phylogenetically, *S. dendroideum*, with its large leaves and flowers, appears to be the least specialized of the group, *S. aoikon* and *S. confusum* intermediate, and *S. cremnophila*, with its thick leaves and adjustment to a semiarid environment, plus its seemingly condensed, elongate inflorescences, the most specialized.

The superficial differences between *Sedum dendroideum* and *S. botterii* have already been considered in the discussion of the latter species. The decision as to which of these is the least specialized is difficult to make. Both species have wide, disjunct ranges. Both are variable, but *S. dendroideum* has become adjusted to a larger variety of environmental niches. Some of its populations regularly endure freezing; others have become adjusted to semiarid conditions. Possibly *S. dendroideum* is the more specialized of the two species, but comparative anatomical studies still are necessary and, of course, fossils, if they could be found, would be very helpful.

An unexpected relationship of *Sedum dendroideum* is with *Villadia batesii*. Though my evidence is all circumstantial, it supports the idea that these two species have hybridized in nature and produced plants of the sort which Praeger named *S. amecamecanum*, based on a collection of Carl Purpus in 1906, his no. 108, from Mt. Iztacci-huatl. I have studied an isotype (US), and I have also had in cultivation plants, distributed in the horticultural trade, which could be parts of the original collection. The three specimens of the isotype are without flowers or fruits. They are labeled as from "rocks near and above timberline." Praeger listed the type locality as Amecameca. Possibly he had this information from Dr. Rose, who sent the specimen to him. In any event, the conclusion from the data on the herbarium label and the published information is that the type locality is on the side of Iztaccihuatl toward Ame-cameca. Praeger described the type as having pale yellow flowers with nectaries whitish basally and deep orange above.

On Sept. 4, 1955, in walking from La Joya, on the southwestern side of Iztaccihuatl, to Amecameca, I saw about 20 plants of *Sedum amecamecanum* on the northern bank and at the base of cliffs in a large ravine tributary to the Milpulco Valley, at an elevational range of 3,430 to 3,450 m. above sea level. The plants were in bud. One appeared very similar to the *S. amecamecanum* which I had cultivated in Ithaca. Other Crassulaceae nearby were *S. dendroideum* and *Villadia batesii*. On Dec. 18, 1955, some plants of *S. amecamecanum* were at the height of flowering, but most were without flowers. *Sedum dendroideum* and *Villadia batesii* also were in flower. Distances between plants of *S. amecamecanum* and *S. dendroideum* were >5 cm., and between S. *amecamecanum* and *Villadia batesii* >4 dm. Plants of *S. amecamecanum* were both in semishade and in the open exposed to the south, south-southeast, and southwest. Altogether I counted 50 plants in an area of 2,000 sq. m. The site is on the north side of the brook, just northwest of a spectacular rock known to natives as the Finger. The pH of the soil about the roots of *S. amecamecanum* ranged from 6.6 to 6.8. Drainage was good. Although small plants were present, all could have developed vegetatively. I found no plants which positively were seedlings. Some plants of *S. amecamecanum* appeared so similar to *Villadia batesii* that close examination was necessary to see the differences. Because time on Iztaccihuatl was precious, I devoted primary attention to *S. amecamecanum*. I made detailed measurements and notes on 10 plants of that, 2 plants of *S dendroideum*, and 2 plants of *Villadia batesii*. The results, based on plants in nature, are summarized in the following table. The intermediate status of *S. amecamecanum* is obvious.

| | *S. dendroideum* | | *S. amecamecanum* | | *V. batesii* | |
|---|---|---|---|---|---|---|
| | $\bar{x}$ | $s$ | $\bar{x}$ | $s$ | $\bar{x}$ | $s$ |
| No. of plants | 2 | | for stems and lvs. 10, for fls. 7 | | 2 | |
| No. of obs. | 6 | | for stems and lvs. 37, for fls. 28 | | 6 | |
| **Stems** | | | | | | |
| Habit | erect or pendulous | — | decumbent, repent, or pendulous | — | erect or procumbent | — |
| | (m.) | | (m.) | (m.) | (m.) | (m.) |
| Length | 1 | — | .26 | .1 | .15 | .06 |
| **Leaves** | (mm.) | (mm.) | (mm.) | (mm.) | (mm.) | (mm.) |
| Length** | 70 | 12.8 | 19.6 | 2.3 | 14 | 0 |
| Width** | 25.3 | 3.1 | 4.5 | .5 | 3 | 0 |
| Thickness** | 2.9 | .3 | 1.7 | .1 | 1.4 | .06 |
| **Inflorescences** | | | | | | |
| No. of flowers | 126 | — | 6 | — | 4 | — |

|  | S. dendroideum | | S. amecamecanum | | V. batesii | |
|---|---|---|---|---|---|---|
|  | $\bar{x}$ | s | $\bar{x}$ | s | $\bar{x}$ | s |
| Sepals | (mm.) | (mm.) | (mm.) | (mm.) | (mm.) | (mm.) |
| Length* | 8.1 | 0 | 8.9 | .8 | 6.8 | .4 |
| Width** | 2.5 | 0 | 2 | .1 | 1.7 | .1 |
| Petals |  |  |  |  |  |  |
| Length | 8.5 | 0 | 8.5 | .4 | 8.1 | 0 |
| Length of connate portion** | 0 | 0 | 2.5 | .2 | 3.9 | 0 |
| Width** | 3.3 | .2 | 3.8 | .2 | 3 | .06 |
| Color | yellow | — | white or pinkish white | — | pinkish white | — |
| Stamens | (mm.) | (mm.) | (mm.) | (mm.) | (mm.) | (mm.) |
| Length of adnation of filaments opposite petals** | .9 | 0 | 2.7 | .2 | 3.9 | 0 |
| Nectaries |  |  |  |  |  |  |
| Length | .7 | .04 | .7 | .04 | .6 | 0 |
| Width | .8 | .09 | .7 | .1 | .5 | 0 |
| Color | white or yellowish white | — | pale yellow or pinkish white | — | dark red | — |

*Sedum amecamecanum* differs highly significantly from both *S. dendroideum* and *Villadia batesii* in six of the characters studied. In each of these characters it is intermediate between the other two species. In addition, a highly significant difference between *S. amecamecanum* and *V. batesii* exists in width of petals and a significant difference in length of sepals, but the differences in these characters (figures underlined in foregoing table) between *S. amecamecanum* and *S. dendroideum* are not significant.

At Ithaca, I have cultivated *Sedum amecamecanum* for at least seventeen years and regarded it as a valid species, though plants rarely flowered and, when they did, the flowers appeared abnormal. When I first saw plants in the field on Sept. 4, 1955, I still believed that *S. amecamecanum* was an undoubted species. On Dec. 18, 1955, however, when the plants were in flower, the relationship with *Villadia batesii* was apparent. In the greenhouse, I have grown all plants studied in the field. Seven have flowered. Since the *S. dendroideum* has not flowered, a comparison of floral parts of plants cultivated under similar conditions is not possible, but the following comparison of leaves shows that some of the differences between the two parents and the hybrids are maintained in cultiva-

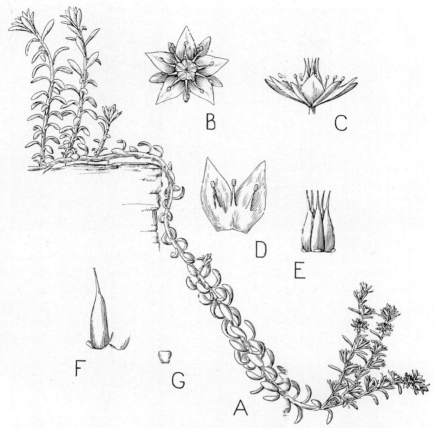

*Fig. 18.* Plant of *Sedum dendroideum* ssp. *monticola* × *Villadia batesii* from Mt. Iztaccihuatl, cultivated at Ithaca, N.Y. A. Habit sketch (x .4). B. Flower from above (1.6). C. Flower from side (x 1.6). D. Two petals and stamens (x 2.4). E. Pistils (x 2.4). F. Single pistil (x 3.2). G. Nectary (x 4).

tion. Although differences among plants of *S. dendroideum* appear to be less in cultivation than in nature, differences in dimensions of leaves among plants of *S. amecamecanum* are greater in cultivation.

| | S. dendroideum | | S. amecamecanum | | V. batesii | |
|---|---|---|---|---|---|---|
| | $\bar{x}$ | s | $\bar{x}$ | s | $\bar{x}$ | s |
| No. of plants | 4 | | 10 | | 2 | |
| No. of obs. | 12 | | 30 | | 6 | |
| Leaves | | | | | | |
| Length** | 52 mm. | 4 mm. | 15 mm. | 2.6 mm. | 14 mm. | .7 mm. |
| Width** | 20 mm. | 0 mm. | 4.9 mm. | .9 mm. | 3 mm. | 0 mm. |
| Thickness** | 2 mm. | 0 mm. | 1.6 mm. | .1 mm. | 1.3 mm. | .1 mm. |

*Fig. 19.* Plants cultivated in the greenhouse, Ithaca, N.Y., from left to right: *Sedum dendroideum* ssp. *monticola* from Iztaccihuatl, *Sedum dendroideum* ssp. *monticola* x *Villadia batesii* from Iztaccihuatl, and *Villadia batesii* from the Sierra de las Cruces, May 31, 1956 (x .2).

Three of the floral characters of greatest importance in distinguishing *Sedum amecamecanum* from *S. dendroideum* and *Villadia batesii*

*Fig. 20.* Flowers of *Sedum dendroideum* ssp. *monticola* x *Villadia batesii* (left) and *Villadia batesii* (right) from plants cultivated in the greenhouse, Ithaca, N.Y., May 31, 1956 (x 4).

were studied on plants in the greenhouse. The plants in cultivation showed less variability than those in nature. The expressions of two of the characters in the greenhouse were highly significantly different from the expressions in nature. The data follow:

|  | In nature | | In greenhouse | |
|---|---|---|---|---|
|  | $\bar{x}$ | s | $\bar{x}$ | s |
| No. of plants | 7 | | 7 | |
| No. of obs. | 28 | | 21 | |
| Sepals | | | | |
| Length | 8.9 mm. | .8 mm. | 7.7 mm. | .8 mm. |
| Petals | | | | |
| Length of | | | | |
| connate portion** | 2.5 mm. | .2 mm. | 1.9 mm. | 0 mm. |
| Color | white or pinkish white | —— | white, rarely creamy white, or even pale yellow | —— |
| Stamens | | | | |
| Length of adnation of filaments opposite petals** | 2.7 mm. | .2 mm. | 2.1 mm. | 0 mm. |

In nature, most anthers of flowers of *Sedum amecamecanum* appeared undeveloped; likewise the ovules appeared abortive. In flowers of plants in cultivation, many pollen grains are small and undeveloped, but the ovules appear well filled out, though they do not develop into seeds. Evidently *S. amecamecanum* is sterile or nearly so. Most of the plants on Iztaccihuatl may be the products of vegetative reproduction. In fact, on the basis of the small amount of variability among plants in cultivation, perhaps only two crosses would be necessary to account for the observed variation in *S. amecamecanum*. One plant, my no. 1, clearly is different from the others. It has longer, broader leaves, but was not in flower on Iztaccihuatl on Dec. 18, 1955, and has not flowered in cultivation. The differences in floral characters of the other plants, observed in the field, disappear in cultivation. Except for plant no. 1, differences in width of leaves among plants are slight. Likewise, except for plants nos. 1 and 4, differences in length of leaves among the cultivated plants are negligible. Since the culture of no. 4 was in poor condition, possibly as a result of infection with nematodes, the shortness of the leaves of that probably is of no significance. In foliage, plant no. 1 is most nearly intermediate between *S. den-*

*droideum* and *Villadia batesii*. Apparently it is what Praeger cultivated and described as *S. amecamecanum*, and also it is the same as
plants which I have cultivated. The other plants appear intermediate between that and *V. batesii*. A possibility is that no. 1 is
an $F_1$ hybrid and that the other plants are the result of a single
backcross to *V. batesii*.

*Sedum amecamecanum*, on the basis of the evidence just cited, seems
to be the result of hybridization of *Sedum dendroideum* and *Villadia
batesii*. Plants intermediate between these two species may be
either $F_1$ hybrids, as perhaps Praeger's type, Jour. Bot. 55: 43
(1917), and my no. 1, or backcrosses to either parental species. The
existence of such bigeneric hybrids and others to be described
under *S. quevae* need not invalidate the generic status of *Villadia*.
Any group of species which have evolved together and developed
one or more important and distinctive characters may constitute
a genus, as long as there are no fertile hybrids or species which
are both reproductively fertile and morphologically intermediate.
By an important distinctive characteristic is meant one with a
complex genetic basis which in the group concerned is relatively
stable. The present evidence does not require combining *Villadia*
and *Sedum*, but it does indicate their close genetic relationship.
Detailed genetic studies, involving study of chromosomes, of many
plants both in nature and in cultivation, are necessary for an
understanding of the mechanics of the hybridization just reported.

## 4. *SEDUM AOIKON* (figs. 21–22)

Among the yellow-flowered species of *Sedum* with flat, spatulate
leaves, *S. aoikon* is distinctive with dense cymes of small flowers
having tiny sepals and orange-yellow petals. Its leaves are shiny
green.

**Description.** Materials: 2 plants cultivated in the greenhouse
at Ithaca, N.Y., of unknown origin in wild. For all characters,
$n = 2$.

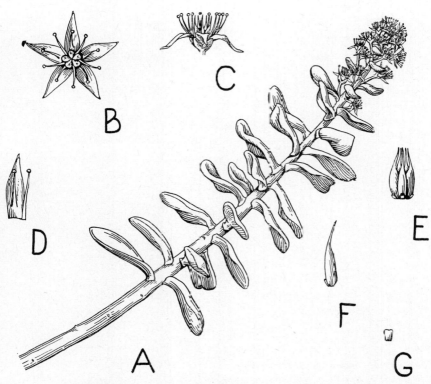

*Fig. 21*. Floriferous branch, flower, and floral parts of a plant of *Sedum aoikon* cultivated in the greenhouse, Ithaca, N.Y. A. Foral stem (x .6). B. Flower from above (x 2.4). C. Flower from side (x 2.4). D. Petal and stamens (x 3.6). E. Pistils (x 3.6). F. Single pistil (x 4.8). G. Nectary (x 6).

| | n-obs. | $\bar{x}$ | $\sigma$ | w |
|---|---|---|---|---|
| Habit | 2 | subshrub | —— | —— |
| Height | 2 | 2.1 dm. | .21 dm. | 2 – 2.3 dm. |
| Leaves | | | | |
| Length | 10 | 52 mm. | 6.4 mm. | 40 –61 mm. |
| Width | 10 | 14 mm. | 1.5 mm. | 12 –17 mm. |
| Thickness | 10 | 1.8 mm. | .1 mm. | 1.6– 2.2 mm. |
| Shape | 10 | spatulate | —— | —— |
| Base | 10 | short-spurred | —— | —— |
| Apex | 10 | rounded, rarely emarginate | —— | —— |
| Color | 10 | lustrous, green | —— | —— |
| Floral stems | | | | |
| Origin | 6 | axillary | —— | —— |

| | n-obs. | x̄ | s | w |
|---|---|---|---|---|
| Color | 6 | green, sometimes suffused with red | —— | —— |
| Inflorescences | 6 | dense | —— | —— |
| No. of flowers | 6 | 20 | —— | 10 −30 |
| Diameter | 7 | 18 mm. | 3.5 mm. | 14 −27 mm. |
| Flowers | | | | |
| Diameter | 6 | 11 mm. | 1.3 mm. | 8 −14 mm. |
| Torus | | | | |
| Length | 5 | .4 mm. | 0 mm. | .3− .6 mm. |
| Sepals | | | | |
| Length | 16 | 1.2 mm. | 0 mm. | .8− 1.4 mm. |
| Length of connate portion | 16 | .3 mm. | 0 mm. | .2− .5 mm. |
| Width | 6 | 1 mm. | .04 mm. | 1 − 1.1 mm. |
| Shape | 16 | ovate | —— | —— |
| Base | 16 | short-spurred | —— | —— |
| Apex | 16 | acute | —— | —— |
| Color | 16 | green | —— | —— |
| Petals | | | | |
| Length | 16 | 5.3 mm. | .3 mm. | 4.5− 6.3 mm. |
| Width | 6 | 1.6 mm. | .1 mm. | 1.4− 1.9 mm. |
| Shape | 16 | lanceolate | —— | —— |
| Apex | 16 | acute, mucronate-appendaged | —— | —— |
| Color | 16 | orange-yellow | —— | —— |
| Stamens | | | | |
| Length of adnation of epipetalous filaments | 6 | 1.1 mm. | 0 mm. | 1 − 1.3 mm. |
| Anthers | | | | |
| Length | 6 | .8 mm. | 0 mm. | .6− .9 mm. |
| Diameter | 6 | .5 mm. | 0 mm. | .4− .5 mm. |
| Nectaries | | | | |
| Length | 6 | .5 mm. | .06 mm. | .4− .6 mm. |
| Width | 6 | .4 mm. | .01 mm. | .4− .5 mm. |
| Shape | 6 | quadrate | —— | —— |
| Color | 6 | translucent | —— | —— |
| Pistils | | | | |
| Length | 6 | 3.8 mm. | 0 mm. | 3.2− 4.7 mm. |
| No. of ovules per ovary | 16 | 23 | —— | 15 −28 |

A plant of one of these clones, grown in a cold frame at Ithaca, produced inflorescences 45–60 mm. in diameter, with the largest cyme comprising 171 flowers. The largest sepal in a sample of seven from this plant was 2.1 mm. long and 1.3 mm. wide, surpassing in both dimensions the variation in the greenhouse. The follicles were widely divergent, 2.4–3.7 mm. long, and the seeds were elliptical, irregularly alveolate, terminally winged and pale brown, .7–.8 mm. long and .2 mm. in diameter.

Fig. 22. *Sedum aoikon* cultivated in the greenhouse, Ithaca, N.Y., Feb. 2, 1951 (x .4).

**Variation.** I have cultivated one of the two plants described above for twelve years and the other for ten years. In this time, they have not varied remarkably in the greenhouse. In 1947, one plant produced a 4-merous flower, and in 1956, the other produced a flower with 6 petals. In 1956, the greatest difference, out of twenty characters studied, was in length of leaves. Except for that, the two plants might be part of the same clone. A further cultural experiment, with adequate replicates, will be necessary to learn whether this difference in length of leaves is real or just the result of slight differences of conditions at the positions on the bench in the greenhouse where the plants are growing.

**Nomenclature.** *Sedum aoikon* Ulbrich, Notizbl. Bot. Gart. u. Mus. Berlin-Dahlem 7: 111 (1917), without designation of a type locality. I published (Clausen, R. T., 1948) a photo of the type which was preserved in the herbarium of the Botanisches Museum in Berlin. The plant was cultivated for several years in the botanical garden there. According to Ulbrich, it attained a height of 1 m., a stature very much greater than that of the plants which I have cultivated. Most of the large, shrubby species attain much lower maximum heights in the greenhouse in Ithaca than they do in the field, and also the variation in height among plants in the greenhouse is less.

A synonym is:

1905. *Sedum "Purpusi"* Rose (not Kuntze, 1903), No. Am. Flora 22: 69. Carl Purpus collected the type in 1904 on rocks and slope between Esperanza and Orizaba, a vast area of diverse climatic and edaphic conditions. The type (US 431,423) comprises four pieces of stem, all with cymes having flowers either in anthesis or in bud, mostly the latter. The cymes are paniculate, each with a definite central axis. The largest leaves are 15–17 mm. long and 6–8 mm. wide. The cymes are dense, congested, and not fully developed. A fragmentary isotype is at the New York Botanical Garden. Although measurements of the floral parts of these dried specimens cannot be accurate, they may be suggestive of the real condition. The sepals appear to be 1.1–1.8 mm. long, and the petals 3–4.7 mm. long and .9–1.2 mm. wide. These authentic samples of *S. purpusii* are not *S. botterii* or *S. hultenii*. Moreover, they probably are not *S. dendroideum*. In their small sepals and petals they seem nearest to *S. aoikon*. This has smaller sepals than any other species of *Sedum* in the Trans-Mexican Volcanic Belt. On the two plants cultivated in Ithaca, the sepals vary but little, the coefficient of variation being 4 per cent. They probably vary more in nature than under the rather uniform conditions in the greenhouse. For that reason, the greater length of the sepals of the dried specimens is not inconsistent with the idea that *S. purpusii* and *S. aoikon* are synonyms.

**Distribution.** I do not know the location of any population of *Sedum aoikon*, although I have searched for it between the city of

Orizaba and Boca del Monte. If the idea is correct that *S. purpusii* is a synonym of *S. aoikon*, then the species should occur somewhere in that region. According to Mrs. Rush (1941), she had a plant which was labeled as from Orizaba.

A plant from the Sierra de Chiapas, made available to me by Edward Alexander, may be *Sedum aoikon*, but without flowers identification is uncertain. The leaves are smaller than in the two plants described above.

**Relationships.** *Sedum aoikon* is most closely related to *S. confusum* and *S. dendroideum*. The following differences between *S. aoikon* and *S. confusum* are significant.

| | | *S. aoikon* | | | | *S. confusum* | |
|---|---|---|---|---|---|---|---|
| $n$ | $n$-obs. | $\bar{x}$ | $s$ | $n$ | $n$-obs. | $\bar{x}$ | $s$ |
| | | (mm.) | (mm.) | | | (mm.) | (mm.) |
| Leaves | | | | | | | |
| Length** | 2 | 10 | 52 | 6.4 | 4 | 11 | 20 | 0 |
| Thickness* | 2 | 10 | 1.8 | .1 | 4 | 11 | 2.6 | .4 |
| Sepals | | | | | | | |
| Length* | 2 | 16 | 1.2 | 0 | 2 | 5 | 2.6 | 0 |

In addition, *S. confusum* has more diffuse cymes without prominent, central axes.

Of the subspecies of *Sedum dendroideum*, ssp. *praealtum* and ssp. *parvifolium* are closest to *S. aoikon*. The distinctions between these have already been discussed in the section on relationships under *S. dendroideum*.

Diagnostic characters of *Sedum aoikon* are the short sepals and thin leaves. Since related species with even shorter sepals and thinner leaves are unknown, the origin of *S. aoikon* through hybridization is less likely than that it arose through the gradual accumulation of small genetic changes. If *S. aoikon* eventually is found in wild situations, isolated from related species, this idea will be strengthened. On the other hand, part of the pollen of the cultivated plants of *S. aoikon* is undeveloped. This might suggest that these plants are hybrids, but corroborative evidence is lacking. Since *S. aoikon* can be separated from *S. dendroideum* by significant differences, it is maintained in specific rank with the suggestion that it is very closely related to *S. dendroideum* ssp. *praealtum* and ssp. *parvifolium* and probably derived from the same ancestral stock.

Reference. Clausen, R. T. (1948).

## 5. *SEDUM CREMNOPHILA* (fig. 23)

*Sedum cremnophila* has the thickest leaves of any species of *Sedum* in the Trans-Mexican Volcanic Belt. These are in rosettes on very stout stems. *Sedum lucidum*, also with thick leaves, but not quite as thick, has bright, shiny, green leaves and white petals. The leaves of *S. cremnophila* appear dull, dark green, and the petals are yellow.

**Description.** Materials: 15 plants, all from the Sierra de Tepoztlán. Measurements marked cult. are for plants in the greenhouse at Ithaca, N.Y.

Plants of *Sedum cremnophila* are subshrubs with the stems erect, decumbent, or pendulous, gray-brown, <4.5 dm. long, 1–2.8 cm. in diameter.

Leaves are obovate or oblanceolate, rounded at apex, dark green, covered with a dull wax. When wax is rubbed off, leaves appear bright green and lustrous. Differences in dimensions between plants in the wild state and in cultivation are not significant.

| | $n$ | $n$-obs. | $\bar{x}$ (mm.) | $s$ (mm.) | $w$ (mm.) |
|---|---|---|---|---|---|
| Length—wild | 4 | 21 | 66 | 18 | 30–98 |
| —cult. | 4 | 32 | 73 | 15 | 40–98 |
| Width—wild | 10 | 45 | 35 | 4.9 | 21–48 |
| —cult. | 4 | 32 | 38 | 7 | 21–54 |
| Thickness—wild | 10 | 45 | 11 | 1.9 | 7–16 |
| —cult. | 4 | 32 | 12.4 | 1.2 | 9–17 |

Five leaves of one plant, measured when fresh and then two years later, after having been dried in the same way as herbarium specimens, changed highly significantly in all dimensions.

| | $\bar{x}$ (mm.) | $s$ (mm.) | $w$ (mm.) |
|---|---|---|---|
| Length—fresh | 90 | 8.5 | 78 –98 |
| —dried | 69 | 4.3 | 64 –74 |
| Width—fresh | 42 | 4.1 | 37 –46 |
| —dried | 28 | 2.6 | 25 –32 |
| Thickness—fresh | 11.4 | 1.1 | 10 –13 |
| —dried | .24 | .05 | .2– .3 |

Inflorescences are mixed, with flowers of middle cincinni opening first and on each cincinnus the lowest flower opening first. In wild state, inflorescences may have <90 flowers.

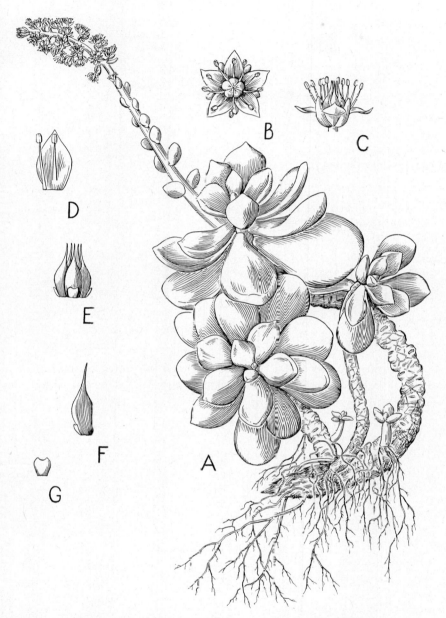

*Fig. 23.* Plant of *Sedum cremnophila* from the Sierra de Tepoztlán, cultivated in
the greenhouse, Ithaca, N.Y.  A. Plant (x .4).  B. Flower from above (x 1.6).
C. Flower from side (x 1.6).  D. Petal and stamens (x 2.4).  E. Pistils (x 2.4).
F. Single pistil (x 3.2).  G. Nectary (x 4).

|                                     | n  | n-obs. | x̄       | s       | w        |
|-------------------------------------|----|--------|---------|---------|----------|
| Lowest cincinnus—length—wild        | 9  | 9      | 7.7 mm. | 1.7 mm. | 5–10 mm. |
| No. of flowers per cyme—cult.       | 6  | 12     | 33      | —       | 4–78     |

Flowers are on short, subglaucous pedicels, rarely 6-merous.

|                          | n | n-obs. | x̄ (mm.) | w (mm.)  |
|--------------------------|---|--------|----------|----------|
| Diameter—wild            | 1 | 8      | 12       | 11 –14   |
| —cult.                   | 1 | 3      | 12       | 12       |
| Torus—length—cult.       | 1 | 3      | 1        | .9– 1    |
| Pedicels—length—cult.    | 1 | 3      | 2.1      | 1 – 3    |

Sepals are clavate, elliptical or elliptic-oblong, green and subglaucous. They are not spurred and may be minutely connate basally. Differences between plants in wild state and in cultivation are not significant.

|                | n | n-obs. | x̄ (mm.) | s (mm.) | w (mm.)   |
|----------------|---|--------|----------|---------|-----------|
| Length—wild    | 9 | 36     | 4.7      | .6      | 3 –5.9    |
| —cult.         | 6 | 17     | 4.5      | .4      | 3.6–5.4   |
| Width—wild     | 1 | 8      | 2        | —       | 1.9–2.2   |
| —cult.         | 1 | 3      | 2.2      | —       | 2 –2.4    |

Petals are lanceolate or ovate, obtuse, mucronate-appendaged, sulphur yellow. Differences between plants in wild state and in cultivation are not significant.

|                | n | n-obs. | x̄ (mm.) | s (mm.) | w (mm.)   |
|----------------|---|--------|----------|---------|-----------|
| Length—wild    | 9 | 36     | 6        | .7      | 4.5–6.8   |
| —cult.         | 6 | 17     | 5.4      | .5      | 4.6–6.2   |
| Width—wild     | 9 | 36     | 2.8      | .3      | 2.5–3.3   |
| —cult.         | 6 | 17     | 2.6      | .4      | 1.9–3.6   |

Stamens have yellow anthers.

|                                            | n | n-obs. | x̄ (mm.) | s (mm.) | w (mm.)   |
|--------------------------------------------|---|--------|----------|---------|-----------|
| Adnation of epipetalous filaments—wild     | 9 | 36     | 1.1      | .1      | .7–1.5    |
| —cult.                                     | 1 | 3      | 1.1      | —       | 1 –1.3    |
| Anthers—length—wild                        | 1 | 4      | 1.2      | —       | 1.1–1.3   |
| —cult.                                     | 1 | 3      | 1        | —       | .9–1      |
| Anthers—diameter—cult.                     | 1 | 3      | .7       | —       | .7        |

Nectaries are obovately subquadrate, retuse, and pale orange.

|  | n | n-obs. | $\bar{x}$ (mm.) | s (mm.) | w (mm.) |
|---|---|---|---|---|---|
| Length—wild | 9 | 36 | .9 | .03 | .7–1.1 |
| —cult. | 6 | 17 | .9 | .1 | .7–1.1 |
| Width—wild | 9 | 36 | .8 | .1 | .5–1.1 |
| —cult. | 6 | 17 | .8 | .2 | .6–1.1 |

Pistils are substipitate, erect, and pale yellow.

|  | n | n-obs. | $\bar{x}$ | w |
|---|---|---|---|---|
| Length—cult. | 1 | 3 | 5.2 mm. | 4.8– 5.5 mm. |
| No. of ovules per ovary—cult. | 1 | 3 | 39 | 35 –44 |

Follicles are erect, with lips of ventral margins .1–.2 mm. wide.

|  | n | n-obs. | $\bar{x}$ (mm.) | w (mm.) |
|---|---|---|---|---|
| Length—wild | 1 | 3 | 3 | 2.9–3.1 |
| Length of beaks—wild | 1 | 3 | 1.1 | .8–1.4 |

Seeds were not found, but observations of plants were not at the proper season for mature fruits and seeds.

According to Johansen, as quoted by Walther (1936), a plant of unknown origin in nature had a somatic number of 60 chromosomes.

**Variation.** Differences in dimensions of leaves, petals, and nectaries and also in length of sepals among plants of *Sedum cremnophila* cultivated under similar conditions suggest that the plants may not be alike genetically. The easiest way to account for these differences is through gene mutation. No evidence exists of hybridization between *S. cremnophila* and any other species. In the Sierra de Tepoztlán, the other species of *Sedum* which occur either in the same habitat with *S. cremnophila* or nearby are *S. longipes*, *S. frutescens*, and *S. jaliscanum*. Of these, only *S. longipes* flowers at the same time as *S. cremnophila*. *Sedum jaliscanum* flowers in the wet season and has mature fruits long before *S. cremnophila* is in anthesis. *Sedum frutescens* appears dormant when *S. cremnophila* is in flower. Because of these differences in time of flowering, no possibility exists of hybridization between *S. cremnophila* and either *S. jaliscanum* or *S. frutescens*. These and *S. longipes* are not the species most closely related to *S. cremnophila*, and they appear not to have affected its pattern of variation.

The massive, fleshy leaves of *Sedum cremnophila* shrink so significantly on drying that foliage of herbarium specimens is worthless for descriptive purposes.

**Nomenclature.** *Sedum cremnophila* R. T. Clausen, Cact. Succ. Jour. 15: 63 (1943). Based on *S. nutans* Rose.

Synonyms are:

1903. *Sedum nutans* Rose, Bull. N.Y. Bot. Gard. 3: 43 (not *S. nutans* Haworth, 1821). Type locality: cliffs, alt. 2,250 m., Sierra de Tepoztlán, Morelos. Type: Cyrus Pringle no. 6,980 (US 48,383), Feb. 8, 1899.
1905. *Cremnophila nutans* Rose, No. Am. Flora 22: 56 (1905). Based on *S. nutans* Rose.

**Distribution.** (fig. 25, p. 100). *Sedum cremnophila* is known only from the Sierra de Tepoztlán and the adjacent Sierra Chalchi to the south.

Cyrus Pringle discovered *Sedum cremnophila* in the Sierra de Tepoztlán in February, 1899. I visited the population there in September and December, 1955. The species is not common. Altogether I counted 142 plants, including seedlings. These occur on knobs of conglomerate, probably of Miocene age, in an area about 2 km. north and south and 50 m. east and west. The knobs are about 1 km. south of the station at El Parque and north of the Aztec temple. The altitudinal range is from 2,210 to 2,260 m. The plants are commonest on the lower parts of the cliffs where they are shaded by trees of *Quercus*. There the soil is clay, and the range of pH is from 5.2 to 6.4. Higher on the cliffs, plants are exposed to sunlight for much of the day. Exposure is to the west, west-north-west, and north-northeast. In the dry season, the cliffs become very arid, but in the wet season, seepage in some places keeps the soil moist. Commonest competitors of *S. cremnophila* on the lower parts of the cliffs are a species of *Selaginella* and mosses. On Dec. 30, 1955, most plants of *S. cremnophila* had floral buds, but some flowers were expanded, some of these were in anthesis, and a few already were past anthesis.

Dr. Faustino Miranda has told me about the occurrence of *Sedum cremnophila* in the Sierra Chalchi. I have seen no specimens from there and did not have time to explore those mountains.

**Relationships.** *Sedum cremnophila* appears to be most closely related to *S. dendroideum*. It has the same habit of growth and also has axillary floral stems. Its leaves are similar in shape, but thicker.

In heavily shaded situations, the stems become elongate and pendulous, as do those of *S. dendroideum*. Adapted to the arid conditions prevailing in the Sierra de Tepoztlán in the dry season, it appears to be a more specialized member of the group of species to which *S. dendroideum* belongs. Further discussion appears in the section on relationships under *S. dendroideum*.

Walther (1936) has discussed possible relationships with *Echeveria linguaefolia*.

Reference. Clausen, R. T. (1943).

## 6. *SEDUM LUCIDUM* (figs. 24 and 25)

The thick, lustrous, green leaves of *Sedum lucidum* are distinctive. The other thick-leaved species of *Sedum* of the Trans-Mexican Volcanic Belt have leaves which are glaucous or dull green. The flowers of *S. lucidum* are on short pedicels, <7 mm. long. The inflorescences are pleiochasial cymes. *Sedum nussbaumerianum*, also with white petals, has long pedicels, 12–18 mm. long, and the cymes appear umbellate.

**Description.** Materials: 20 plants—6 from the Cerro Borrego on the western side of Orizaba, Vera Cruz; 1, the type, from a hillside at Orizaba; 7 from Río Blanco, Vera Cruz; and 6 from Maltrata, Vera Cruz. Measurements marked cult. are of plants cultivated in the greenhouse at Ithaca, N.Y.

Plants of *Sedum lucidum* are subshrubs with the stems much branched, <4.5 dm. long, gray, brown, or gray-brown, rarely cristate. For wild plants, the differences among populations in diameter of stems are highly significant, but for plants in cultivation, the differences among populations in both height and diameter of stems are not significant.

| | $n$ | $n$-obs. | $\bar{x}$ (dm.) | $s$ (dm.) | $w$ (dm.) |
|---|---|---|---|---|---|
| Height at time of flowering | | | | | |
| Cerro Borrego—cult. | 4 | 4 | 2.5 | 1.1 | 1.5– 3.5 |
| Type—cult. | 1 | 1 | 1.4 | — | 1.4 |
| Río Blanco—cult. | 2 | 2 | 1.1 | .4 | .8– 1.4 |
| Maltrata—cult. | 4 | 4 | 2.4 | 1 | 1.3– 3.6 |

| | $n$ | $n$-obs. | $\bar{x}$ (dm.) | $s$ (dm.) | $w$ (dm.) |
|---|---|---|---|---|---|
| Stems—diameter | | | | | |
| Cerro Borrego | 5 | 25 | 4.6 | .3 | 3 – 6 |
| Río Blanco | 6 | 23 | 4.2 | 1 | 2 – 6.9 |
| Maltrata | 6 | 21 | 7.3 | .9 | 5 – 9 |
| Cerro Borrego—cult. | 6 | 10 | 4.8 | 1 | 4 – 6 |
| Type—cult. | 1 | 2 | 5.5 | — | 5.5 |
| Río Blanco—cult. | 6 | 9 | 4.9 | .8 | 4 – 6 |
| Maltrata—cult. | 6 | 8 | 6.7 | 1.2 | 5.5–10 |

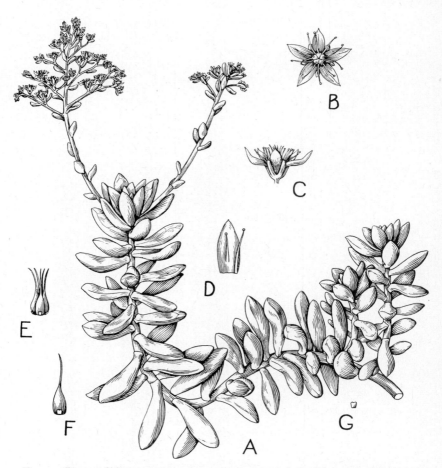

*Fig. 24.* Plant of *Sedum lucidum* from the original collection near Orizaba by Eric Walther, cultivated in the greenhouse, Ithaca, N.Y. A. Plant (x .4). B. Flower from above (x 1.6). C. Flower from side (x 1.6). D. Petal and stamens (x 2.4). E. Pistils (x 2.4). F. Single pistil (x 3.2). G. Nectary (x 4).

Leaves are plano-convex, obovate, oblanceolate-elliptical, oblanceolate, or elliptical, rounded, obtuse, or acute, sometimes apiculate, carinate and slightly angulate, upcurved, lustrous, green, sometimes red toward apex. On the basis of wild plants, differences in length, width, and thickness of leaves are highly significant between the sample from Maltrata and those from Cerro Borrego and Río Blanco, but when the plants are cultivated under uniform conditions, only the difference in thickness remains highly significant. The other differences among populations are not significant. The plants did not respond equally in cultivation, and the greater variation in dimensions of leaves among most of the cultivated plants may result from this.

| | $n$ | $n$-obs. | $\bar{x}$ (mm.) | $s$ (mm.) | $w$ (mm.) | |
|---|---|---|---|---|---|---|
| Length | | | | | | |
| Cerro Borrego | 6 | 34 | 22 | 3.7 | 13 | −36 |
| Río Blanco | 7 | 32 | 22 | 2.2 | 12 | −29 |
| Maltrata | 6 | 36 | 35 | 4.7 | 20 | −47 |
| Cerro Borrego—cult. | 6 | 48 | 31 | 5.9 | 22 | −48 |
| Type—cult. | 1 | 9 | 39 | — | 33 | −48 |
| Río Blanco—cult. | 6 | 46 | 38 | 3.1 | 23 | −52 |
| Maltrata—cult. | 6 | 50 | 39 | 2.9 | 25 | −55 |
| Width | | | | | | |
| Cerro Borrego | 6 | 34 | 11 | 1.2 | 8 | −15 |
| Río Blanco | 7 | 32 | 12 | 2.4 | 7 | −18 |
| Maltrata | 6 | 36 | 17 | 1.9 | 12 | −23 |
| Cerro Borrego—cult. | 6 | 48 | 14 | 2.1 | 10 | −20 |
| Type—cult. | 1 | 9 | 14 | — | 13 | −16 |
| Río Blanco—cult. | 6 | 46 | 15 | 2 | 11 | −22 |
| Maltrata—cult. | 6 | 50 | 16 | 2.5 | 11 | −22 |
| Thickness | | | | | | |
| Cerro Borrego | 6 | 34 | 6.1 | 0 | 5 | − 7 |
| Río Blanco | 7 | 32 | 5.6 | 1.1 | 3 | − 8 |
| Maltrata | 6 | 36 | 9.4 | .7 | 7 | −13 |
| Cerro Borrego—cult. | 5 | 41 | 5.6 | 1.2 | 3.2− | 9 |
| Type—cult. | 1 | 9 | 7.5 | — | 6 | − 9 |
| Río Blanco—cult. | 5 | 39 | 6.5 | 0 | 4.6−10 | |
| Maltrata—cult. | 6 | 50 | 8.7 | .5 | 6 | −12 |

Ten leaves from two plants on the Cerro Borrego, dried in November, 1955, and kept as herbarium specimens, when measured in July, 1957, had shrunk in all dimensions, but not significantly except in thickness, which difference is highly significant.

| | $\bar{x}$ (mm.) | $s$ (mm.) | $w$ (mm.) |
|---|---|---|---|
| Length—fresh | 25 | 6.8 | 13 –36 |
| —dried | 22 | 5.7 | 11.5–30 |
| Width—fresh | 12 | 2.4 | 8 –15 |
| —dried | 11 | 2.1 | 8 –14 |
| Thickness—fresh | 6.3 | .7 | 5 – 7 |
| —dried | .4 | .18 | .2– .8 |

Inflorescences are pleiochasial cymes of 4–12 cincinni or dichasia, on axillary floriferous stems. Although the mature floriferous stems clearly are axillary, developmental studies may be necessary to determine whether they begin at the apex of the primary shoot and then are surpassed by a lateral branch which later appears to be a continuation of the main stem.

| | $n$ | $n$-obs. | $\bar{x}$ | $w$ |
|---|---|---|---|---|
| No. of flowers per cyme | | | | |
| Cerro Borrego | 1 | 1 | 9 | 9 |
| Maltrata | 1 | 1 | 52 | 52 |
| Cerro Borrego—cult. | 4 | 5 | 34 | 18–49 |
| Río Blanco—cult. | 2 | 2 | 47 | 11–83 |
| Maltrata—cult. | 4 | 6 | 68 | 21–111 |

Flowers are on pedicels which are thickened upward.

| | $n$ | $n$-obs. | $\bar{x}$ (mm.) | $s$ (mm.) | $w$ (mm.) |
|---|---|---|---|---|---|
| Pedicels—length | | | | | |
| Cerro Borrego | 1 | 1 | 2 | — | 2 |
| Maltrata | 1 | 5 | 4 | — | 1 – 6.7 |
| Cerro Borrego—cult. | 4 | 35 | 3.6 | 1 | 1 – 6.1 |
| Type—cult. | 1 | 2 | 2.5 | — | 2 – 3 |
| Río Blanco—cult. | 2 | 18 | 4 | 1.2 | 2 – 6 |
| Maltrata—cult. | 4 | 31 | 4.3 | 1.2 | 1.7– 7 |
| Flowers—diameter | | | | | |
| Cerro Borrego—cult. | 1 | 1 | 13 | — | 13 |
| Type—cult. | 1 | 2 | 10 | — | 9 –11 |
| Maltrata—cult. | 1 | 9 | 13.3 | — | 12 –14 |
| Torus—length | | | | | |
| Maltrata—cult. | 1 | 9 | .9 | — | .7– 1.2 |

Sepals are ovate or oblong, rarely spurred, green, sometimes speckled with pink. The difference in cohesion of sepals between plants from Maltrata and those from Cerro Borrego and Río Blanco is significant.

| | $n$ | $n$-obs. | $\bar{x}$ (mm.) | $s$ (mm.) | $w$ (mm.) |
|---|---|---|---|---|---|
| Length | | | | | |
| Cerro Borrego | 1 | 2 | 2.6 | — | 2.4–2.8 |
| Maltrata | 1 | 5 | 3.3 | — | 3.1–3.6 |
| Cerro Borrego—cult. | 4 | 36 | 3 | .3 | 2.2–4.2 |
| Type—cult. | 1 | 2 | 2.3 | — | 2 –2.6 |
| Río Blanco—cult. | 2 | 18 | 3.9 | 0 | 3.1–4.9 |
| Maltrata—cult. | 4 | 36 | 3.1 | .6 | 2.4–4.8 |
| Length of cohesion | | | | | |
| Cerro Borrego—cult. | 3 | 27 | .2 | .04 | 0 – .4 |
| Río Blanco—cult. | 1 | 9 | .1 | — | 0 – .1 |
| Maltrata—cult. | 4 | 30 | .3 | .05 | .2– .5 |
| Width | | | | | |
| Cerro Borrego | 1 | 2 | 1.5 | — | 1.4–1.6 |
| Maltrata | 1 | 5 | 2 | — | 1.9–2.1 |
| Type—cult. | 1 | 2 | 9 | — | .8–1 |
| Maltrata—cult. | 1 | 9 | 1.5 | — | 1.1–1.9 |

Petals are lanceolate or elliptic-oblong, obtuse, mucronate-appendaged, white or rarely pinkish white. The difference in length of petals is significant between plants in cultivation from Cerro Borrego and those from Río Blanco and Maltrata.

| | $n$ | $n$-obs. | $\bar{x}$ (mm.) | $s$ (mm.) | $w$ (mm.) |
|---|---|---|---|---|---|
| Length | | | | | |
| Cerro Borrego | 1 | 2 | 5.6 | — | 5.2–6 |
| Maltrata | 1 | 5 | 7 | — | 6.7–7.8 |
| Cerro Borrego—cult. | 4 | 36 | 5.3 | .5 | 5.4–7.3 |
| Type—cult. | 1 | 1 | 5 | — | 6 |
| Río Blanco—cult. | 2 | 15 | 7.2 | .5 | 6.5–8.2 |
| Maltrata—cult. | 4 | 36 | 7.3 | .4 | 6.4–8.3 |
| Length of cohesion | | | | | |
| Maltrata | 1 | 5 | .7 | — | .7– .8 |
| Cerro Borrego—cult. | 4 | 36 | .03 | .06 | 0 – .4 |
| Type—cult. | 1 | 1 | .4 | — | .4 |
| Río Blanco—cult. | 2 | 18 | 0 | 0 | 0 |
| Maltrata—cult. | 4 | 36 | .2 | .4 | 0 –1.2 |
| Width | | | | | |
| Cerro Borrego | 1 | 2 | 2 | — | 1.9–2.2 |
| Maltrata | 1 | 5 | 2.5 | — | 2.4–2.6 |
| Cerro Borrego—cult. | 4 | 36 | 2.7 | .2 | 2.3–3.2 |
| Type—cult. | 1 | 1 | 2.2 | — | 2.2 |
| Río Blanco—cult. | 2 | 18 | 3.2 | .9 | 2.4–4.2 |
| Maltrata—cult. | 4 | 36 | 2.7 | .3 | 2.1–3.1 |

Stamens have white filaments and yellow anthers.

| | n | n-obs. | x̄ (mm.) | s (mm.) | w (mm.) |
|---|---|---|---|---|---|
| Adnation of epipetalous filaments | | | | | |
| Cerro Borrego—cult. | 4 | 36 | 1.4 | .1 | .9–1.8 |
| Type—cult. | 1 | 1 | 1.4 | — | 1.4 |
| Río Blanco—cult. | 2 | 18 | 1.7 | .2 | 1.2–2.4 |
| Maltrata—cult. | 4 | 36 | 1.6 | .1 | 1 –2.2 |
| Anthers—length | | | | | |
| Cerro Borrego | 1 | 1 | .8 | — | .8 |
| Maltrata | 1 | 1 | 1 | — | 1 |
| Maltrata—cult. | 1 | 9 | .9 | — | .8–1 |
| Anthers—diameter | | | | | |
| Maltrata—cult. | 1 | 9 | .5 | — | .4– .6 |

Nectaries are quadrate, emarginate, pale yellow or white.

| | n | n-obs. | x̄ (mm.) | s (mm.) | w (mm.) |
|---|---|---|---|---|---|
| Length | | | | | |
| Cerro Borrego | 1 | 2 | .4 | — | .4– .5 |
| Maltrata | 1 | 5 | .7 | — | .7 |
| Cerro Borrego—cult. | 4 | 36 | .8 | .1 | .7–1 |
| Type—cult. | 1 | 1 | .7 | — | .7 |
| Río Blanco—cult. | 2 | 18 | .8 | .1 | .7– .9 |
| Maltrata—cult. | 4 | 36 | .9 | .1 | .7–1.2 |
| Width | | | | | |
| Cerro Borrego | 1 | 2 | .5 | — | .5– .6 |
| Maltrata | 1 | 5 | .7 | — | .6– .7 |
| Type—cult. | 1 | 1 | .6 | — | .6 |
| Maltrata—cult. | 1 | 9 | .7 | — | .7– .8 |

Pistils are erect and pale green.

| | n | n-obs. | x̄ | w |
|---|---|---|---|---|
| Length | | | | |
| Type—cult. | 1 | 1 | 4.4 mm. | 4.4 mm. |
| Maltrata—cult. | 1 | 9 | 3.9 mm. | 3.2– 6 mm. |
| No. of ovules per ovary | | | | |
| Maltrata—cult. | 1 | 9 | 30 | 27 –36 |

Follicles are erect, with lips of ventral margins .1 mm. wide.

| | n | n-obs. | x̄ (mm.) |
|---|---|---|---|
| Length | | | |
| Cerro Borrego | 1 | 1 | 2.4 |

Seeds were not seen.

Uhl, quoted in the reference listed below, reported a gametic number of 34 chromosomes for the type plant.

**Variation.** At Maltrata, plants of *Sedum lucidum* have thicker stems and leaves than those at Río Blanco and on the Cerro Borrego. On the basis of data from wild plants, the population at Maltrata differs highly significantly from the other two in four vegetative characters. When plants from the three populations are cultivated under similar conditions, however, those from Maltrata differ highly significantly from the others only in one vegetative character and significantly in one floral character. On the other hand, cultivated plants from the Cerro Borrego differ significantly from those from Río Blanco and Maltrata in shorter petals. In this character, the type plant matches plants from the Cerro Borrego. The three populations are not uniform genetically, but are not sufficiently different to be subspecies.

Variation within populations of *Sedum lucidum* is great. Under conditions of similar culture, plants within each of the three populations differ in both vegetative and floral characteristics. This diversity may have a genetic basis. Further, it cannot be explained by hybridization at the present time. On the Cerro Borrego, the only other Crassulaceae appeared to be two species of *Echeveria*, neither of which was crossing with the *Sedum*. Similarly, at Río Blanco, the only other species of Crassulaceae near plants of *S. lucidum* was a species of *Echeveria*. Within a kilometer of *S. lucidum* were *Kalanchoe pinnata*, *S. dendroideum* ssp. *praealtum*, and *S. hemsleyanum*. I saw no evidence of hybridization involving any of these. At Maltrata, *S. lucidum* occurs in close association with *S. dendroideum* ssp. *dendroideum*, *S. hemsleyanum*, and *S. stahlii*. At the time of my visit on Nov. 6, 1955, all except *S. stahlii* had floral buds. I could not find evidence that any of them were hybridizing. Mutation is the most reasonable explanation of the diversity within populations of *S. lucidum*. If interspecific hybridization has been involved, it must have occurred in the past. It is not taking place now.

**Nomenclature.** *Sedum lucidum* R. T. Clausen, Cact. Succ. Jour. 23: 125 (1951). Type locality: steep hillside near Orizaba, Vera Cruz. Type: plant cultivated in greenhouse, Ithaca, N.Y., Jan. 3, 1951, C44–12 (CU), originally collected in 1935 by Eric

Walther. The original description is defective in stating that the cymes are dichasial. Some parts of the inflorescences may be dichasia, but not the whole inflorescences.

**Distribution.** I know *Sedum lucidum* from three locations, all in the drainage of the Río Blanco, just south of the eastern end of the Trans-Mexican Volcanic Belt, in an area which I consider

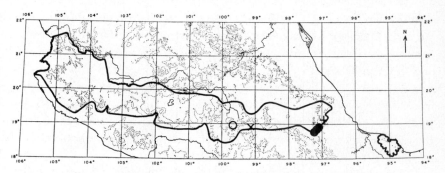

Fig. 25. Known distribution of *Sedum lucidum* (•), *Sedum* of the Tiscalatengo Gorge (o), *S. nussbaumerianum* (+), and *S. cremnophila* (x).

part of the Sierra Madre del Sur. Some of the details concerning the populations at the three locations are indicated in the following table:

| Location | n-plants | Area (km.) | Alt. range (m.) | pH | Drainage |
|----------|----------|------------|-----------------|-----|----------|
| Cerro Borrego | 22 | .02 x .015 | 1,509–1,524 | 7.2–7.8 | good |
| Río Blanco | 166 | .6 x .1 | 1,280–1,415 | 7.4–7.6 | good |
| Maltrata | 176 | .1 x .05 | 1,770–1,834 | 7.2–7.4 | excessive |

Eric Walther collected *Sedum lucidum* near Orizaba in 1935. Since the species may occur on several of the slopes near there, I am not sure which is the exact type locality, but suspect that it may be the Cerro Borrego on the western side of the city of Orizaba. I visited there on Nov. 4 and Nov. 5, 1955. The plants occurred on cliffs of limestone, exposed to the west, west-southwest, southwest, or south-southwest, below the western crest of the mountain and about 200 m. northwest of the monument on its southern summit. They were rooted in organic matter and loam and were either in partial shade or exposed to the sun for much of the day except the early morning. Trees of a species of *Quercus* most often shaded the *Sedum*. Commonest competitors were species of mosses and lichens. In November, 1955, plants of *S. lucidum* were not in flower. A branch with floral buds, collected on Nov. 5, was in flower on Nov. 29. In the greenhouse at Ithaca, plants have flowered in January, February, and early March.

I found the population of *Sedum lucidum* at Río Blanco. 5 km. southwest of Orizaba, on Nov. 9, 1955. The plants there were on cliffs of limestone on both the northern and southern sides of the valley. Exposure was to the north, northeast, east, and southeast. The plants either were in sun for most of the day or were partially shaded. Their roots usually were in sandy loam, but sometimes in organic matter. Competitors included *Selaginella extensa* and an unidentified species of Bromeliaceae. Nearby. but not in close association with the *Sedum*, was *Echeveria microcalyx*. At the time of my visit, *S. lucidum* was not in flower. In the greenhouse at Ithaca, plants have bloomed in January and March.

I discovered *Sedum lucidum* at Maltrata on Nov. 6, 1955. The plants there were on limestone about .5 km. west-southwest of the center of the village, where the road to Esperanza is nearest to the cliffs on the western side of the town. Exposure was to the southeast, and the plants were in full sun, rooted in sandy loam in crevices of the rocks. *Sedum dendroideum* ssp. *dendroideum*, *S. hemsleyanum*, and *S. stahlii* all were competitors. *Muhlenbergia microsperma* also was a frequent competitor. A seedling of *S. lucidum* indicated that the species was reproducing from seed. but survival of seedlings on the hot, dry rocks must be very low. On Nov. 6, many plants of *S. lucidum* had floral buds. A branch collected then flowered in the city of Mexico on Nov. 26. Plants in the greenhouse in Ithaca have flowered in January, February, and March.

**Relationships.** *Sedum lucidum* looks like a small, thick-leaved, white-flowered relative of *S. dendroideum* with small erect follicles. Probably it is closest to *S. dendroideum* ssp. *dendroideum*, but where these two occur together at Maltrata, they do not hybridize. Since both have floral buds at the same time. they probably are in anthesis simultaneously. Intrinsic barriers to crossability must prevent the production of hybrids. The relationships of *S. lucidum* with the two species to be discussed next will be considered in the accounts of those.

Reference. Clausen, R. T. (1951).

## 7. *SEDUM OF THE TISCALATENGO GORGE*
(figs. 26 and 27)

Several species of *Sedum* occur in the gorge of the Tiscalatengo River between Villa Guerrero and Tenancingo in the state of Mexico. The one being discussed here resembles *S. lucidum* in its thick leaves, axillary floral stems, and white flowers, but differs in having its stems and leaves glaucous, sepals both longer and clavate, and anthers red. *Sedum nussbaumerianum* differs in having acute, yellow-green leaves, cymes which appear umbellate, and flowers on long pedicels with tiny, acute sepals. *Sedum allantoides, S. pachyphyllum,* and *S. treleasei* of the Sierra Madre del Sur all have

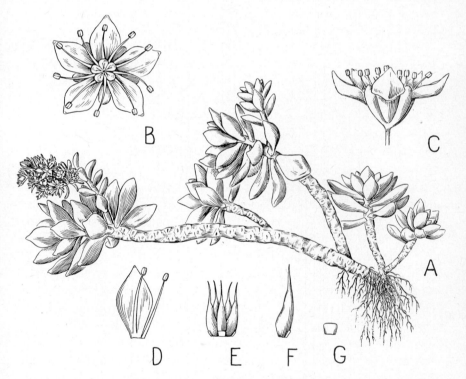

*Fig. 26.* Plant of the *Sedum* of the Tiscalatengo Gorge, cultivated in the greenhouse, Ithaca, N.Y.  A. Plant (x .5).  B. Flower from above (x 2.3).  C. Flower from side (x 2.3).  D. Petal and stamens (x 2.7).  E. Pistils (x 2.7).  F. Single pistil (x 3.6).  G. Nectary (x 4.5).

leaves about as thick as broad. *Sedum pachyphyllum* and *S. treleasei* have yellow flowers. *Sedum allantoides* has terminal floral stems.

**Description.** Materials: 5 plants—4 from the gorge of the Tiscalatengo River between Tenancingo and Villa Guerrero and 1 from Edward Alexander from the "Barranca de Texalotengo" below Rancho Santo Tobías near Villa Guerrero. Measurements marked cult. are of plants cultivated in the greenhouse at Ithaca, N.Y.

Plants of the *Sedum* of the Tiscalatengo Gorge are subshrubs with much-branched stems, <2.2 dm. long, gray-brown, and glaucous.

| | $n$ | $n$-obs. | $\bar{x}$ (mm.) | $s$ (mm.) | $w$ (mm.) |
|---|---|---|---|---|---|
| Stems—diameter | | | | | |
| Tiscalatengo Gorge | 4 | 19 | 7.8 | .2 | 7–9 |
| —cult. | 4 | 7 | 8 | .8 | 6–9 |
| Barranca de Texalatengo—cult. | 1 | 1 | 8 | — | 8 |

Leaves are clavately elliptic-oblanceolate or obovate, short-spurred, obtuse, upcurved, pale green, glaucous, sometimes with red mucronate tips, in rosettes 25–110 mm. in diameter at the ends of the stems. The difference in thickness between wild plants and those in cultivation is not significant.

| | $n$ | $n$-obs. | $\bar{x}$ (mm.) | $s$ (mm.) | $w$ (mm.) |
|---|---|---|---|---|---|
| Length | | | | | |
| Tiscalatengo Gorge | 4 | 19 | 25.2 | 3.5 | 13 –36 |
| —cult. | 4 | 52 | 30.5 | 14.1 | 14 –63 |
| Barranca de Texalotengo—cult. | 1 | 9 | 37.1 | — | 32 –46 |
| Width | | | | | |
| Tiscalatengo Gorge | 4 | 19 | 15.7 | 0 | 10 –18 |
| —cult. | 4 | 52 | 15.2 | 5.9 | 10 –29 |
| Barranca de Texalotengo—cult. | 1 | 9 | 18.5 | — | 16 –22 |
| Thickness | | | | | |
| Tiscalatengo Gorge | 4 | 19 | 4.6 | .9 | 3.5– 6.5 |
| —cult. | 4 | 51 | 6.2 | 1.4 | 3.6–10 |
| Barranca de Texalotengo—cult. | 1 | 9 | 6.3 | — | 7 –10 |

Inflorescences are pleiochasial cymes on axillary floral stems. As in *Sedum lucidum*, the position of the point of origin of the floral stems has not been determined.

|  | *n* | *n-obs.* | $\bar{x}$ | *w* |
|---|---|---|---|---|
| No. of flowers per cyme |  |  |  |  |
| Tiscalatengo Gorge—cult. | 3 | 3 | 14 | 10–21 |
| Barranca de Texalatengo—cult. | I | I | 19 | 19 |

*Fig. 27. Sedum* of the Tiscalatengo Gorge, cultivated in the greenhouse, Ithaca, N.Y., March 14, 1956 (x 1.5).

Flowers are pedicellate.

|  | *n* | *n-obs.* | $\bar{x}$ *(mm.)* | *s* *(mm.)* | *w* *(mm.)* |
|---|---|---|---|---|---|
| Pedicels—length |  |  |  |  |  |
| Tiscalatengo Gorge—cult. | I | 5 | 5.2 | — | 3.6– 6.5 |
| Flowers—diameter |  |  |  |  |  |
| Tiscalatengo Gorge—cult. | 3 | 16 | 12.6 | 2.1 | 8 –15 |
| Torus—length |  |  |  |  |  |
| Tiscalatengo Gorge—cult. | 2 | 11 | 1.4 | 0 | 1.2– 1.8 |

Sepals are clavate, oblanceolate-oblong, not spurred, very un-equal, glaucous, pale green speckled with pink at apices.

| | $n$ | $n$-obs. | $\bar{x}$ (mm.) | $s$ (mm.) | $w$ (mm.) |
|---|---|---|---|---|---|
| Length | | | | | |
| Tiscalatengo Gorge—cult. | 3 | 16 | 6.4 | .8 | 5 –7.6 |
| Barranca de Texalotengo—cult. | 1 | 4 | 7 | — | 5.9–8 |
| Width | | | | | |
| Tiscalatengo Gorge—cult. | 3 | 16 | 2.4 | 1 | 1.6–4.2 |

Petals are elliptical, acute or obtuse, minutely mucronate-appendaged, white, sometimes very pale yellowish green on dorsal keel above middle.

| | $n$ | $n$-obs. | $\bar{x}$ (mm.) | $s$ (mm.) | $w$ (mm.) |
|---|---|---|---|---|---|
| Length | | | | | |
| Tiscalatengo Gorge—cult. | 3 | 16 | 7.1 | .7 | 5.4–7.9 |
| Barranca de Texalotengo—cult. | 1 | 4 | 6 | — | 5.6–6.4 |
| Width | | | | | |
| Tiscalatengo Gorge—cult. | 3 | 16 | 3.2 | .1 | 2.8–3.6 |
| Barranca de Texalotengo—cult. | 1 | 4 | 3 | — | 2.8–3.3 |

Stamens have dark red anthers; pollen is well developed.

| | $n$ | $n$-obs. | $\bar{x}$ (mm.) | $s$ (mm.) | $w$ (mm.) |
|---|---|---|---|---|---|
| Epipetalous filaments—length of adnation | | | | | |
| Tiscalatengo Gorge—cult. | 3 | 16 | .8 | .2 | .4–1.3 |
| Barranca de Texalotengo—cult. | 1 | 4 | .6 | — | .5– .8 |
| Epipetalous filaments—length of free parts | | | | | |
| Tiscalatengo Gorge—cult. | 3 | 13 | 4.2 | .7 | 2.7–5.3 |
| Barranca de Texalotengo—cult. | 1 | 4 | 1.6 | — | 1.2–2.2 |
| Anthers—length | | | | | |
| Tiscalatengo Gorge—cult. | 3 | 12 | 1 | .1 | .8–1.3 |
| Barranca de Texalotengo—cult. | 1 | 1 | 1 | — | 1 |
| Anthers—diameter | | | | | |
| Tiscalatengo Gorge—cult. | 2 | 10 | .7 | .08 | .6– .8 |

Nectaries are reniform or subquadrate, truncate or emarginate, and white.

| | $n$ | $n$-obs. | $\bar{x}$ (mm.) | $s$ (mm.) | $w$ (mm.) |
|---|---|---|---|---|---|
| Length | | | | | |
| Tiscalatengo Gorge—cult. | 3 | 16 | .6 | 0 | .4– .7 |
| Barranca de Texalotengo—cult. | 1 | 4 | .6 | — | .5– .8 |
| Width | | | | | |
| Tiscalatengo Gorge—cult. | 3 | 16 | .8 | .02 | .7–1.2 |
| Barranca de Texalotengo—cult. | 1 | 4 | .8 | — | .7–1 |

Pistils are erect, white, with styles about as long as ovaries. A flower of a plant from the Tiscalatengo Gorge had only 4 pistils.

| | $n$ | $n$-obs. | $\bar{x}$ | $s$ | $w$ |
|---|---|---|---|---|---|
| Length | | | | | |
| Tiscalatengo Gorge—cult. | 3 | 15 | 5.1 mm. | .2 mm. | 4.5– 6   mm. |
| Barranca de Texalotengo—cult. | 1 | 4 | 4.2 mm. | — | 3.7– 4.9 mm. |
| No. of ovules per ovary | | | | | |
| Tiscalatengo Gorge—cult. | 2 | 11 | 39 | — | 34 –47 |
| Barranca de Texalotengo—cult. | 1 | 4 | 40 | — | 36 –42 |

Follicles and seeds were not found, but observations in the field were not at the proper season for these.

**Variation.** My plants from the Tiscalatengo Gorge and Alexander's plant from the Barranca de Texalotengo are similar. The plants could all have been derived from the same population, but that may not be the case since the Tiscalatengo Gorge is several kilometers above the Rancho Santo Tobías.

Eleven differences among four plants from the Tiscalatengo Gorge, cultivated under similar conditions, suggest that these plants may have different genetic constitutions. No related species of *Sedum* occurs in association with the plants being discussed here, and no evidence exists of hybridization with any other species. If the observed variability has a genetic basis, it might be explained most easily as caused by gene mutation.

**Nomenclature.** A specific epithet for the *Sedum* of the Tiscalatengo Gorge still has not been formally published. Since Edward Alexander, who first brought the species to my attention in February, 1947, has expressed a desire to name it, I am leaving it unnamed here.

**Distribution.** (fig. 25, p. 100). The known distribution of the *Sedum* of the Tiscalatengo Gorge is in the drainage of the Tenancingo River in the vicinity of Villa Guerrero in the state of Mexico. The information from Alexander suggests that his plant came from a gorge southeast of Villa Guerrero, whereas my plants are from northeast of there, in the gorge about 1 km. below the bridge of the highway between Tenancingo and Villa Guerrero. The population comprised at least 73 plants on cliffs of andesite, facing west, on the east side of the gorge. The plant lowest on the cliffs was 30 m. above the river. Most plants were inaccessible, but Carlos Palomé and I, on Jan. 1, 1956, were able to go along a ledge to one which I photographed and studied in detail. In addition, Palomé, with a pole, knocked down stems with rosettes of three other plants. These comprise my sample. The plant which I reached was rooted in clay with a pH of 5.4. In the afternoon it was exposed to the sun, but in the morning it would have been in the shade. *Echeveria gibbiflora* was on the same cliffs, as were a species of grass, a mint, and mosses. *Rhus toxicodendron* grew nearby. *Sedum oxypetalum* was within a kilometer, and *S. tortuosum* and a species related to *S. longipes* were within 5 km.

**Relationships.** Species related to the *Sedum* of the Tiscalatengo Gorge are *S. pachyphyllum*, *S. treleasei*, and *S. lucidum*. The first two of these have yellow flowers; the last has shiny, green leaves. Additional differences between the species of the Tiscalatengo Gorge and *S. lucidum*, when both are cultivated under similar conditions, are the following:

|  | *Sedum* of the Tiscalatengo Gorge | | | *S. lucidum* | | |
|---|---|---|---|---|---|---|
|  | $n$ | n-obs. | $\bar{x}$ | $n$ | n-obs. | $\bar{x}$ |
| Sepals—length** | 3 | 16 | 6.4 mm. | 10 | 90 | 3.2 mm. |
| Adnation of epipetalous filaments** | 3 | 16 | .8 mm. | 10 | 90 | 1.5 mm. |
| Anthers—color | 3 | 12 | dark red | 1 | 9 | yellow |
| Nectaries—length** | 3 | 16 | .6 mm. | 10 | 90 | .8 mm. |

Besides having yellow flowers with yellow anthers, *Sedum treleasei* differs in having shorter pedicels and sepals and lanceolate petals, but more knowledge of the variation of this species is necessary before a satisfactory comparison will be possible. Similarly, more information is necessary concerning the variation of *S. pachyphyllum*.

## 8. *SEDUM NUSSBAUMERIANUM* (fig. 28)

The leaves of *Sedum nussbaumerianum* are thick, acute, and yellow-green. The cymes appear like umbels, and the white flowers are on long, slender pedicels. The two species most similar are *S. adolphii* and *S. lucidum*. *Sedum adolphii* has longer, broader leaves prominently carinate dorsally and cymes with elongate, primary

*Fig. 28. Sedum nussbaumerianum* cultivated in the greenhouse, Ithaca, N.Y., Feb. 14, 1938 (x 1).

axes. It is not known from any locality in the wild and is poorly understood. Possibly it and *S. nussbaumerianum* are subspecies of a single species which should be called *S. adolphii*, but on the basis of available evidence the status of these two as separate species is just as likely. *Sedum lucidum* has shiny, green leaves, cymes with elongate, primary axes, and flowers on short pedicels <7 mm. long.

**Description.** Materials: 3 plants from horticultural sources, of unknown origin in nature. All measurements are of plants cultivated in the greenhouse at Ithaca, N.Y. Those marked pr. are of flowers preserved in alcohol. Those marked h. are of herbarium specimens.

Plants of *Sedum nussbaumerianum* are subshrubs with decumbent, reddish brown, glabrous stems. <7 cm. high, <4.2 dm. long, and <7 mm. in diameter.

Leaves are plane ventrally, convex and obscurely carinate dorsally, oblanceolate-elliptical, acute, glabrous, yellow-green, yellow, or orange.

|  | n | n-obs. | x̄ (mm.) | s (mm.) | w (mm.) |
|---|---|---|---|---|---|
| Length | 2 | 24 | 29.5 | 0 | 22 −39 |
| Width | 2 | 24 | 12.5 | 0 | 10 −16 |
| Thickness | 2 | 24 | 6.5 | 0 | 5.4− 8.2 |

Inflorescences are pleiochasial cymes, appearing umbellate because of the shortness of the primary axes, on axillary floral stems.

|  | n | n-obs. | x̄ | w |
|---|---|---|---|---|
| No. of flowers per cyme—h. | 1 | 5 | 28 | 18–38 |
| Primary axes of cymes—length—h. | 1 | 5 | 5.4 mm. | 2–11 mm. |

Flowers are on long, slender, white pedicels, slightly fragrant, rarely 4-merous.

|  | n | n-obs. | x̄ (mm.) | w (mm.) |
|---|---|---|---|---|
| Pedicels—length | 1 | 2 | 15 | 12 −18 |
| —length—h. | 1 | 12 | 11 | 8 −16 |
| Flowers—diameter—pr. | 1 | 5 | 15 | 14 −16 |
| Torus—length—pr. | 1 | 5 | 1 | .8− 1.5 |

Sepals are ovate, acute, very pale green.

|  | n | n-obs. | x̄ (mm.) | w (mm.) |
|---|---|---|---|---|
| Length—pr. | 1 | 5 | 2.4 | 2.1–2.6 |
| Length of cohesion—pr. | 1 | 5 | .9 | .6–1.2 |
| Width—pr. | 1 | 5 | 1.4 | 1.1–1.6 |

Petals are lanceolate, acute, white.

|  | n | n-obs. | x̄ (mm.) | w (mm.) |
|---|---|---|---|---|
| Length | 1 | 2 | 6.5 | 6 –7 |
| —pr. | 1 | 5 | 7.8 | 7.3–8.4 |
| Width—pr. | 1 | 5 | 3 | 2.8–3.2 |

Stamens have white filaments and salmon-pink anthers.

|  | n | n-obs. | x̄ (mm.) | w (mm.) |
|---|---|---|---|---|
| Adnation of epipetalous filaments—pr. | 1 | 5 | 1.2 | .8–1.6 |
| Anthers—length—pr. | 1 | 5 | 1 | .9–1.1 |
| —diameter—pr. | 1 | 5 | .6 | .5– .7 |

Nectaries are quadrate, truncate, emarginate, white or tinged with pink.

|  | n | n-obs. | x̄ (mm.) | w (mm.) |
|---|---|---|---|---|
| Length—pr. | 1 | 5 | .6 | .5–.6 |
| Width—pr. | 1 | 5 | .5 | .5–.6 |

Pistils are erect and white.

|  | n | n-obs. | x̄ | w |
|---|---|---|---|---|
| Length—pr. | 1 | 5 | 6.4 mm. | 6.1– 7 mm. |
| No. of ovules per ovary—pr. | 1 | 5 | 32 | 29 –33 |

Follicles and seeds were not available.

Uhl, quoted in the reference listed below, reported gametic numbers of 64 chromosomes for three cultivated plants.

**Variation.** Cultivated plants of *Sedum nussbaumerianum* are similar. All could belong to a single clone.

**Nomenclature.** *Sedum nussbaumerianum* Bitter, Notizbl. Bot. Gart. u. Mus. Berlin-Dahlem 8 (74): 281 (1923). Type locality: sulphur spring, ravine at Zacuapan, Vera Cruz. Type: cultivated in botanical garden in Bremen, originally collected in 1907 by Carl Purpus. I have studied a topotype from Zacuapan, collected in 1906 by Purpus (US 1,490,475). This consists of two cymes and a portion of stem with two leaves. The characters cited by Bitter as distinguishing *S. nussbaumerianum* from *S. adolphii* are not diagnostic, but others, cited below under relationships, may be satisfactory for separation.

**Distribution.** My only information about the distribution of *Sedum nussbaumerianum* is derived from Bitter's original description and the label with the specimen in the United States National Herbarium. In 1955 I made two trips into the District of Axocuapan ( = Zacuapan) and explored the deep ravine there, but without finding *S. nussbaumerianum*. The area is vast. One might spend many weeks exploring it thoroughly. Nor did I see *S. nussbaumerianum* in cultivation in Mexico.

In cultivation at Ithaca, plants flower in the greenhouse from late January to early April.

**Relationships.** *Sedum adolphii* is most closely related to *S. nussbaumerianum*. Often the two species are confused. In the horticultural trade both may be listed as *S. adolphii*. Some differences between them, as determined from plants cultivated under similar conditions, are the following:

|  | *S. nussbaumerianum* | | | *S. adolphii* | | |
|---|---|---|---|---|---|---|
|  | n | n-obs. | x̄ (mm.) | n | n-obs. | x̄ (mm.) |
| Leaves—length | 2 | 24 | 29.5 | 1 | 12 | 42 |
| —width | 2 | 24 | 12.5 | 1 | 12 | 18 |
| —thickness | 2 | 24 | 6.5 | 1 | 12 | 8.3 |
| Cymes—length of primary axes | 1 | 5 | 5.4 | 1 | 1 | 25 |

A cultivated plant from the Lecouona sisters, Banderilla, Vera Cruz, received through the courtesy of Edward Alexander, of the New York Botanical Garden, is intermediate in length of leaves, av. 36 mm., between *Sedum adolphii* and *S. nussbaumerianum*, but is like the latter in width, av. 13 mm., and thickness, av. 6.2 mm., of leaves. This plant has not flowered, nor is any information available concerning its origin.

Possibly *Sedum nussbaumerianum*, *S. adolphii*, *S. lucidum*, and the species of the Tiscalatengo Gorge all are derived from the same ancestral stock. *Sedum lucidum* impresses me as the least specialized of the four, and *S. nussbaumerianum* as the most specialized. Differences between these two, based on plants cultivated under similar conditions, are indicated below:

|  | *S. lucidum* | | | *S. nussbaumerianum* | | |
|---|---|---|---|---|---|---|
|  | n | n-obs. | x̄ (mm.) | n | n-obs. | x̄ (mm.) |
| Leaves—length** | 19 | 153 | 36.3 | 2 | 24 | 29.5 |
| —width** | 19 | 153 | 15.2 | 2 | 24 | 12.5 |
| Pedicels—length | 10 | 84 | 3.9 | 1 | 14 | 11.9 |
| Sepals—length of cohesion | 8 | 66 | .2 | 1 | 5 | .9 |

In addition, the leaves of *Sedum nussbaumerianum* are yellower.

According to Charles Cass, a disease of *Sedum nussbaumerianum* appeared in southern California in about 1941. The disease spread rapidly. It is worst in winter. The leaves of diseased plants become spotted with red. Eventually the spots become dark, almost black. Dr. Clark Rogerson has identified a fungus from the leaves as *Alternaria tenuis*, one of the Fungi Imperfecti, which is nonpathogenic. The pathogen is unknown. Since the appearance of the disease, nurserymen in California have been trying to produce through hybridization a *Sedum* with yellow leaves which is immune. Some plants which I received from Cass may be hybrids of *S. nussbaumerianum* and *Graptopetalum paraguayense*. One of these flowered in Ithaca in 1950 and again in 1959. Its pollen appeared about 75 per cent well developed, but the plant did not set any seed. It is contrasted below with both suspected parental species.

| | *Graptopetalum paraguayense* | | *Hybrid* | *Sedum nussbaumerianum* | |
|---|---|---|---|---|---|
| | $\bar{x}$ | $s$ | $\bar{x}$ | $\bar{x}$ | $s$ |
| No. of plants | for leaves 3, for pedicels and floral parts 2 | | 1 | for leaves 2, for pedicels and floral parts 1 | |
| No. of obs. | for leaves 27, for pedicels 5, for floral parts 4 | | for leaves 12, for pedicels and floral parts 3 | for leaves 24, for pedicels 14, for floral parts 5 | |
| Leaves | | | | | |
| Length | 32.3 mm. | 1 mm. | 34.8 mm. | 29.5 mm. | 0 mm. |
| Width | 15.5 mm. | .6 mm. | 16.3 mm. | 12.5 mm. | 0 mm. |
| Thickness | 6.5 mm. | 1.6 mm. | 4.8 mm. | 6.5 mm. | 0 mm. |
| Bloom | glaucous | | subglaucous | not glaucous | |
| Color | gray-green to pink | | pale green suffused with pink | yellow-green, yellow, or orange | |
| Pedicels | | | | | |
| Length | 9.2 mm. | 0 mm. | 7 mm. | 11.9 mm. | — |
| Sepals | | | | | |
| Length | 4.6 mm. | .3 mm. | 2.9 mm. | 2.4 mm. | — |
| Petals | | | | | |
| Length | 9.4 mm. | .3 mm. | 8.6 mm. | 7.8 mm. | — |
| Length of cohesion | 2.8 mm. | — | .9 mm. | 0 mm. | — |
| Concavities | present | | present | absent | |

| | Graptopetalum paraguayense | | Hybrid | Sedum nussbaumerianum | |
|---|---|---|---|---|---|
| | $\bar{x}$ | $s$ | $\bar{x}$ | $\bar{x}$ | $s$ |
| Color | white, finely speckled with red | | white or pinkish white with red dots on margins | white | |
| Pistils | | | | | |
| Length | 7.3 mm. | 0 mm. | 7 mm. | 6.4 mm. | — |

Another plant, received in flower in 1949, looked like a hybrid between *Graptopetalum amethystinum* and *Sedum nussbaumerianum*. Others, received as *G. paraguayense* x *S. nussbaumerianum*, appeared more like combinations of the *Graptopetalum* with other species of *Sedum*, as *S. pachyphyllum* and *S. treleasei*. Such possible intergeneric hybrids suggest a close genetic relationship between *Sedum* and *Graptopetalum*.

Reference. Clausen, R. T. (1951).

## 9. *SEDUM OXYPETALUM* (figs. 29–32)

Old plants of *Sedum oxypetalum* are shrubs which have stout trunks with the bark peeling in papery layers. The leaves are oblanceolate or obovate, retuse or emarginate, green, and deciduous. The petals are pale yellow streaked with pink. The follicles are widely divergent, and the branchlets with fruits break off at maturity. No other species of *Sedum* of the Trans-Mexican Volcanic Belt has deciduous branchlets. Only *S. frutescens*, *S. quevae*, and *S. tortuosum*, besides *S. oxypetalum*, have deciduous leaves, but these others have the leaves neither consistently retuse nor emarginate. *Sedum oxypetalum*, *S. frutescens*, *S. quevae*, and *S. griseum* are the only species of the area with peeling bark. Of the four, only *S. frutescens* and *S. oxypetalum* have stout trunks. The leaves of *S. frutescens* are distinctive, being elliptic-linear or elliptic-oblong, and the petals

*Fig. 29. Sedum oxypetalum,* plant in leafless condition on the southern crest of the ravine at La Angostura, D.F., March 28, 1949.

are white. In addition, the fruiting branchlets of *S. frutescens* are not deciduous.

Texiyotl, plate 38 of the Badianus manuscript (Emmart, 1940), might be *Sedum oxypetalum*, but Reko (1947) identified it as *S. bourgaei*. It was used for treating the swelling of cheeks and in a lotion for burns.

**Description.** Materials: 33 plants—6 from Huixquilucan, Mexico; 2 from La Angostura, D.F.; 11 from the lava from Xitli, in the valley south of Mexico, D.F.; 2 from San Nicolás, D.F.; 8 from the Sierra de Tepoztlán, Morelos; 2 from the lava northeast of Cuernavaca, Morelos; and 2 from the gorge of the Tiscalatengo River. Measurements marked cult. are of plants cultivated in the greenhouse at Ithaca, N.Y.

Plants of *Sedum oxypetalum* are shrubs with much-branched stems; trunks of flowering plants are 2–10 cm. in diameter; bark peels in papery layers; twigs are papillose; branchlets with fruits are deciduous from definite layers of abscission.

| | $n$ | $\bar{x}$ (m.) | $s$ (m.) | $w$ (m.) |
|---|---|---|---|---|
| Height at time of flowering | | | | |
| Huixquilucan | 1 | 1 | — | 1 |
| La Angostura | 2 | .9 | .6 | .5–1.3 |
| Lava from Xitli | 6 | 1 | .3 | .7–1.5 |
| San Nicolás | 1 | 1 | — | 1 |
| Sierra de Tepoztlán | 5 | .7 | .2 | .6–1 |
| Tiscalatengo Gorge | 1 | .6 | — | .6 |
| Huixquilucan—cult. | 1 | .4 | — | .4 |
| La Angostura—cult. | 1 | .4 | — | .4 |
| Lava from Xitli—cult. | 3 | .5 | .1 | .4– .7 |
| San Nicolás—cult. | 1 | .3 | — | .3 |
| Sierra de Tepoztlán—cult. | 3 | .5 | .03 | .4– .5 |
| Tiscalatengo Gorge—cult. | 1 | .2 | — | .2 |

Leaves are oblanceolate or obovate, retuse or emarginate, finely papillose, green, deciduous after plants have flowered. Differences among populations in dimensions of leaves are not significant, whether based on plants in the wild or in cultivation, but leaves of plants cultivated in the greenhouse at Ithaca are highly significantly longer and broader than those of plants in the wild.

| | $n$ | $n$-obs. | $\bar{x}$ (mm.) | $s$ (mm.) | $w$ (mm.) | |
|---|---|---|---|---|---|---|
| **Length** | | | | | | |
| Huixquilucan | 6 | 25 | 14.9 | 2.1 | 11 | −20 |
| Lava from Xitli | 11 | 33 | 23.7 | 3.2 | 16 | −39 |
| San Nicolás | 2 | 15 | 19.8 | 12.7 | 11 | −33 |
| Sierra de Tepoztlán | 8 | 24 | 23.7 | 6.2 | 17 | −42 |
| Lava NE of Cuernavaca | 2 | 20 | 20.7 | 8.2 | 14 | −28 |
| Tiscalatengo Gorge | 2 | 6 | 18.3 | 0 | 17 | −20 |
| Huixquilucan—cult. | 1 | 3 | 49 | — | 35 | −57 |
| La Angostura—cult. | 1 | 3 | 23.3 | — | 22 | −24 |
| Lava from Xitli—cult. | 6 | 18 | 35.2 | 9.9 | 19 | −51 |
| San Nicolás—cult. | 1 | 3 | 25 | — | 22 | −30 |
| Sierra de Tepoztlán—cult. | 3 | 9 | 38.5 | 2.7 | 32 | −44 |
| Tiscalatengo Gorge—cult. | 2 | 6 | 28.3 | 0 | 22 | −35 |
| **Width** | | | | | | |
| Huixquilucan | 6 | 25 | 7.6 | .8 | 6 | −11 |
| Lava from Xitli | 11 | 33 | 9.2 | 1.1 | 6 | −15 |
| San Nicolás | 2 | 15 | 8.3 | 2.7 | 5 | −14 |
| Sierra de Tepoztlán | 8 | 24 | 9.3 | 3.7 | 5 | −21 |
| Lava NE of Cuernavaca | 2 | 20 | 8.6 | 3.7 | 5 | −12 |
| Tiscalatengo Gorge | 2 | 6 | 5.7 | 0 | 5 | − 6 |
| Huixquilucan—cult. | 1 | 3 | 16 | — | 13 | −18 |
| La Angostura—cult. | 1 | 3 | 10.7 | — | 10 | −12 |
| Lava from Xitli—cult. | 6 | 18 | 13.1 | 2 | 10 | −19 |
| San Nicolás—cult. | 1 | 3 | 11 | — | 10 | −12 |
| Sierra de Tepoztlán—cult. | 3 | 9 | 10.8 | 3.3 | 7 | −16 |
| Tiscalatengo Gorge—cult. | 2 | 6 | 10.3 | 0 | 9 | −12 |
| **Thickness** | | | | | | |
| Huixquilucan | 1 | 10 | 1 | — | 1 | − 1.1 |
| San Nicolás | 2 | 15 | .9 | .1 | .7− | 1.2 |
| Lava NE of Cuernavaca | 2 | 20 | .9 | .2 | .4− | 1.3 |
| La Angostura—cult. | 1 | 1 | 1 | — | 1 | |
| San Nicolás—cult. | 1 | 3 | 1.1 | — | 1.1− | 1.2 |
| Sierra de Tepoztlán—cult. | 1 | 3 | .9 | — | .7− | 1.2 |

Ten leaves selected from three plants at Huixquilucan, measured in fresh condition on Aug. 18, 1955, and then dried and kept as herbarium specimens for two years, had shrunk highly significantly in length and thickness and significantly in width.

| | $\bar{x}$ (mm.) | $s$ (mm.) | $w$ (mm.) | |
|---|---|---|---|---|
| Length—fresh | 17.6 | 1.8 | 14 | −20 |
| —dried | 14.4 | 1.8 | 11 | −17 |

| | $\bar{x}$ (mm.) | $s$ (mm.) | $w$ (mm.) |
|---|---|---|---|
| Width—fresh | 8.6 | .8 | 6 −11 |
| —dried | 6.7 | .4 | 5 − 9 |
| Thickness—fresh | 1 | .06 | 1 − 1.1 |
| —dried | .1 | .06 | .1− .2 |

Inflorescences are dichasial cymes terminal on primary shoots and on branches.

| | $n$ | $n$-obs. | $\bar{x}$ | $w$ |
|---|---|---|---|---|
| No. of flowers per cyme | | | | |
| La Angostura—cult. | 1 | 2 | 4 | 3− 5 |
| San Nicolás—cult. | 1 | 1 | 44 | 44 |
| Sierra de Tepoztlán—cult. | 2 | 4 | 56 | 31–117 |

Flowers have a musty odor and are rarely 4- or 6-merous. The tori of some flowers of two plants collected on the lava from Xitli terminate in slender, subulate projections above the level of attachment of the pistils.

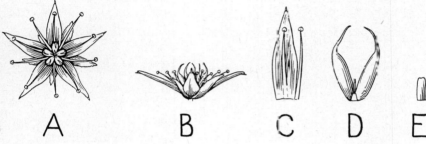

Fig. 30. Flower of a cultivated plant of *Sedum oxypetalum* originally collected on the lava from Xitli. A. Flower from above (x 2.4). B. Flower from side (x 2.4). C. Petal and two stamens (x 3.6). D. Pistils (x 4.8). E. Nectary (x 6).

| | $n$ | $n$-obs. | $\bar{x}$ (mm.) | $s$ (mm.) | $w$ (mm.) |
|---|---|---|---|---|---|
| Flowers—diameter | | | | | |
| La Angostura—cult. | 1 | 4 | 12.5 | — | 12 −13 |
| Lava from Xitli—cult. | 1 | 6 | 11.3 | — | 10 −12 |
| San Nicolás—cult. | 1 | 3 | 12.6 | — | 12 −13 |
| Sierra de Tepoztlán—cult. | 2 | 4 | 12.7 | 0 | 12 −14 |
| Torus—length | | | | | |
| La Angostura—cult. | 1 | 2 | .6 | — | .5− .8 |
| Lava from Xitli—cult. | 3 | 15 | .8 | .2 | .4− 1.8 |
| Sierra de Tepoztlán—cult. | 1 | 3 | 6 | — | .4− .7 |

| | $n$ | $n$-obs. | $\bar{x}$ | $s$ | $w$ |
|---|---|---|---|---|---|
| Anthers—diameter | | | | | |
| Lava from Xitli—cult. | 1 | 3 | 5 | — | .5 |

Nectaries are oblong or obovate-oblong, truncate, rounded, or emarginate, pale yellow or creamy white. Nectaries of plants in the wild are significantly longer and wider than those of plants cultivated in the greenhouse at Ithaca.

| | $n$ | $n$-obs. | $\bar{x}$ (mm.) | $s$ (mm.) | $w$ (mm.) |
|---|---|---|---|---|---|
| Length | | | | | |
| Huixquilucan | 6 | 25 | 1.2 | .1 | 1 −1.4 |
| Lava from Xitli | 6 | 20 | 1.3 | .1 | .9−1.5 |
| Sierra de Tepoztlán | 5 | 15 | 1.1 | .1 | .8−1.3 |
| Huixquilucan—cult. | 1 | 3 | 1.2 | — | 1 −1.3 |
| La Angostura—cult. | 1 | 2 | 1.1 | — | 1 −1.2 |
| Lava from Xitli—cult. | 4 | 12 | 1.1 | 0 | 1 −1.4 |
| San Nicolás—cult. | 1 | 3 | 1.1 | — | 1 −1.2 |
| Sierra de Tepoztlán—cult. | 3 | 12 | 1 | .04 | .7−1.4 |
| Tiscalatengo Gorge—cult. | 1 | 3 | .7 | — | 7− .8 |
| Width | | | | | |
| Huixquilucan | 6 | 25 | .6 | .1 | .4− .8 |
| Lava from Xitli | 6 | 20 | .6 | 0 | .5− .8 |
| Sierra de Tepoztlán | 5 | 15 | .5 | .02 | .4− .6 |
| Huixquilucan—cult. | 1 | 3 | .5 | — | .5 |
| La Angostura—cult. | 1 | 2 | .4 | — | .4 |
| Lava from Xitli—cult. | 4 | 12 | .4 | .04 | .4− .5 |
| San Nicolás—cult. | 1 | 3 | .6 | — | .6 |
| Sierra de Tepoztlán—cult. | 3 | 12 | .5 | 0 | .5− .8 |
| Tiscalatengo Gorge—cult. | 1 | 3 | .4 | — | .4− .5 |

Sepals are lanceolate, unequal, short-spurred, acute, green.

| | n | n-obs. | x̄ (mm.) | s (mm.) | w (mm.) |
|---|---|---|---|---|---|
| Length of longest sepals | | | | | |
| La Angostura—cult. | 1 | 5 | 3.1 | — | 1.6-4 |
| Lava from Xitli—cult. | 1 | 6 | 3.1 | — | 2.3-4.1 |
| San Nicolás—cult. | 1 | 3 | 3.9 | — | 3.6-4.4 |
| Sierra de Tepoztlán—cult. | 2 | 5 | 2.5 | .2 | 1.5-3.2 |
| Width of longest sepals | | | | | |
| La Angostura—cult. | 1 | 5 | 1 | — | .6-1.2 |
| Lava from Xitli—cult. | 1 | 6 | .9 | — | .7-1 |
| San Nicolás—cult. | 1 | 3 | 1.1 | — | .8-1.3 |
| Sierra de Tepoztlán—cult. | 1 | 3 | 1 | — | .9-1.2 |

Petals are lanceolate, acute, mucronate-appendaged, pinkish or greenish white or pale yellow streaked or speckled with pink, often deep pink below middle and dorsally. Differences among populations in the wild are significant in length and highly significant in width, but differences among populations in the same characters, based on plants cultivated in a similar environment, are not significant. Likewise, the length and width of petals of plants in the wild are not significantly different from those in cultivation.

| | n | n-obs. | x̄ (mm.) | s (mm.) | w (mm.) |
|---|---|---|---|---|---|
| Length | | | | | |
| Huixquilucan | 6 | 25 | 6.4 | .5 | 5.6-7.6 |
| Lava from Xitli | 6 | 18 | 7.1 | .7 | 5.3-7.9 |
| Sierra de Tepoztlán | 5 | 15 | 5.4 | .6 | 4.4-6.9 |

Pistils are erect when flowers are in anthesis and are yellow-green speckled with pink.

| | n | n-obs. | x̄ | | w |
|---|---|---|---|---|---|
| Length | | | | | |
| La Angostura—cult. | 1 | 1 | 4 mm. | | 4 mm. |
| San Nicolás—cult. | 1 | 3 | 4 mm. | | 3.9- 4.2 mm. |
| Sierra de Tepoztlán—cult. | 1 | 3 | 4.6 mm. | | 4.2- 4.9 mm. |
| No. of ovules per ovary | | | | | |
| San Nicolás—cult. | 1 | 3 | 13 | | 11 -14 |
| Sierra de Tepoztlán—cult. | 1 | 3 | 15 | | 12 -18 |

Follicles are widely divergent, with lips of ventral margins .1-.4 mm. wide and beaks 1.2-1.7 mm. long. Differences in length of follicles among populations in the wild are highly significant.

| | n | n-obs. | x̄ (mm.) | s (mm.) | w (mm.) |
|---|---|---|---|---|---|
| Length | | | | | |
| La Angostura | 1 | 2 | 3.2 | — | 3 -3.5 |
| Lava from Xitli | 6 | 18 | 2.9 | .1 | 2.5-3.3 |
| San Nicolás | 1 | 10 | 3.4 | — | 2.9-3.7 |
| Lava NE of Cuernavaca | 3 | 15 | 2.8 | 0 | 2.4-3.2 |
| Tiscalatengo Gorge | 2 | 6 | 2.4 | .1 | 2.2-2.5 |
| Huixquilucan—cult. | 1 | 3 | 2.8 | — | 2.8-2.9 |
| Lava from Xitli—cult. | 1 | 3 | 2.4 | — | 2.1-2.8 |
| San Nicolás—cult. | 1 | 3 | 2.3 | — | 1.8-2.8 |

Seeds are pyriform, smooth, and brown. Differences among populations, in both length and width of seeds, are highly significant.

| | n | n-obs. | x̄ (mm.) | s (mm.) | w (mm.) |
|---|---|---|---|---|---|
| Length | | | | | |
| La Angostura | 1 | 2 | .6 | — | .5- .7 |
| Lava from Xitli | 6 | 18 | .9 | 0 | .7-1.1 |
| Lava NE of Cuernavaca | 3 | 15 | .9 | .04 | .7-1 |
| Tiscalatengo Gorge | 2 | 6 | .8 | 0 | .7- .8 |
| Diameter | | | | | |
| La Angostura | 1 | 1 | .2 | — | .2 |
| Lava from Xitli | 6 | 18 | .3 | 0 | .2- .4 |
| Lava NE of Cuernavaca | 3 | 15 | .3 | .04 | .3- .4 |
| Tiscalatengo Gorge | 2 | 6 | .2 | 0 | .2- .3 |

**Variation.** On the basis of study of plants in nature, differences among populations are highly significant in five characters and significant in one character. When plants are grown in a similar environment, differences in three of these characters lose their

*Fig. 31. Sedum oxypetalum,* branch of a cultivated plant from the Sierra de Tepoztlán, showing withered condition of the branchlet after the time of anthesis, Oct. 5, 1956 (x 1.2).

significance; the other three characters were not checked, or the samples were inadequate. In cultivation, plants differ in five characters, suggesting that genetic distinctions may exist among plants within populations. A possible explanation for the origin of such differences, if they are genetic, is mutation. No evidence exists of hybridization with any other species.

Other species of *Sedum* occurring in association with *S. oxypetalum* at one or more sites are *S. bourgaei, S. frutescens,* and *S. jaliscanum.* Additional species occurring within a kilometer of it are *S. cremno-phila* and *S. longipes.* Of these, only *S. jaliscanum* flowers in the wet season, at the same time as *S. oxypetalum. Sedum jaliscanum* is a biennial herb with tubers and white flowers. Where it and *S. oxypetalum* occur together, they do not hybridize.

**Nomenclature.** *Sedum oxypetalum* H. B. K., Nov. Gen. et Sp. Plant. 6: 37–38 (1823). Type locality: Mexican gardens, without designation of a definite place. Type: in the National Museum of Natural History in Paris, France. I have studied a photo of this through the courtesy of the Chicago Natural History Museum. The word *oxypetalum* means sharp petal.

Synonyms are:

1887. *Sedum arborescens* Sessé et Mociño, Flora Mexicana, ed. 1, p. 128. Type locality: between rocks close to the city of Mexico. Type: location uncertain.

1894. *Sedum peregrinum* Sessé et Mociño, Flora Mexicana, ed. 2, p. 118. Type locality: mountains in the vicinity of the city of Mexico. Type: a collection of Sessé, Mociño, Castillo, and Maldonado (Bot. Gard., Madrid), 1787–1804.

**Distribution.** *Sedum oxypetalum* is endemic in the Trans-Mexican Volcanic Belt, occurring from the Sierra Nevada west to the Michoacán Volcanic Region. Information for populations which I have studied is indicated in the following table:

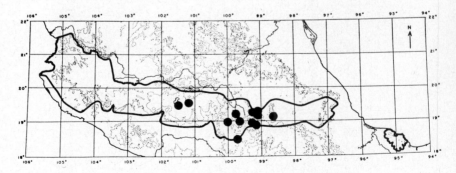

*Fig. 32.* Known distribution of *Sedum oxypetalum.*

| Location | n-plants | Area | Alt. range | pH | Drainage |
|---|---|---|---|---|---|
| Huixquilucan | 81 | 1,250 sq. m. | 2,695–2,705 m. | 6.4 | good |
| La Angostura | >50 | >1,000 sq. m. | ab. 2,400 m. | — | good |
| Lava from Xitli | 73 | several sq. km. | 2,340–2,450 m. | 5.6–6.8 | moderate |
| San Nicolás | > 5 | >10 sq. m. | 2,500 m. | 6.2 | moderate |
| Sierra de Tepoztlán | 63 | 1,000 sq. m. | 2,295–3,000 m. | 5.2–5.6 | good |
| Lava NE of Cuernavaca | ab. 200 | 1 sq. km. | 2,380 m. | — | good |
| Tiscalatengo Gorge | 12 | 50 sq. m. | 2,210 m. | — | good |

Populations additional to those listed above and the discoverers of each are: Iztaccihuatl, Salto de Agua, Joseph Purpus (US—photo); Tacubaya, Paul Maury (NY); eastern slope of Mt. Ajusco, observed by me, but not collected; Sierra Chalchi, Faustino Miranda (oral report); near Toluca, Rose and Painter (US); near Taxco, Moore and Wood (photo); Tequesquipan, District of Temascaltepec, George Hinton (NY); Campanario, Cerro Azul, Gerfroy Arsène (US); and Pátzcuaro, Cyrus Pringle (Vt).

About 6 km. northeast of Huixquilucan, on Aug. 17, 1955, I found *Sedum oxypetalum* growing on conglomerate, exposed to the south-southeast. Plants were in bud or anthesis. Common competitors were *Eysenhardtia polystachya*, *Notholaena aurea*, *Villadia batesii*, and a species of moss. Except for the *Villadia*, no other Crassulaceae were in the vicinity.

Along the Toluca road, Edward Balls collected *Sedum oxypetalum* in 1938. I studied plants on the northern side of that road, at La Angostura, on March 28, 1949. At that time, the plants were leafless. The only other species of Crassulaceae nearby was *Echeveria secunda*.

In 1866, Eugène Bourgeau collected *Sedum oxypetalum* on the Pedregal in the Valley of Mexico. I studied plants there on Aug. 19, 1955, when they were in anthesis, and again on Nov. 25, when they had mature fruits. The plants were widely scattered and occurred in small groups on low cliffs or in the bottoms of large holes in the lava. Possibly the total population of *S. oxypetalum* on the lava from Xitli comprised more than a thousand plants, but exploration of several kilometers of lava resulted in the discovery of only 73 plants, one group east of Eslava and another just south of the new University City. The exposure of plants was in all directions. Commonest competing species were *Polypodium thyssanolepis*, a shrubby mint, and species of *Selaginella* and *Gnaphalium*.

phytic. These two species are not likely to be confused, yet they probably are rather closely related.

*Sedum dendroideum* has large, shiny green leaves and bright yellow flowers on axillary floral stems. It is easy to distinguish from *S. oxypetalum*, but both are big shrubs with similar floral structure.

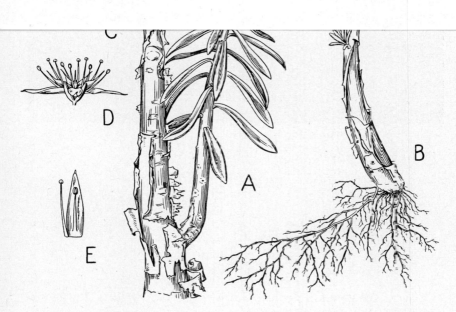

*Fig. 33.* Plants of *Sedum frutescens* cultivated in the greenhouse, Ithaca, N.Y. A. Plant from Taxco (x .4). B. Another plant from Taxco (x .4). C. Flower from above (x 1.6). D. Flower from side (x 1.6). E. Petal and two stamens (x 2.4). F. Pistils (x 3.2). G. Nectary (x 4).

No other *Sedum* was nearby, and although *Villadia batesii* is frequent on the lava, I nowhere saw it close to *S. oxypetalum*.

At Contreras, Paul Maury collected *Sedum oxypetalum* in 1890. I saw it at San Nicolás, above there, on July 29, 1955. On that date, plants still had fruits from the preceding year, but neither floral buds nor flowers. They were exposed to the northwest and were associated with *S. hourgaei*

Some of the distinctions between them, based on plants cultivated under similar conditions, are indicated below:

|  | *S. dendroideum* | | | | *S. oxypetalum* | | | |
| --- | --- | --- | --- | --- | --- | --- | --- | --- |
|  | n | n-obs. | x̄ | s | n | n-obs. | x̄ | s |
| Leaves |  |  |  |  |  |  |  |  |
| Length** | 16 | 48 | 47 mm. | 3.7 mm. | 14 | 42 | 34 mm. | 7.8 mm. |
| Width** | 16 | 48 | 17 mm. | 1.3 mm. | 14 | 42 | 12.1 mm. | 2.2 mm. |
| Thickness** | 16 | 48 | 2 mm. | .1 mm. | 3 | 7 | 1 mm. | .2 mm. |
| Petals |  |  |  |  |  |  |  |  |
| Color | 1 | 3 | yellow | | 11 | 36 | pinkish or greenish white or pale yellow streaked or speckled with pink. | |
| No. of ovules per ovary** | 2 | 5 | 57 | — | 2 | 5 | 14 | — |

*Sedum torulosum*, now definitely known from the Sierra Madre del Sur, where it was collected by T. MacDougall, may be, aside from *S. frutescens*, the most closely related species to *S. oxypetalum*. It too is a large shrub with thick stems, deciduous leaves, and terminal inflorescences. It differs from *S. oxypetalum* in its prominently torulose stems, leaves rounded at apex and pruinose when young, lemon-yellow petals, very short, red nectaries, and linear-lanceolate sepals which become reflexed and wither soon after

southeast of Villa Guerrero, Mexico; and 9 from the ravine of the Chacoalco River on the northern side of Taxco, Guerrero. Measurements marked cult. are of plants cultivated in the greenhouse at Ithaca, N.Y.

Plants of *Sedum frutescens* are shrubs with much-branched stems; the bark is usually pale brown, peeling in papery layers; twigs are finely papillose.

*Fig. 34. Sedum frutescens* 8 dm. high in the Sierra de Tepoztlán, Sept. 15, 1955.

|  | n | x̄ | s | w |
| --- | --- | --- | --- | --- |
| Height of mature plants |  |  |  |  |
| Sierra de Tepoztlán | 5 | .92 m. | .11 m. | .8 – 1 m. |
| Height at time of flowering |  |  |  |  |
| Sierra de Tepoztlán—cult. | 1 | .4 m. | — | .4 m. |
| Taxco—cult. | 1 | .18 m. | — | .18 m. |
| Diameter of trunks of mature plants |  |  |  |  |
| Sierra de Tepoztlán | 5 | 9.8 cm. | 4 cm. | 6 –16 cm. |

Leaves are generally elliptic-linear or elliptic-oblong and acute, sometimes oblanceolate-oblong and obtuse, rarely submarginate, convex dorsally, concave ventrally, finely papillose on margins. On the basis of study of plants in the wild, differences among populations in both length and width of leaves are significant. On

the basis of study of plants in a completely random experiment in
the greenhouse, however, only the difference in length is significant.
Plants in the greenhouse had significantly wider leaves than they
did in the wild.

| | $n$ | $n$-obs. | $\bar{x}$ (mm.) | $s$ (mm.) | $w$ (mm.) |
|---|---|---|---|---|---|
| Length | | | | | |
| Sierra de Tepoztlán | 5 | 26 | 27 | 11.6 | 14  −58 |
| Lava NE of Cuernavaca | 3 | 30 | 23 | 4.5 | 16  −31 |
| Tenancingo Gorge | 1 | 10 | 43 | — | 34  −52 |
| Taxco | 9 | 47 | 37 | 5.6 | 20  −56 |
| Sierra de Tepoztlán—cult. | 4 | 20 | 26 | 0 | 19  −33 |
| Lava NE of Cuernavaca—cult. | 1 | 5 | 23 | — | 17  −32 |
| Taxco—cult. | 3 | 15 | 40 | 6.4 | 24  −57 |
| Width | | | | | |
| Sierra de Tepoztlán | 5 | 26 | 4.7 | .6 | 4  − 6 |
| Lava NE of Cuernavaca | 3 | 30 | 4.4 | 0 | 4  − 5 |
| Tenancingo Gorge | 1 | 10 | 4.5 | — | 3  − 6 |
| Taxco | 9 | 47 | 5.8 | 1.2 | 3  − 9 |
| Sierra de Tepoztlán—cult. | 4 | 20 | 5.8 | .7 | 5  − 8 |
| Lava NE of Cuernavaca—cult. | 1 | 5 | 6 | — | 5  − 7 |
| Taxco—cult. | 3 | 15 | 6.7 | 0 | 5  − 9 |
| Thickness | | | | | |
| Sierra de Tepoztlán | 5 | 26 | 1.6 | .2 | 1  − 2 |
| Lava NE of Cuernavaca | 3 | 30 | 1.3 | .02 | .7− 1.5 |
| Tenancingo Gorge | 1 | 10 | 1.4 | — | 1.2− 1.8 |
| Taxco | 9 | 47 | 1.4 | .2 | 1  − 2.1 |
| Sierra de Tepoztlán—cult. | 4 | 20 | 1.3 | .2 | 1.1− 1.8 |
| Lava NE of Cuernavaca—cult. | 1 | 5 | 1.2 | — | 1  − 1.3 |
| Taxco—cult. | 3 | 15 | 1.6 | .1 | 1.2− 2.4 |

Ten leaves, five from each of two plants, collected at Taxco on
Aug. 25, 1955, and measured when fresh, then pressed as herbarium specimens, were measured in dried condition on Aug. 25,
1957. The difference in thickness is highly significant, but the
other differences are not significant.

| | $\bar{x}$ (mm.) | $s$ (mm.) | $w$ (mm.) |
|---|---|---|---|
| Length—fresh | 36 | 4.8 | 26  −41 |
| —dried | 32 | 4.5 | 26  −37 |
| Width—fresh | 5.2 | .6 | 4  − 6 |
| —dried | 4.8 | .4 | 4  − 5 |
| Thickness—fresh | 1.3 | .2 | 1  − 1.5 |
| —dried | .05 | .02 | .02−  .1 |

Inflorescences are terminal cymes, either dichasial or of several cincinni.

|                          | n | x̄ |
|--------------------------|---|----|
| No. of flowers per cyme  |   |    |
| Taxco—cult.              | 1 | 17 |

Flowers are rarely 6-merous.

|                              | n | n-obs. | x̄ (mm.) | w (mm.) |
|------------------------------|---|--------|---------|---------|
| Diameter                     |   |        |         |         |
| Sierra de Tepoztlán—cult.    | 1 | 10     | 11.7    | 11 –13  |
| Taxco—cult.                  | 1 | 5      | 16      | 15 –17  |
| Torus—length                 |   |        |         |         |
| Taxco—cult.                  | 1 | 3      | .7      | .6– .8  |

Sepals are oblong, short-spurred, obtuse, green.

|                              | n | n-obs. | x̄ (mm.) | w (mm.)    |
|------------------------------|---|--------|---------|------------|
| Length                       |   |        |         |            |
| Sierra de Tepoztlán—cult.    | 1 | 10     | 2.5     | 2.1–3.2    |
| Taxco—cult.                  | 1 | 4      | 3.5     | 2.5–4.1    |
| Width                        |   |        |         |            |
| Sierra de Tepoztlán—cult.    | 1 | 6      | 1       | .9–1.2     |
| Taxco—cult.                  | 1 | 4      | 1.1     | .8–1.2     |

Petals are lanceolate, obtuse or acute, mucronate-appendaged, white, pale green or pale pink on dorsal keel toward apex.

|                              | n | n-obs. | x̄ (mm.) | w (mm.)   |
|------------------------------|---|--------|---------|-----------|
| Length                       |   |        |         |           |
| Sierra de Tepoztlán—cult.    | 1 | 10     | 5.9     | 5.5–6.8   |
| Taxco—cult.                  | 1 | 4      | 8.2     | 7.3–9     |
| Width                        |   |        |         |           |
| Sierra de Tepoztlán—cult.    | 1 | 10     | 2.1     | 1.8–2.6   |
| Taxco—cult.                  | 1 | 4      | 2.4     | 2.2–2.5   |

Stamens have subglobose, red anthers. Pollen is well developed.

|                                     | n | n-obs. | x̄ (mm.) | w (mm.)  |
|-------------------------------------|---|--------|---------|----------|
| Adnation of epipetalous filaments   |   |        |         |          |
| Taxco—cult.                         | 1 | 3      | 1.1     | .6–1.5   |
| Anthers—length                      |   |        |         |          |
| Sierra de Tepoztlán—cult.           | 1 | 1      | .7      | .7       |
| Taxco—cult.                         | 1 | 2      | .6      | .6– .7   |

|  | $n$ | $n$-obs. | $\bar{x}$ (mm.) | $w$ (mm.) |
|---|---|---|---|---|
| Anthers—diameter |  |  |  |  |
| Sierra de Tepoztlán—cult. | 1 | 1 | .6 | .6 |
| Taxco—cult. | 1 | 2 | .5 | .5– .6 |

Nectaries are spatulate or obovate, emarginate and erose, and white.

|  | $n$ | $n$-obs. | $\bar{x}$ (mm.) | $w$ (mm.) |
|---|---|---|---|---|
| Length |  |  |  |  |
| Sierra de Tepoztlán—cult. | 1 | 10 | .7 | .6– .7 |
| Taxco—cult. | 1 | 3 | 1.2 | 1 –1.3 |
| Width |  |  |  |  |
| Sierra de Tepoztlán—cult. | 1 | 10 | .3 | .3– .4 |
| Taxco—cult. | 1 | 3 | .8 | .7– .8 |

Pistils are divergent and greenish white.

|  | $n$ | $n$-obs. | $\bar{x}$ | $w$ |
|---|---|---|---|---|
| Length |  |  |  |  |
| Taxco—cult. | 1 | 4 | 5.4 mm. | 4.4– 5.4 mm. |
| No. of ovules per ovary |  |  |  |  |
| Taxco—cult. | 1 | 3 | 11 | 11 –12 |

Follicles are widely divergent, with lips of ventral margins .1–.2 mm. wide and beaks 1–1.8 mm. long.

|  | $n$ | $n$-obs. | $\bar{x}$ (mm.) | $w$ (mm.) |
|---|---|---|---|---|
| Length |  |  |  |  |
| Taxco | 1 | 7 | 2.6 | 2.4–3.2 |

Seeds were not available for study. According to Fröderström (1930–1935), they are "lanceolate, smooth, 0.9 x 0.25 mm."

**Variation.** Unfortunately, *Sedum frutescens* was not in flower in the period when I was in the Trans-Mexican Volcanic Belt in 1955, and only two plants have flowered in the greenhouse. The plant from Taxco which flowered differed from that which originated in the Sierra de Tepoztlán in diameter of flowers, length and width of petals, and length and width of nectaries. In each of these characters the plant from Taxco was larger. Similarly, three plants from Taxco, in cultivation at Ithaca, had significantly longer leaves than four plants from the Sierra de Tepoztlán and

An additional locality for *Sedum frutescens*, besides the ones visited by me, is Campanario, on the southern side of the Cerro Azul near

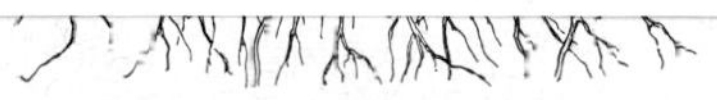

Fig. 36. Plant of *Sedum quevae* from near Santa María Atlihuizía, Tlaxcala, cultivated in the greenhouse, Ithaca, N.Y. A. Plant (x .4). B. Flower from above (x 1.6). C. Flower from side (x 1.6). D. Petal and stamens (x 2.4). E. Pistils (x 2.4). F. Single pistil (x 3.2). G. Nectary (x 4). H. Portion of stem and one leaf (x 1.6).

| El Tezcal—cult. | 3 | 7 | .5 | .1 | .5– .6 |
|---|---|---|---|---|---|

Nectaries are thick, subquadrate or reniform, truncate, white or very pale yellow, rarely pinkish. Differences in width between plants from northwest of Malinche and those from El Tezcal are significant both in the wild and in cultivation under similar conditions, but in the wild the nectaries of plants from El Tezcal are one plant from the lava northeast of Cuernavaca. This evidence suggests that plants at Taxco may comprise a subspecies different from the one in the Sierra de Tepoztlán, but more information is

Morelia, at an altitude of 2,000 m. Arsène (US) collected it there with floral buds in December, 1910.

**Relationships.** *Sedum frutescens* is most like *S. oxypetalum.* In general aspect, plants of these two species appear very similar. They differ in only a few characters, but apparently do not hybridize. Since they flower in different seasons and usually grow in different habitats, no possibility exists that they might cross in the

|  | $n$ | $n$-obs. | $\bar{x}$ (mm.) | $s$ (mm.) | $w$ (mm.) |
|---|---|---|---|---|---|
| Flowers—diameter |  |  |  |  |  |
| NW of Malinche | 3 | 6 | 12 | 1.3 | 11 −13 |
| NW of Malinche—cult. | 6 | 13 | 12 | .7 | 10 −14 |
| El Tezcal—cult. | 3 | 6 | 12 | .9 | 12 −14 |
| Torus—length |  |  |  |  |  |
| NW of Malinche—pr. | 1 | 3 | 1.3 | — | 1.1− 1.4 |
| NW of Malinche—cult. | 5 | 11 | 1 | 0 | 6 . . . |

narrower and in cultivation wider than those of plants from northwest of Malinche.

|  | $n$ | $n$-obs. | $\bar{x}$ (mm.) | $s$ (mm.) | $w$ (mm.) |
|---|---|---|---|---|---|
| Length |  |  |  |  |  |
| NW of Malinche | 4 | 14 | .5 | 0 | .4−.5 |
| El Tezcal | 3 | 5 | .4 | 0 | .4−.5 |
| Lachivía—h. | 1 | 1 | .5 | — | .5 |
| NW of Malinche—cult. | 6 | 12 | .5 | .1 | .4−.9 |
| El Tezcal—cult. | 3 | 9 | .6 | .05 | .5−.7 |
| Width |  |  |  |  |  |
| NW of Malinche | 4 | 14 | .7 | .05 | .6−.9 |
| El Tezcal | 3 | 5 | .5 | 0 | .5−.7 |
| Lachivía—h. | 1 | 1 | .6 | — | .6 |
| NW of Malinche—cult. | 6 | 12 | .7 | 0 | .5−.8 |
| El Tezcal—cult. | 3 | 9 | .8 | 0 | .7−.9 |

Pistils are erect and white or greenish white. One flower of a plant from El Tezcal, otherwise 5-merous, had only 4 pistils.

|  | $n$ | $n$-obs. | $\bar{x}$ | $s$ | $w$ |
|---|---|---|---|---|---|
| Length |  |  |  |  |  |
| NW of Malinche—cult. | 6 | 12 | 5.3 mm. | .3 mm. | 4.8− 6.1 mm. |
| El Tezcal—cult. | 3 | 9 | 5.7 mm. | .2 mm. | 5.1− 6.2 mm. |
| No. of ovules per ovary |  |  |  |  |  |
| NW of Malinche—cult. | 5 | 11 | 33 | — | 26 −40 |
| El Tezcal—cult. | 3 | 9 | 40 | — | 33 −52 |

Follicles are erect and pale brown or reddish brown.

|  | $n$ | $n$-obs. | $\bar{x}$ (mm.) | $w$ (mm.) |
|---|---|---|---|---|
| Length |  |  |  |  |
| NW of Malinche | 1 | 10 | 3.5 | 2.8−3.8 |

Seeds are elliptic-oblong, smooth, and yellow-brown.

|  | $n$ | $n$-obs. | $\bar{x}$ (mm.) | $w$ (mm.) |
|---|---|---|---|---|
| Length |  |  |  |  |
| NW of Malinche | 1 | 10 | .7 | .6−.7 |
| Width |  |  |  |  |
| NW of Malinche | 1 | 10 | .3 | .2−.3 |

**Variation.** Before consideration of the variation of *Sedum quevae,* more information is necessary concerning the origin of the plants on which the comments are based. The sample in cultivation from northwest of Malinche comprises six plants. One is from near the waterfalls at Santa María Atlihuitzía; three are from a quadrat of 2 sq. m. on the bank of the road near San Bernabé, about 6 km. northeast of Tlaxcala and about 2.5 km. south of Santa María Atlihuitzía; and two are from Santa Elena, about 2 km. northeast of San Bernabé and about 8 km. northeast of Tlaxcala. Cultivated in the greenhouse, these six plants differ in at least eight characters. In all except one of the eight characters, the greatest differences exist among the three plants selected from the quadrat. The greatest difference in the eighth character was between the two plants from Santa Elena. Instead of samples from different sites varying from each other, the greatest differences are among plants from the same site. A plant 1 m. east of the quadrat on the bank near San Bernabé appears to be a sterile hybrid between *S. quevae* and *Villadia scopulina*. The possibility exists that the variability among plants of apparent *S. quevae* may be the result of back-crossing; but in only two characters, namely, length of petals and pistils, is the variation of the three plants at San Bernabé in the direction of the *Villadia*. Further, the sterility of the hybrid does not suggest that backcrossing is likely. Another plant, apparently also a hybrid, from Santa Elena, similarly is sterile.

The population at El Tezcal appears to be small and homogeneous. The three plants studied are similar. Two of these are the most widely separated plants in the population, about 12 m. apart; the third is from within 1 dm. of the second. On the basis of study in the field, the plants at El Tezcal are not the same as those northwest of Malinche, differing significantly in five characters, namely, in length and width of both sepals and petals and in width of nectaries. Such evidence suggests possible subspecific distinction, but when plants of both populations are grown under similar conditions, the differences disappear except the one concerned with the nectaries; in addition, the leaves of plants from El Tezcal are significantly shorter. Whereas the nectaries are significantly narrower in the field, they are significantly broader in the greenhouse. The nectaries of the plants from northwest of Malinche are of the same average width both in the field and in the greenhouse. An opinion whether the population at El Tezcal is a distinctive subspecies should await further exploration for other possible populations and should also await more adequate sampling of the known populations of *Sedum quevae.*

A plant from Lachivía has longer, wider leaves than those from elsewhere. Possibly a subspecies with larger leaves exists in the Sierra Madre del Sur, but before judgment is possible, information is necessary concerning the variances of dimensions of leaves among plants in the population at Lachivía or elsewhere in the area of occurrence. Once the variances among plants are known, an estimate will be possible of what should be an adequate sample from there. Until such a sample has been studied, appraisal of the subspecific status of plants from Lachivía must remain uncertain.

**Nomenclature.** *Sedum quevae* Raymond Hamet, Bot. Jahrb. 50, Beibl. 114: 25–26 (1914). Type locality: Aseseca, Puebla. Type: Arsène's no. 193, collected Nov. 20, 1906, reported to be in the herbarium of the University of Montpellier. I have not seen the type, but have studied specimens from other localities, all in Puebla, cited by Hamet in the original description: Acatzingo Cerro Guadalupe, Hacienda Alamos and ravines near that hacienda. Details of the original description are in agreement with the data for my samples described above. Hamet named the species for Professor Queva of the University of Dijon, in whose laboratory he studied.

A synonym is:

1918. *Sedum falconis* T. S. Brandegee, Univ. Calif. Pub. Bot. 6: 498 Type locality: rocks, Cerro del Gavilán, near San Luis Tultitlanapa, Puebla. Type: Carl Purpus' no. 4,227, collected in August, 1909 (UC 136,828). Fröderström (1930–1935, pt. 4, pl. 21) published a photograph of the type.

*Sedum arsenii* (Fröderström, 1930–1935, pt. 4, p. 30) was never validly published.

**Distribution.** *Sedum quevae* occurs in the southern part of the Trans-Mexican Volcanic Belt, from the region of Acatzingo westsouthwest of the peak of Orizaba west to El Tezcal northeast of Cuernavaca, and also in the central part of the Sierra Madre del Sur, at Lachivía, Oaxaca. I have studied in the field the two populations listed below:

| Location | n-plants | Area | Alt. range | pH | Drainage |
|----------|----------|------|-----------|-----|----------|
| NW of Malinche | 81 | 10 sq. km. | 2,270–2,360 m. | 5.6–6.2 | good |
| El Tezcal | 10 | 120 sq. m. | 1,755–1,760 m. | 6.4–7.2 | good to excessive |

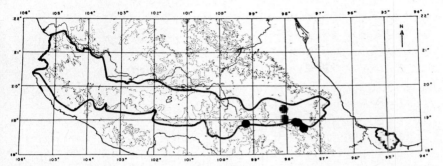

*Fig. 37.* Part of known distribution of *Sedum quevae.*

Other populations and the discoverers of each are: "Aseseca, Arsène (Montpellier)"; Acatzingo, Arsène (US); vicinity of Puebla, Arsène (US); and Cerro del Gavilán, Carl Purpus (UC).

In the region northwest of Malinche, *Sedum quevae* occurs on conglomerate in small groups of about 20 plants per site. Exposure is to the north, northwest, and southeast. In 1954, Edward Alexander told me about a *Sedum* with white flowers, in bloom on Aug. 26, 1945, which grew near San Bernabé, east of Tlaxcala. Possibly that was *S. quevae.* I have studied plants in that region in 1949 and again in 1955. At Santa María Altihuitzía, domestic animals eat the tender new shoots of the *Sedum.* All plants there either were under the protection of thorny branches of leguminous shrubs or were on steep, rocky slopes. Plants there and at San Bernabé had floral buds on Aug. 23, 1955. On Oct. 18, some were in flower. Competing species at San Bernabé included *Barbula spiralis* (identified by Professor Andrews), *Notholaena aurea, Ipomaea* (? *longipedunculata*), *Stevia paniculata, Aegopogon tenellus,* a shrubby mint, and *Villadia scopulina.*[4] At Santa Elena, besides *V. scopulina,* other Crassulaceae within 200 m. of *S. quevae* were *S. moranense* and *V. misera,* the latter in flower on Aug. 23, 1955.

I first saw *Sedum quevae* at El Tezcal, about 9 km. southwest of Tepoztlán, on Aug. 30, 1955. At that time, the plants had floral buds, but *S. jaliscanum,* growing in the same habitat on the lava, was in anthesis. By Nov. 17, *S. quevae* was in anthesis, and all plants of *S. jaliscanum* were withered and in fruit. No other Crassulaceae were in the vicinity. Exposure of plants of *S. quevae* was to

---

[4] *Villadia* **scopulina,** (Rose) comb. nov., fundata super *Altamiranoa scopulina* Rose, Bull. N.Y. Bot. Gard. 3: 32 (1903).

the east and northeast. Common competing species on the lava included *Prionosciadium nelsonii*, *Dahlia coccinea*, and *Jaegeria hirta*.

**Relationships.** On the basis of gross morphology, species related to *Sedum quevae* are *S. oxypetalum*, *S. frutescens*, *S. tortuosum*, *S. retusum*, and *S. tuberculatum*. All are subshrubs with papillose twigs and leaves broader than thick. *Sedum quevae* differs from all of these in having tubers, petals which are connate basally, and follicles which are erect, with margins not markedly enlarged as corky ridges. Plants of *S. frutescens* and *S. oxypetalum* have stout trunks. *Sedum tortuosum* is an epiphyte with long, winged seeds. *Sedum retusum* has prominently retuse leaves, petals which usually are pink basally, orange nectaries, pink ovaries, and papillose seeds. *Sedum tuberculatum* has oblanceolate sepals and yellow nectaries. Since none of the supposedly related species occur at the same sites with *S. quevae*, hybridization cannot occur.

The two apparent hybrids between *Sedum quevae* and *Villadia scopulina* indicate another relationship. In the field, I thought that both plants were *S. quevae*. Since I did not appreciate the significance of these two plants and was not investigating *Villadia* at the time of their discovery, I neither studied variation in the population of *V. scopulina* nor collected more than one plant of it for culture. The hybrid at Santa Elena had remarkably narrow leaves, apparently an etiolated condition resulting from growth in the shade of a narrow ravine. I confidently expected that this plant would have broader leaves when grown in the greenhouse in an experiment with other samples of *S. quevae*. Instead, it continues to differ in its narrower leaves from *S. quevae*. It flowers profusely in the greenhouse, and its petals become spotted with red pigment from the anthers. Evidently the cells of the tissue of the anthers break down, with the result that the red pigment diffuses. Pollen does not develop, and the ovules abort. At both places where I found the supposed hybrids, *S. quevae* and *V. scopulina* occur near together, within 2 m. of each other at each site. Plants of the two species flower at the same time, namely, at the end of the wet season. The characteristics of the supposed hybrids are a recombination of those of the suspected parental species, but transgressive in length of sepals, as shown in the following table in which all data are for plants grown under similar conditions in the greenhouse at Ithaca.

*Fig. 38. Villadia scopulina, Sedum quevae* x *V. scopulina*, and *S. quevae*, from left to right, all from northwest of Mt. Malinche, cultivated in the greenhouse, Ithaca, N.Y., Oct. 5, 1956 (ca. x .1).

|  | Sedum quevae | | Supposed $F_1$ hybrids | | Villadia scopulina |
|  | $\bar{x}$ | $s$ | $\bar{x}$ | $s$ | $\bar{x}$ |
|---|---|---|---|---|---|
| No. of plants |  |  |  |  |  |
| For height and leaves | 5 |  | 2 |  | 1 |
| For floral parts | 6 |  | 2 |  | 1 |
| No. of obs. |  |  |  |  |  |
| For height | 5 |  | 2 |  | 2 |
| For leaves | 11 |  | 8 |  | 10 |
| For sepals and petals | 12 |  | 8 |  | 10 |
| For stamens | 11 |  | 5 |  | 10 |
|  | (dm.) | (dm.) | (dm.) | (dm.) | (dm.) |
| Height | 3.2 | 1.1 | 1.8 | 0 | .6 |
|  | (mm.) | (mm.) | (mm.) | (mm.) | (mm.) |
| Leaves |  |  |  |  |  |
| Length | 28.4 | 6.4 | 24 | 4.2 | 15.5 |
| Width | 7.2 | 1.3 | 3.2 | .6 | 2.1 |
| Sepals |  |  |  |  |  |
| Length | 4.5 | 1 | 9 | 2.6 | 4.5 |
| Width | 2.4 | .3 | 1.7 | .5 | 1.1 |

|  | Sedum quevae | | Supposed $F_1$ hybids | | Villadia scopulina |
|  | $\bar{x}$ (mm.) | $s$ (mm.) | $\bar{x}$ (mm.) | $s$ (mm.) | $\bar{x}$ (mm.) |
|---|---|---|---|---|---|
| Petals |  |  |  |  |  |
| Length | 6.7 | .5 | 6.8 | .8 | 6.2 |
| Length of connate portion | .5 | .1 | 1.7 | .2 | 2.5 |
| Width | 2.1 | .03 | 2.3 | .1 | 2.4 |
| Stamens |  |  |  |  |  |
| Length of filaments opposite petals | 3.5 | .5 | 2 | .6 | 1.2 |
| Length of adnation of filaments to petals | 1.3 | .3 | 1.7 | 0 | 2.6 |

The sepals of the hybrids are longer and wider than those of plants of either parental species. Further, the petals are longer.

*Fig. 39.* Flowers of *Sedum quevae* (left) and *S. quevae* x *Villadia scopulina* (right) from plants cultivated in the greenhouse, Ithaca, N.Y., May 31, 1956 (x 4.3).

The hybrids and *Villadia scopulina* differ from *Sedum quevae* in three characters, but on the other hand they and *S. quevae* differ from the *Villadia* in one character. Four differences between the two hybrid plants suggest that they are different genetically, probably the result of independent crossing of different biotypes of either or both parental species. Variability among the five plants of the sample of *S. quevae* from northwest of Malinche may be the result of backcrossing of $F_1$ hybrids, but since these appear to be sterile, it may also be the result of gene mutation within *S. quevae*.

*Fig. 40. Sedum quevae* x *Villadia scopulina*, two plants from northwest of Mt. Malinche, from San Bernabé (left) and Santa Elena (right), cultivated in the greenhouse, Ithaca, N.Y., May 31, 1956 (x 2.4).

## 12. *SEDUM BOURGAEI* (figs. 41 and 42)

Only two species of *Sedum* of the Trans-Mexican Volcanic Belt are subshrubs with linear leaves. These are *S. bourgaei* and *S. griseum*. Both have white petals. *Sedum bourgaei* has thinner, green leaves, usually less than 1.4 mm. thick; oblong, dark purple nectaries, mostly .2–.5 mm. wide; and smooth bark. Branches two years old are red or reddish brown. *Sedum griseum* has thicker, often subglaucous leaves, generally 1.4 mm. or more thick; reniform, creamy white nectaries, .7–1.5 mm. wide; and bark which peels in thin layers. Its branches are gray-brown.

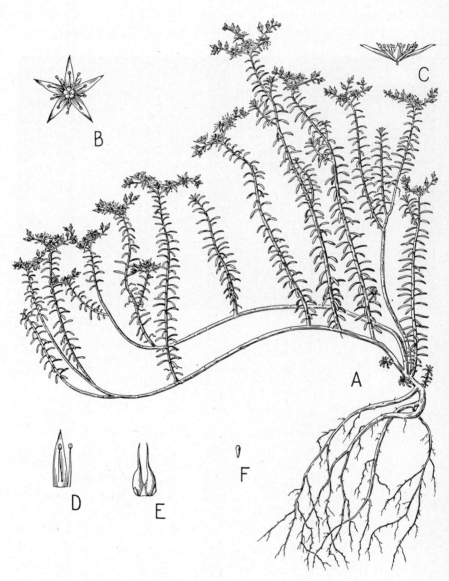

*Fig. 41.* Plant of *Sedum bourgaei* from 19 km. east of Zitácuaro, Michoacán, cultivated in the greenhouse, Ithaca, N.Y. A. Habit sketch (x .4). B. Flower from above (x 1.6). C. Flower from side (x 1.6). D. Petal and stamens (x 2.4). E. Pistils (x 3.2). F. Nectary (x 4).

**Description.** Materials: 25 plants—1 from the Sierra de las Cruces, D.F.; 4 from San Nicolás, D.F.; 7 from the northern slope of Mt. Ajusco, D.F.; 11 from 19 km. east of Zitácuaro, Michoacán; 1 from the Sierra de Ozumatlán, Michoacán; and 1 from 8 km. south of Pátzcuaro, Michoacán. Measurements marked cult. are of plants cultivated in the greenhouse at Ithaca.

Plants of *Sedum bourgaei* are subshrubs with stems erect, decumbent, or pendulous, much branched, and with smooth bark; twigs are green and papillose; two-year-old branches are red or reddish brown; bark of older portions of stems is smooth and gray-brown. Differences among populations in height of flowering plants are highly significant based on data from the field, but not significant based on plants in cultivation under similar conditions. Likewise the difference between plants in the wild and in cultivation is not significant.

|  | $n$ | $\bar{x}$ (dm.) | $s$ (dm.) | $w$ (dm.) |
|---|---|---|---|---|
| Height at time of flowering |  |  |  |  |
| Sierra de la Cruces | 1 | 6 | — | 6 |
| Ajusco | 2 | 4.5 | 0 | 4.5 |
| Zitácuaro | 9 | 2.6 | .5 | 2 −3.3 |
| Sierra de Ozumatlán | 1 | 3.8 | — | 3.8 |
| San Nicolás—cult. | 1 | 1.5 | — | 1.5 |
| Ajusco—cult. | 1 | 4.7 | — | 4.7 |
| Zitácuaro—cult. | 4 | 3.4 | .5 | 3 −4.2 |
| Sierra de Ozumatlán—cult. | 1 | 3.7 | — | 3.7 |
| Pátzcuaro—cult. | 1 | 3.4 | — | 3.4 |

Leaves are linear, sessile, sometimes very short-spurred, obtuse, green, glabrous or minutely papillose, plano-convex or biconvex. Differences in length of leaves among 5 populations in the wild are highly significant, and differences in width and thickness are significant, but differences among populations in length, width, and thickness, based on 9 plants from 4 populations, cultivated under similar conditions, are not significant. Neither are differences in length, width, and thickness significant between plants in the wild and those in cultivation. All measurements are of fully expanded leaves. Those on new shoots have smaller dimensions than the ones listed.

| | n | n-obs. | x̄ (mm.) | s (mm.) | w (mm.) |
|---|---|---|---|---|---|
| Length | | | | | |
| Sierra de las Cruces | 1 | 1 | 15 | — | 15 |
| San Nicolás | 4 | 34 | 13.5 | 3.6 | 9 −22 |
| Ajusco | 7 | 33 | 17.4 | 4.1 | 9 −31 |
| Zitácuaro | 11 | 55 | 9.3 | 2.2 | 6 −15 |
| Sierra de Ozumatlán | 1 | 5 | 13.3 | — | 11.6−15.9 |
| San Nicolás—cult. | 1 | 1 | 5.3 | — | 5.3 |
| Ajusco—cult. | 3 | 14 | 12.4 | 0 | 11 −14 |
| Zitácuaro—cult. | 4 | 8 | 14.1 | 6.6 | 6.4−23.5 |
| Sierra de Ozumatlán—cult. | 1 | 2 | 15.5 | — | 15 −16 |
| Pátzcuaro—cult. | 1 | 1 | 17 | — | 17 |
| Width | | | | | |
| Sierra de las Cruces | 1 | 1 | 2 | — | 2 |
| San Nicolás | 4 | 34 | 1.7 | .1 | 1.2− 2.2 |
| Ajusco | 7 | 33 | 2.1 | .2 | 1.5− 2.4 |
| Zitácuaro | 11 | 55 | 1.7 | .2 | 1.5− 2.1 |
| Sierra de Ozumatlán | 1 | 5 | 1.7 | — | 1.6− 1.8 |
| San Nicolás—cult. | 1 | 1 | 1.5 | — | 1.5 |
| Ajusco—cult. | 3 | 14 | 2 | 0 | 1.9− 2.2 |
| Zitácuaro—cult. | 4 | 8 | 2.1 | .4 | 1.5− 2.4 |
| Sierra de Ozumatlán—cult. | 1 | 2 | 2 | — | 1.8− 2.2 |
| Pátzcuaro—cult. | 1 | 1 | 2 | — | 2 |
| Thickness | | | | | |
| Sierra de las Cruces | 1 | 1 | 1.2 | — | 1.2 |
| San Nicolás | 4 | 34 | 1 | .1 | .6− 1.4 |
| Ajusco | 7 | 33 | 1.1 | .1 | .9− 1.4 |
| Zitácuaro | 11 | 55 | .8 | .1 | .6− 1.1 |
| Sierra de Ozumatlán | 1 | 5 | .6 | — | .6− .7 |
| San Nicolás—cult. | 1 | 1 | 1.1 | — | 1.1 |
| Ajusco—cult. | 3 | 14 | 1.2 | .2 | 1 − 1.7 |
| Zitácuaro—cult. | 4 | 8 | 1 | .2 | .7− 1.2 |
| Sierra de Ozumatlán—cult. | 1 | 2 | .8 | — | .7− 1 |
| Pátzcuaro—cult. | 1 | 1 | 1 | — | 1 |

Inflorescences are terminal cymes of 1–7 cincinni. The elongation of stems in successive years is by shoots which develop from axillary buds below the inflorescences.

| | n | n-obs. | x̄ | s | w |
|---|---|---|---|---|---|
| No. of flowers per cyme | | | | | |
| Sierra de las Cruces | 1 | 2 | 11 | — | 2 −20 |
| Zitácuaro | 1 | 5 | 17 | — | 9 −24 |
| Sierra de Ozumatlán | 1 | 5 | 12 | — | 7 −16 |
| San Nicolás—cult. | 1 | 1 | 3 | — | 3 |

| | $n$ | $n$-obs. | $\bar{x}$ | $s$ | $w$ |
|---|---|---|---|---|---|
| Ajusco—cult. | 2 | 3 | 25 | — | 14 -41 |
| Zitácuaro—cult. | 4 | 6 | 29 | — | 11 -57 |
| Sierra de Ozumatlán—cult. | 1 | 2 | 28 | — | 23 -33 |
| Pátzcuaro—cult. | 1 | 2 | 25 | — | 15 -36 |
| Floral stems—diam. at bases of cymes | | | (mm.) | (mm.) | (mm.) |
| Zitácuaro | 2 | 10 | 1.1 | .1 | .9- 1.2 |
| —cult. | 4 | 6 | 1.6 | .4 | .9- 2 |

Flowers are rarely 4- or 6-merous and either sessile or on pedicels to 4 mm. long. Differences in diameter among populations, both in the wild and in cultivation, are not significant, nor are differences between plants in the wild and those in cultivation significant.

| | $n$ | $n$-obs. | $\bar{x}$ | $s$ | $w$ |
|---|---|---|---|---|---|
| | | | (mm.) | (mm.) | (mm.) |
| Diameter | | | | | |
| Ajusco | 2 | 6 | 15.8 | 0 | 15 -17 |
| Zitácuaro | 6 | 14 | 13 | 1.7 | 11 -16 |
| Sierra de Ozumatlán | 1 | 5 | 12 | — | 11 -13 |
| Ajusco—cult. | 1 | 1 | 12 | — | 12 |
| Zitácuaro—cult. | 4 | 8 | 12.1 | 3.7 | 7 -15.5 |
| Sierra de Ozumatlán—cult. | 1 | 2 | 12.5 | — | 12 -13 |
| Pátzcuaro—cult. | 1 | 2 | 12 | — | 11 -13 |
| Torus—length | | | | | |
| Zitácuaro—cult. | 2 | 4 | .9 | .1 | .8- 1.1 |
| Sierra de Ozumatlán—cult. | 1 | 2 | 1 | — | 1 |

Sepals are minutely spurred at bases, lanceolate or oblong, obtuse, unequal, green. Differences in length of sepals among 4 populations, based on 13 plants in the wild, are significant, but differences among 4 populations, based on 7 plants in cultivation, are not significant.

| | $n$ | $n$-obs. | $\bar{x}$ | $s$ | $w$ |
|---|---|---|---|---|---|
| | | | (mm.) | (mm.) | (mm.) |
| Longest sepals—length | | | | | |
| Sierra de las Cruces | 1 | 1 | 5 | — | 5 |
| Ajusco | 2 | 6 | 5.8 | 1.2 | 4.2-7.5 |
| Zitácuaro | 9 | 38 | 3.3 | .6 | 2 -5.4 |
| Sierra de Ozumatlán | 1 | 5 | 3.6 | — | 2.9-4.2 |
| San Nicolás—cult. | 1 | 1 | 2.7 | — | 2.7 |
| Ajusco—cult. | 1 | 2 | 3 | — | 3 -3.1 |
| Zitácuaro—cult. | 4 | 8 | 3.5 | .3 | 2.7-4.8 |
| Sierra de Ozumatlán—cult. | 1 | 2 | 4.7 | — | 4.2-5.3 |
| Pátzcuaro—cult. | 1 | 1 | 3.8 | — | 3.8 |

| | $n$ | $n$-obs. | $\bar{x}$ (mm.) | $s$ (mm.) | $w$ (mm.) |
|---|---|---|---|---|---|
| Longest sepals—length of spurs | | | | | |
| Sierra de Ozumatlán | 1 | 5 | .3 | — | .2– .4 |
| Ajusco—cult.—cold frame | 1 | 1 | .1 | — | .1 |
| Longest sepals—width | | | | | |
| Sierra de las Cruces | 1 | 1 | 1 | — | 1 |
| Zitácuaro | 1 | 5 | 1 | — | .9–1 |
| Sierra de Ozumatlán | 1 | 5 | 1 | — | .9–1.1 |
| San Nicolas—cult. | 1 | 1 | 1.1 | — | 1.1 |
| Ajusco—cult. | 1 | 2 | .9 | — | .9 |
| Zitácuaro—cult. | 1 | 1 | 1.2 | — | 1.2 |

Petals are lanceolate, somewhat hooded, acute or acuminate, mucronate-appendaged, white, pale green or pink on dorsal keels above middle. Differences in length and length of cohesion of petals are of no significance, either among populations or between plants in the wild and those in cultivation. Differences among populations in width of petals, though not significant in the wild, are significant in the greenhouse, based on 7 plants from 4 populations cultivated under similar conditions. Plants from near Zitácuaro have the narrowest petals.

| | $n$ | $n$-obs. | $\bar{x}$ (mm.) | $s$ (mm.) | $w$ (mm.) |
|---|---|---|---|---|---|
| Length | | | | | |
| Sierra de las Cruces | 1 | 2 | 6.2 | — | 5.5–7 |
| Ajusco | 2 | 6 | 7.9 | 0 | 7.5–8.2 |
| Zitácuaro | 9 | 38 | 6.4 | 1 | 5 –8.4 |
| Sierra de Ozumatlán | 1 | 5 | 6.1 | — | 5.8–6.5 |
| San Nicolás—cult. | 1 | 1 | 5.2 | — | 5.2 |
| Ajusco—cult. | 2 | 13 | 5.9 | .1 | 5.3–6.4 |
| Zitácuaro—cult. | 4 | 8 | 6.4 | 1.6 | 4.2–8.4 |
| Sierra de Ozumatlán—cult. | 1 | 2 | 6.7 | — | 6.6–6.9 |
| Pátzcuaro—cult. | 1 | 1 | 5.8 | — | 5.8 |
| Length of cohesion | | | | | |
| Zitácuaro | 2 | 10 | .2 | .1 | .1– .4 |
| Sierra de Ozumatlán | 1 | 5 | .1 | — | .1– .2 |
| San Nicolás—cult. | 1 | 1 | 0 | — | 0 |
| Ajusco—cult. | 2 | 12 | .2 | .2 | 0 – .4 |
| Zitácuaro—cult. | 4 | 8 | .1 | .1 | 0 – .4 |
| Sierra de Ozumatlán—cult. | 1 | 2 | .2 | — | .2– .3 |
| Pátzcuaro—cult. | 1 | 1 | 0 | — | 0 |

|  | n | n-obs. | x̄ (mm.) | s (mm.) | w (mm.) |
|---|---|---|---|---|---|
| Width |  |  |  |  |  |
| Sierra de las Cruces | 1 | 1 | 1 | — | 1 |
| Ajusco | 2 | 6 | 2.1 | 0 | 2 −2.2 |
| Zitácuaro | 9 | 38 | 1.7 | .2 | 1.1–2.1 |
| Sierra de Ozumatlán | 1 | 5 | 1.7 | — | 1.7–2.1 |
| San Nicolás—cult. | 1 | 1 | 1.8 | — | 1.8 |
| Ajusco—cult. | 1 | 2 | 2 | — | 2 |
| Zitácuaro—cult. | 4 | 8 | 1.6 | 0 | 1.5–1.8 |
| Sierra de Ozumatlán—cult. | 1 | 5 | 2 | — | 1.9–2.2 |
| Pátzcuaro—cult. | 1 | 1 | 2 | — | 2 |

Stamens have white filaments and red or purple, rarely yellow, anthers. Pollen is well developed. Differences among populations in length and diameter of anthers are not significant.

|  | n | n-obs. | x̄ (mm.) | s (mm.) | w (mm.) |
|---|---|---|---|---|---|
| Adnation of epipetalous filaments |  |  |  |  |  |
| Sierra de las Cruces | 1 | 1 | 1 | — | 1 |
| Zitácuaro | 2 | 6 | .6 | .02 | .5– .6 |
| Sierra de Ozumatlán | 1 | 5 | 1.1 | — | .9–1.3 |
| Ajusco—cult.—cold frame | 1 | 1 | .5 | — | .5 |
| Ajusco—cult. | 1 | 11 | .4 | — | .4– .5 |
| Zitácuaro—cult. | 4 | 8 | .5 | 0 | .2– .8 |
| Sierra de Ozumatlán—cult. | 1 | 2 | 1 | — | 1 −1.1 |
| Pátzcuaro—cult. | 1 | 1 | .2 | — | .2 |
| Anthers—length |  |  |  |  |  |
| Ajusco | 2 | 5 | .7 | .1 | .6– .8 |
| Zitácuaro | 8 | 23 | .7 | .05 | .6– .8 |
| Sierra de Ozumatlán | 1 | 4 | .7 | — | .6– .7 |
| Ajusco—cult.—cold frame | 1 | 1 | .7 | — | .7 |
| Zitácuaro—cult. | 1 | 2 | .8 | — | .8 |
| Sierra de Ozumatlán—cult. | 1 | 2 | .7 | — | .7– .8 |
| Anthers—diameter |  |  |  |  |  |
| Zitácuaro—cult. | 1 | 2 | .4 | — | .4– .5 |
| Sierra de Ozumatlán—cult. | 1 | 2 | .4 | — | .4– .5 |

Nectaries are spatulate-oblong, truncate, emarginate, and dark purple. Differences in length among populations are not significant, but the nectaries of 13 plants in the wild are significantly longer than those of 7 of these plants in cultivation. Differences in width are significant among 3 populations in the wild, but not significant among samples from these same populations in cultivation.

| | n | n-obs. | x̄ (mm.) | s (mm.) | w (mm.) |
|---|---|---|---|---|---|
| **Length** | | | | | |
| Sierra de las Cruces | 1 | 2 | .7 | — | .7– .8 |
| Ajusco | 2 | 6 | .9 | 0 | .8–1 |
| Zitácuaro | 9 | 38 | .9 | .1 | .6–1.1 |
| Sierra de Ozumatlán | 1 | 5 | .9 | — | .8–1 |
| San Nicolás—cult. | 1 | 1 | .7 | — | .7 |
| Ajusco—cult. | 2 | 13 | .7 | .1 | .5– .8 |
| Zitácuaro—cult. | 4 | 8 | .8 | .1 | .6– .9 |
| Sierra de Ozumatlán—cult. | 1 | 2 | .8 | — | .8– .9 |
| Pátzcuaro—cult. | 1 | 1 | .7 | — | .7 |
| **Width** | | | | | |
| Sierra de las Cruces | 1 | 1 | .1 | — | .1 |
| Ajusco | 2 | 6 | .3 | .1 | .2– .4 |
| Zitácuaro | 9 | 38 | .3 | .04 | .2– .3 |
| Sierra de Ozumatlán | 1 | 5 | .4 | — | .4 |
| San Nicolás—cult. | 1 | 1 | .3 | — | .3 |
| Ajusco—cult. | 2 | 13 | .3 | .03 | .2– .3 |
| Zitácuaro—cult. | 4 | 8 | .3 | 0 | .3 |
| Sierra de Ozumatlán—cult. | 1 | 2 | .4 | — | .4– .5 |
| Pátzcuaro—cult. | 1 | 1 | .3 | — | .3 |

Pistils are erect, white or greenish white, often pinkish basally.
Differences in length among populations are not significant.

| | n | n-obs. | x̄ | s | w |
|---|---|---|---|---|---|
| **Length** | | | | | |
| Sierra de las Cruces | 1 | 1 | 5 mm. | — | 5 mm. |
| Ajusco—cult.—cold frame | 1 | 1 | 3.4 mm. | — | 3.4 mm. |
| Zitácuaro—cult. | 4 | 8 | 4.4 mm. | 1.1 mm. | 3.4– 6 mm. |
| Sierra de Ozumatlán—cult. | 1 | 2 | 4.6 mm. | — | 4.4– 4.8 mm. |
| Pátzcuaro—cult. | 1 | 1 | 3.4 mm. | — | 3.4 mm. |
| **No. of ovules per ovary** | | | | | |
| Ajusco—cult.—cold frame | 1 | 1 | 13 | — | 13 |
| Zitácuaro—cult. | 4 | 8 | 14 | — | 10 –18 |
| Sierra de Ozumatlán—cult. | 1 | 2 | 16 | — | 13 –20 |

Follicles are erect or divergent, pale brown, with lips of ventral
margins .1–.2 mm. wide and beaks 1.1–2.7 mm. long. Differences
in length among populations are not significant.

| | n | n-obs. | x̄ (mm.) | s (mm.) | w (mm.) |
|---|---|---|---|---|---|
| **Length** | | | | | |
| Sierra de las Cruces | 1 | 1 | 2.5 | — | 2.5 |
| San Nicolás | 4 | 34 | 2.4 | .2 | 1.5–3 |
| Zitácuaro | 1 | 5 | 2.5 | — | 2.4–2.7 |

Seeds are elliptical, reticulate, and brown.

|  | $n$ | $n$-obs. | $\bar{x}$ (mm.) | $w$ (mm.) |
|---|---|---|---|---|
| Length |  |  |  |  |
| Sierra de las Cruces | I | I | .7 | .7 |
| San Nicolás | I | 4 | .6 | .6–.7 |
| Diameter |  |  |  |  |
| Sierra de las Cruces | I | I | .2 | .2 |
| San Nicolás | I | 3 | .3 | .2–.3 |

**Variation.** Plants in the five populations which I have observed in the field appear very much alike. On the basis of study of nineteen gross morphological characters of plants in the wild, differences among populations in five characters are significant, two of them highly significant. Plants from near Zitácuaro, growing either in the open or in partial shade, had the lowest stature, shortest leaves, and shortest sepals. Plants on Mt. Ajusco had the widest leaves, and a plant in the Sierra de Ozumatlán had the widest nectaries. When plants from these three populations are brought together and grown side by side in the greenhouse, they are more alike, and differences in these five characters are not significant; but plants from near Zitácuaro have significantly narrower petals than do samples from the other populations, and the epipetalous stamens are less adnate than in flowers of a plant from the Sierra de Ozumatlán. Scant basis exists for delimiting subspecies among the populations studied.

Within populations, plants differ in the wild in thirteen out of nineteen characters studied. That some of this variation is environmental is attested by the fact that plants grown under similar conditions differed in only nine of these thirteen characters, namely, in length, width, and thickness of leaves, diameter of flowers, length and length of cohesion of petals, length and width of nectaries, and length of pistils. They suggest the possibility of some genetic variation in *Sedum bourgaei*.

No evidence exists that *Sedum bourgaei* hybridizes with any other species. At San Nicolás it is intermixed with *S. oxypetalum*, but the latter flowers in the rainy season in the summer, whereas *S. bourgaei* flowers in the dry season in the autumn and winter. In the Sierra de las Cruces, *S. bourgaei* occurs in association with *Echeveria secunda* and *Villadia batesii*. These all may be in anthesis at the same time, but apparently they do not cross. Similarly, *S. bourgaei* and *V. batesii* occur close together on Mt. Ajusco without crossing. In the Sierra de la Marquesa, near Zitácuaro, and in the Sierra de Ozumatlán, *S. bourgaei* is not closely associated with any other species of Crassulaceae. Except for the possibility of an intergeneric cross, the present ecological distribution of *S. bourgaei* is unfavorable for hybridization.

Some plants from near Zitácuaro had tuberous roots, up to 8 mm. in diameter. In 1887, Sereno Watson described one of Edward Palmer's collections from Río Blanco, northwest of Guadalajara, as a new species, *Sedum "Guadalajarana."* According to him this had slender stems; a tuberiferous rootstock; very narrowly linear, clasping, glaucous leaves, 6 mm. ("3 lines") long or less; acuminate sepals; and petals 3 mm. long. Authentic specimens of this species do have shorter, narrower leaves than plants of *S. bourgaei* and also shorter petals, but the sepals are obtuse, not acuminate, and the leaves are short-spurred, not clasping. Praeger (1921) wrote that the leaves are glaucous and subterete, not flattened, that the stems are wiry, that the petals are reddish at their bases, that the carpels are green (not white), and that the nectaries are shorter than in *S. bourgaei* and pale red. Since I have not studied populations of *S. guadalajaranum*, either at Río Blanco or in the gorge near Guadalajara, I am not yet ready to evaluate its taxonomic status. Possibly it is a subspecies of *S. bourgaei*. In any case, despite the tuberous roots, the plants from near Zitácuaro differ from *S. guadalajaranum* in several characters: stouter stems; longer, wider, green leaves; pistils white, sometimes pink basally; and longer nectaries. They must be identified as *S. bourgaei*.

**Nomenclature.** *Sedum bourgaei* Hemsley, Diag. Pl. Nov. 1: 11 (1878). Type locality: San Nicolás. Type: Bourgeau's collection no. 933, collected on July 27, 1866, reported to be in the herbarium at Kew. I have studied an isotype (US 48,556).

A synonym is:

1887. *Sedum acre* Sessé et Mociño (non L.), Flora Mexicana, ed. 1, p. 129. Type locality: Mexico. Type: a collection of Sessé, Mociño, Castillo, and Maldonado (Bot. Gard., Madrid), 1787–1804, available through the courtesy of the Chicago Natural History Museum. The descriptive adjective *ovatis*, as used in the description, scarcely applies to the linear leaves of the specimen.

**Distribution.** *Sedum bourgaei* occurs in the central part of the volcanic belt, from Mt. Ajusco west to Pátzcuaro, and also on the

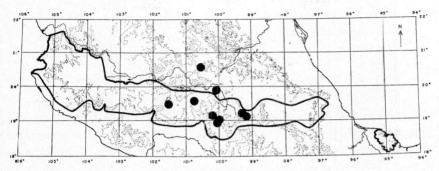

*Fig. 42.* Known distribution of *Sedum bourgaei*.

adjacent Central Mexican Plateau. Data for six populations which I have studied are summarized in the following table:

| Location | n-plants | Area (m.) | Alt. range (m.) | pH | Drainage |
|---|---|---|---|---|---|
| Ajusco | > 34 | > 20 x 10 | 3,260–3,270 | 6.8 | moderate |
| San Nicolás | 110 | 30 x 20 | 2,490–2,510 | 6.2 | moderate |
| Sierra de las Cruces | — | — | 3,000–3,200 | — | — |
| Sierra de la Marquesa | 54 | — | 3,300 | — | moderate |
| E of Zitácuaro | 800 ± | 500 x 20 | 2,700–2,720 | 6.4–7 | moderate |
| Sierra de Ozumatlán | 42 | 5 x 4 | 2,860 | 6.6 | moderate |

Populations additional to those listed above and the discoverers of each are: Ixtapan (US), Mesón Viejo (Mexu, US), Sierrita (US), and Timbres (NY), all four in the District of Temascaltepec and found by George Hinton; "local" in pine forest, alt. 2,340 m., Zitácuaro-Cacique, District of Zitácuaro, Hinton (NY, US); hills of Pátzcuaro, Cyrus Pringle (GH, Mexu, NY, US, Vt); Cerro de las Campanas, Querétaro, Gerfroy Arsène (US); and Tultenango ("Tutulongo" on label) Canyon, Joseph Rose (US).

Carlos Palomé and I found *Sedum bourgaei* on Mt. Ajusco on Oct. 12, 1955. The plants occur there on the lower portion of the northern slope. The exact site is the western crest of a canyon which is part of the ridge known as the Espinaza del Diablo. They are exposed to the northeast and east in an area where *Abies religiosa* is the dominant tree. The plants were in bud and anthesis on Oct. 12. Plants of *Villadia batesii*, occurring within 10 cm. of

*S. bourgaei*, were also in bud. The flowering times of the two species must be similar, but I found no hybrids. In the greenhouse at Ithaca, a plant from Mt. Ajusco has flowered in June, and in the cold frame in August.

Bourgeau discovered *Sedum bourgaei* at San Nicolás in 1866. Possibly he collected his specimens at the same place where I obtained my sample on July 29, 1955. On that date plants had old fruits, but no floral buds or flowers. On Sept. 17, 1930, south of Contreras, Russell and Souviron (US) collected plants in flower. The locality is in the vicinity of the type population. The plants which I studied were on cliffs on the southern side of a small ravine just south of Cañada Magdalena and were exposed to the northwest; they were associated with *S. oxypetalum*, which was also not in flower on July 29. Important among the competing species were *Buddleja parviflora, Garrya longifolia, Quercus reticulata, Symphoricarpos microphyllus*, and mosses. In the greenhouse at Ithaca, a plant has flowered in November.

Pringle collected *Sedum bourgaei* on ledges at 3,050 m. in the Sierra de las Cruces on Feb. 11, 1899. I saw it there, about a kilometer southwest of Desierto de los Leones, on April 2, 1949. Plants were in flower on that date. They were on rocks on a steep mountainside in a forest of *Abies religiosa*. Associated species were *Echeveria secunda, Villadia batesii, Heuchera hemsleyana, Ribes pringlei*, and *Asplenium castaneum*.

Plants which I saw in the Sierra de la Marquesa on Aug. 17, 1955, were mostly on cliffs, sometimes pendulous, exposed to the north and west. About ten plants were growing in moss under *Abies religiosa*.

The large population about 19 km. east of Zitácuaro and 1 km. east of Macho de Agua is on the south side of the highway from Toluca to Zitácuaro. The plants occur for about .5 km. along the road on a rocky mountainside exposed to the north. I studied them there in 1955 on Sept. 21, Oct. 5, Nov. 30, and Dec. 15. Plants had floral buds on Sept. 21. On the other dates, besides floral buds, flowers were in anthesis. Competing species included *Alnus arguta* and *Halenia brevicornis*. In the greenhouse at Ithaca, plants have flowered in June, July, November, December, January, and February.

The small population in the Sierra de Ozumatlán, studied on

Dec. 1, 1955, was on a steep slope on the northern side of a small landslide between Mil Cumbres and Las Trojes. The plants were growing in volcanic ash over conglomerate, exposed to the southwest, in the shade of a species of *Pinus* with five leaves per fascicle. In the greenhouse at Ithaca, a plant from this population has been in flower in November, December, and April.

**Relationships.** The species most closely related to *Sedum bourgaei* are *S. guadalajaranum* and *S. griseum*. The problem of *S. guadalajaranum* has already been discussed above under variation. A comparison with *S. griseum* appears in the discussion of relationships under that species. The much larger shrub, *S. frutescens*, having stout trunks with peeling bark, obviously differs in vegetative characters from *S. bourgaei*. Differences between the two species in length and width of leaves, based on plants cultivated under similar conditions, are highly significant.

|  | S. bourgaei | | | | S. frutescens | | |
|---|---|---|---|---|---|---|---|
| n | n-obs. | $\bar{x}$ (mm.) | s (mm.) | n | n-obs. | $\bar{x}$ (mm.) | s (mm.) |
| Leaves | | | | | | | |
| Length** 8 | 15 | 13.2 | 5.9 | 8 | 40 | 31 | 3.9 |
| Width** 8 | 15 | 2 | .1 | 8 | 40 | 6.2 | .4 |

The pistils of *Sedum bourgaei* are erect, but those of *S. frutescens* are widely divergent. In addition, the nectaries of *S. bourgaei* are dark purple, and those of *S. frutescens* are white.

Illustrations. Hemsley (1879–1888), vol. 5, pl. 20; Praeger (1921) p. 155, fig. 82.

## 13. *SEDUM GRISEUM* (figs. 43–44)

Plants of *Sedum griseum* resemble those of *S. bourgaei* in being subshrubs with linear leaves, papillose twigs, and white flowers. They differ in having stems with gray-brown bark which peels in thin layers; often subglaucous, thicker leaves, usually 1.4 mm. or more thick; thicker floral stems; broader sepals; and reniform,

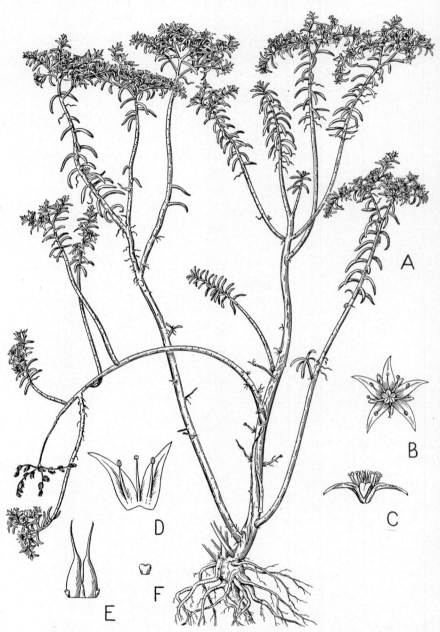

*Fig. 43.* Plant of *Sedum griseum* from the Sierra de Ozumatlán, Michoacán, cultivated in the greenhouse, Ithaca, N.Y.  A. Habit sketch (x .4).  B. Flower from above (x 1.6).  C. Flower from side (x 1.6).  D. Petals and stamens (x 2.4). E. Pistils (x 3.2).  F. Nectary (x 4).

pale yellow or creamy white nectaries, .7–1.5 mm. wide. No other species of the Trans-Mexican Volcanic Belt is likely to be confused with *S. griseum*.

**Description.** Materials: 22 plants—8 from the Sierra de Ozumatlán, Michoacán; 13 from southwest of San Lorenzo, Michoacán; and 1 from the New York Botanical Garden without information concerning place of origin in the wild. Measurements marked cult. are of plants cultivated under similar conditions in the greenhouse at Ithaca, N.Y.

Plants of *Sedum griseum* are subshrubs with erect or sometimes procumbent, much-branched stems having gray-brown bark; twigs are pale green or gray-brown and papillose; two-year-old branches are gray-brown or gray-green; bark of older portions of stems cracks and peels in thin layers. In the field, the difference in height between plants in the Sierra de Ozumatlán and at San Lorenzo is significant, but the difference between samples from these localities in the greenhouse is not significant; neither is the difference significant between plants in the wild and those in cultivation.

| | $n$ | $\bar{x}$ (dm.) | $s$ (dm.) | $w$ (dm.) |
|---|---|---|---|---|
| Height at time of flowering | | | | |
| Sierra de Ozumatlán | 5 | 2.5 | .6 | 2 –3.2 |
| San Lorenzo | 10 | 5.3 | 2.3 | 1.8–8.7 |
| Sierra de Ozumatlán—cult. | 4 | 2.5 | .6 | 1.6–3.8 |
| San Lorenzo—cult. | 4 | 3.2 | 1.5 | 2 –5.5 |
| Origin unknown—cult. | 1 | 1.3 | — | 1.3 |

Leaves are linear or lanceolate-linear, biconvex in cross section, sessile, obtuse, green or yellow-green, becoming suffused with red, often subglaucous, finely papillose, sometimes sparingly hirtellous dorsally. Differences in length and width of leaves between the population in the Sierra de Ozumatlán and that at San Lorenzo are not significant, either in the field or in cultivation; but differences in length and thickness between plants in the wild and those in cultivation are significant, the difference in length being highly significant. The difference in thickness between populations is significant in the wild, but not significant on the basis of plants cultivated under similar conditions.

| | n | n-obs. | x̄ (mm.) | s (mm.) | w (mm.) |
|---|---|---|---|---|---|
| **Length** | | | | | |
| Sierra de Ozumatlán | 8 | 57 | 11.9 | 1.5 | 5.9–16.1 |
| San Lorenzo | 12 | 66 | 12.6 | 2.2 | 6.7–19 |
| Sierra de Ozumatlán—cult. | 4 | 12 | 21.7 | 2.7 | 12 –28 |
| San Lorenzo—cult. | 4 | 11 | 15.4 | 3.3 | 10.2–20.7 |
| Origin unknown | 1 | 5 | 12.3 | — | 11.8–13 |
| **Width** | | | | | |
| Sierra de Ozumatlán | 8 | 57 | 2.3 | .2 | 1.7– 2.9 |
| San Lorenzo | 12 | 66 | 2.3 | .2 | 1.7– 2.9 |
| Sierra de Ozumatlán—cult. | 4 | 12 | 2.7 | .3 | 2.4– 3.2 |
| San Lorenzo—cult. | 3 | 9 | 2.3 | .4 | 2 – 3 |
| Origin unknown—cult. | 1 | 5 | 2.3 | — | 2.2– 2.4 |
| **Thickness** | | | | | |
| Sierra de Ozumatlán | 8 | 57 | 1.4 | .1 | 1 – 1.8 |
| San Lorenzo | 12 | 66 | 1.6 | .1 | .9– 2.1 |
| Sierra de Ozumatlán—cult. | 4 | 12 | 2 | .2 | 1.6– 2.3 |
| San Lorenzo—cult. | 4 | 11 | 1.5 | .4 | 1.1– 2.1 |
| Origin unknown—cult. | 1 | 5 | 1.6 | — | 1.5– 1.8 |

Ten leaves collected from two plants at San Lorenzo on Sept. 29, 1955, and measured on that date were dried as herbarium specimens and measured again on Dec. 6, 1957. They had shrunk in all dimensions, highly significantly in both width and thickness.

| | x̄ (mm.) | s (mm.) | w (mm.) |
|---|---|---|---|
| Length—fresh | 15.9 | 1.9 | 13 –19 |
| —dried | 14.6 | 1.8 | 12 –18 |
| Width—fresh | 2.2 | .2 | 1.8– 2.4 |
| —dried | 1.9 | .2 | 1.7– 2.4 |
| Thickness—fresh | 1.5 | .1 | 1.4– 1.8 |
| —dried | .1 | 0 | .1 |

Inflorescences are cymes of 1–12 cincinni. The stems with terminal cymes usually elongate by the development of shoots from axillary buds, but sometimes the cincinni proliferate and bear additional cymes in a subsequent season. Differences between populations in the diameters of the floral stems at the bases of the cymes are not significant, whether based on plants in the wild or on those in cultivation, but the plants in cultivation have highly significantly thicker stems than those in the wild.

| | $n$ | $n\text{-}obs.$ | $\bar{x}$ | $s$ | $w$ | |
|---|---|---|---|---|---|---|
| No. of flowers per cyme | | | | | | |
| Sierra de Ozumatlán | 5 | 22 | 20 | — | 5 | – 43 |
| San Lorenzo | 10 | 46 | 12 | — | 2 | – 31 |
| Sierra de Ozumatlán—cult. | 4 | 12 | 73 | — | 31 | –215 |
| Origin unknown—cult. | 1 | 5 | 5 | — | 3 | – 7 |
| Floral stems—diam. at | | | | | | |
| bases of cymes | | | | | | |
| Sierra de Ozumatlán | 5 | 23 | 1.8 mm. | .3 mm. | 1.2– | 2.3 mm. |
| San Lorenzo | 10 | 46 | 1.6 mm. | .3 mm. | 1 – | 2.7 mm. |
| Sierra de Ozumatlán—cult. | 4 | 10 | 3 mm. | .8 mm. | 2 – | 4.5 mm. |
| San Lorenzo—cult. | 3 | 6 | 2.4 mm. | .4 mm. | 1.5– | 3.2 mm. |
| Origin unknown—cult. | 1 | 5 | 1.2 mm. | — | 1 – | 1.3 mm. |

Flowers are rarely 6-merous or with 2 petals fused and corollas 4-merous. A flower of a plant from San Lorenzo had 4 sepals and 6 petals. The flowers are either sessile or on pedicels <3 mm. long. The difference between the populations in the diameter of the flowers is not significant.

| | $n$ | $n\text{-}obs.$ | $\bar{x}$ (mm.) | $s$ (mm.) | $w$ (mm.) | |
|---|---|---|---|---|---|---|
| Diameter | | | | | | |
| Sierra de Ozumatlán | 3 | 9 | 10 | 1.3 | 7 | –12 |
| San Lorenzo | 10 | 46 | 11 | 0 | 8 | –14 |
| Sierra de Ozumatlán—cult. | 1 | 2 | 12 | — | 11 | –13 |
| Torus—length | | | | | | |
| Sierra de Ozumatlán | 1 | 3 | 1 | — | .8– | 1.2 |
| —cult. | 1 | 2 | 1 | — | .8– | 1.3 |
| Origin unknown—cult. | 1 | 2 | .9 | — | .9 | |

Sepals are short-spurred, lanceolate, ovate, or lanceolate-oblong, obtuse or acute, pale green, sometimes reddish at tips, unequal. Differences between the two populations in the length and width of the sepals are not significant, whether based on plants in the wild or on those cultivated under similar conditions. Sepals of plants cultivated in the greenhouse at Ithaca are highly significantly longer than those of plants in the wild.

| | $n$ | $n\text{-}obs.$ | $\bar{x}$ (mm.) | $s$ (mm.) | $w$ (mm.) |
|---|---|---|---|---|---|
| Length | | | | | |
| Sierra de Ozumatlán | 5 | 22 | 3.2 | .3 | 2.4–4 |
| San Lorenzo | 10 | 46 | 3.6 | .3 | 2.5–5 |
| Sierra de Ozumatlán—cult. | 4 | 12 | 6.2 | 1.1 | 4.3–8.1 |
| San Lorenzo—cult. | 3 | 6 | 5.4 | 1.3 | 3.7–7.7 |
| Origin unknown—cult. | 1 | 2 | 2.5 | — | 2.4–2.6 |

| | n | n-obs. | x̄ (mm.) | s (mm.) | w (mm.) |
|---|---|---|---|---|---|
| **Length of spurs** | | | | | |
| Sierra de Ozumatlán | 5 | 22 | .5 | .1 | .3– .8 |
| —cult. | 1 | 2 | .5 | — | .5– .6 |
| **Width** | | | | | |
| Sierra de Ozumatlán | 5 | 22 | 1.5 | .1 | 1.1–1.8 |
| San Lorenzo | 10 | 46 | 1.7 | .2 | 1.1–2.2 |
| Sierra de Ozumatlán—cult. | 4 | 12 | 1.9 | .1 | 1.6–2 |
| San Lorenzo—cult. | 2 | 4 | 1.8 | .05 | 1.5–2.1 |
| Origin unknown—cult. | 1 | 2 | .9 | — | .9–1 |

Petals are lanceolate, obtuse or acute, mucronate-appendaged, sometimes slightly hooded, white, pale yellow or green on dorsal keels above middle, sometimes red at apices. Plants in the wild at San Lorenzo have significantly longer and highly significantly wider petals than do those in the Sierra de Ozumatlán, but plants in the Sierra de Ozumatlán have the petals highly significantly more connate. When plants are cultivated under similar conditions, these differences are not significant. The petals of plants cultivated in the greenhouse at Ithaca are highly significantly more connate than those of plants in the wild.

| | n | n-obs. | x̄ (mm.) | s (mm.) | w (mm.) |
|---|---|---|---|---|---|
| **Length** | | | | | |
| Sierra de Ozumatlán | 5 | 22 | 6.3 | .4 | 5.1–7.1 |
| San Lorenzo | 10 | 46 | 7.1 | .4 | 6.1–8.7 |
| Sierra de Ozumatlán—cult. | 4 | 12 | 7.1 | 0 | 6.6–8 |
| San Lorenzo—cult. | 3 | 6 | 7.2 | .5 | 6.7–8 |
| Origin unknown—cult. | 1 | 2 | 6.5 | — | 6.4–6.7 |
| **Length of connate portion** | | | | | |
| Sierra de Ozumatlán | 5 | 22 | .3 | .04 | .2– .5 |
| San Lorenzo | 10 | 46 | .1 | .1 | 0 – .5 |
| Sierra de Ozumatlán—cult. | 4 | 12 | .4 | .04 | .2– .8 |
| San Lorenzo—cult. | 2 | 4 | .4 | 0 | .2– .9 |
| Origin unknown—cult. | 1 | 1 | .3 | — | .3 |
| **Width** | | | | | |
| Sierra de Ozumatlán | 5 | 22 | 2.1 | .2 | 1.6–2.5 |
| San Lorenzo | 10 | 46 | 2.4 | .1 | 2 –2.8 |
| Sierra de Ozumatlán—cult. | 4 | 12 | 2.5 | .1 | 2.1–3 |
| San Lorenzo—cult. | 3 | 6 | 2.5 | .04 | 2.3–2.7 |
| Origin unknown—cult. | 1 | 2 | 1.8 | — | 1.7–1.9 |

Stamens have white filaments and yellow anthers; pollen is well developed. The difference in length of adnation of the epipetalous filaments between the plants in the Sierra de Ozumatlán and those at San Lorenzo is not significant, but four cultivated plants from the Sierra de Ozumatlán have the filaments highly significantly less adnate than do samples of plants in the wild in either population.

| | n | n-obs. | $\bar{x}$ (mm.) | s (mm.) | w (mm.) |
|---|---|---|---|---|---|
| Adnation of epipetalous filaments | | | | | |
| Sierra de Ozumatlán | 3 | 5 | 2.1 | .3 | 1.5–2.5 |
| San Lorenzo | 10 | 46 | 2.4 | .3 | 2 –3.6 |
| Sierra de Ozumatlán—cult. | 4 | 12 | 1.7 | .5 | 1.1–2.3 |
| Anthers—length | | | | | |
| Sierra de Ozumatlán | 1 | 1 | 1 | — | 1 |
| San Lorenzo | 8 | 23 | .8 | .1 | .5–1 |
| Sierra de Ozumatlán—cult. | 1 | 1 | .7 | — | .7 |
| Anthers—diameter | | | | | |
| Sierra de Ozumatlán—cult. | 1 | 1 | .6 | — | .6 |

Nectaries are reniform, emarginate, pale yellow or creamy white. Under similar conditions of cultivation, nectaries of three plants from San Lorenzo are significantly longer than those of four plants from the Sierra de Ozumatlán. A highly significant difference in width of nectaries between the populations in the wild is not significant on the basis of plants in cultivation.

| | n | n-obs. | $\bar{x}$ (mm.) | s (mm.) | w (mm.) |
|---|---|---|---|---|---|
| Length | | | | | |
| Sierra de Ozumatlán | 5 | 22 | .6 | 0 | .5– .7 |
| San Lorenzo | 10 | 46 | .6 | .1 | .5– .9 |
| Sierra de Ozumatlán—cult. | 4 | 12 | .6 | 04 | .6– .8 |
| San Lorenzo—cult. | 3 | 6 | .8 | 0 | .6– .9 |
| Origin unknown—cult. | 1 | 2 | .7 | — | .6– .8 |
| Width | | | | | |
| Sierra de Ozumatlán | 5 | 22 | .9 | .1 | .7–1.1 |
| San Lorenzo | 10 | 46 | 1.1 | .1 | .8–1.5 |
| Sierra de Ozumatlán—cult | 4 | 12 | 1 | .1 | .7–1.4 |
| San Lorenzo—cult. | 3 | 5 | 1.1 | .1 | .9–1.2 |
| Origin unknown—cult. | 1 | 2 | .8 | — | .8– .9 |

Pistils are erect and greenish white.

| | n | n-obs. | x̄ | s | w |
|---|---|---|---|---|---|
| Length | | | | | |
| Sierra de Ozumatlán—cult. | 4 | 12 | 5.5 mm. | .6 mm. | 4.6– 6.9 mm. |
| Origin unknown—cult. | 1 | 2 | 4.2 mm. | — | 4.1– 4.3 mm. |
| No. of ovules per ovary | | | | | |
| Sierra de Ozumatlán—cult. | 4 | 12 | 20 | — | 13 –28 |
| Origin unknown—cult. | 1 | 2 | 21 | — | 21 –22 |

Follicles are erect and brown.

| | n | n-obs. | x̄ (mm.) | s (mm.) | w (mm.) |
|---|---|---|---|---|---|
| Length | | | | | |
| San Lorenzo | 1 | 1 | 3 | — | 3 |
| Sierra de Ozumatlán—cult. | 1 | 5 | 3.4 | — | 3 –3.8 |
| San Lorenzo—cult. | 2 | 10 | 3.6 | 0 | 2.8–4.3 |

Seeds are pyriform, brown, very finely and irregularly reticulate.

| | n | n-obs. | x̄ (mm.) | w (mm.) |
|---|---|---|---|---|
| Length | | | | |
| Sierra de Ozumatlán—cult. | 1 | 5 | .6 | .6–.7 |
| Diameter | | | | |
| Sierra de Ozumatlán—cult. | 1 | 5 | .3 | .2–.3 |

**Variation.** Plants in the two populations which I have studied in the field are similar. On the basis of study of the wild plants, those at San Lorenzo differ significantly from those in the Sierra de Ozumatlán in six characters: taller stems; thicker leaves; longer, wider, less connate petals; and wider nectaries. When plants from these populations are cultivated under similar conditions in the greenhouse, however, no differences exist in two of the six characters, and the differences in the remaining four are not significant. Evidently the differences observed in the field are environmental modifications. Only one difference is significant between the two samples of plants in cultivation. That is in the length of the nectaries. The plants from San Lorenzo have longer nectaries.

The single plant from the New York Botanical Garden, without information concerning place of origin, differs from my other plants in several characters. It is lower in stature at time of flowering and has shorter, more glaucous leaves, fewer flowers per cyme, more slender floral stems, shorter, narrower sepals and petals, and narrower nectaries. In most of these characters, it falls within the expected range of variation of plants from the Sierra de Ozumatlán and San Lorenzo. Whether it is typical of the population from which it originally came and whether these differences would be significant if more plants were available remain questions. In some respects, namely, height length and glaucescence of leaves, and length of sepals, the plant from the New York Botanical Garden more exactly agrees with Praeger's original description of *Sedum griseum* than do my plants from the two populations mentioned. The possibility exists that the plant from New York is part of the clone which Praeger described. Present data favor the inclusion of the plants from the Sierra de Ozumatlán and San Lorenzo in the same species with this plant of unknown origin. Should more plants like the last become available and should some characters prove to distinguish it significantly from the others, subspecific recognition may be necessary, in which case this variation must be regarded as the one including the nomenclatural type.

Plants within populations differ in fourteen characters in the field. Under conditions of cultivation, plants differ in only six out of eleven of these same characters studied. The sample from the Sierra de Ozumatlán is the more variable Plants from there differ in five characters, whereas plants from San Lorenzo differ in only two characters. The only other species of Crassulaceae occurring with *Sedum griseum*, either in the Sierra de Ozumatlán or at San Lorenzo, is *Echeveria retusa*. That does not hybridize with the *Sedum* at either locality. If the observed variation in populations of *S. griseum* has a genetic basis, gene mutations may be the cause.

**Nomenclature.** *Sedum griseum* Praeger, Jour. Bot. 55: 43 (1917). Type locality: not designated, but probably somewhere in Mexico. Type: a plant from the New York Botanical Garden labeled "*S. Bourgaei*, No. 2." I have not seen a type specimen, but have used Praeger's (1921) illustration, fig. 84, as a basis for interpretation of the species. Fröderström's (1930–1935) figs. 157–162 and pl. 16 illustrate *S. bourgaei*.

**Distribution.** *Sedum griseum* occurs in the Michoacán Volcanic Region of the Trans-Mexican Volcanic Belt and also on the Central Mexican Plateau in the state of Guanajuato and possibly elsewhere. Below are data for the two populations which I have studied in the field:

| *Location* | *n-plants* | *Area* | *Alt. range* | *pH* | *Drainage* |
|---|---|---|---|---|---|
| Sierra de Ozumatlán | 229 | 2 km. x 20 m. | 2,260–2,290 m. | 6.8–7.2 | good to excessive |
| San Lorenzo | 427 | 200 m. x 50 m. | 2,190–2,235 m. | 6.2–7.4 | good |

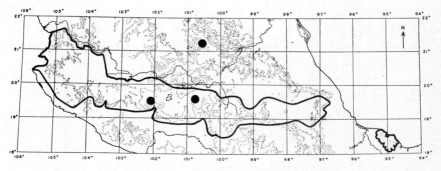

*Fig. 44.* Known distribution of *Sedum griseum.*

In about 1946, C. L. Gilly collected *Sedum griseum,* his no. 131, from east of San Luis de la Paz, Guanajuato. A living specimen of that collection has been available to me through the kindness of Edward Alexander. It is like the plant of unknown origin, from the New York Botanical Garden, discussed above. In 1905, Rose obtained specimens of *S. griseum* from cultivation at Tula, Hidalgo, and from near San Juan del Río, Querétaro. Whether the specimen from the latter locality was wild or cultivated is not clear. The report of *S. griseum* from the hills of Pátzcuaro is based on specimens of *S. bourgaei,* and possibly this is also true of the report of its occurrence on the Nevado de Toluca. I have searched in vain on the Nevado for *S. griseum,* and I doubt its occurrence there at 3,172 m.

I visited the population of *Sedum griseum* in the Sierra de Ozumatlán on Sept. 21 and 25 and Dec. 1, 1955. In September, the plants had floral buds. By December, many flowers were in anthesis, others were postanthesis, and some were still in bud. The plants were on cliffs of conglomerate and amygdaloidal basalt, facing southeast and east, along the highway from Zitácuaro to Morelia, between El Alamo and Las Trojes, that is, from north of km. 280 to south of km. 281. The plants occurred in groups and were mostly exposed to the sun throughout the day. The only other species of Crassulaceae in the vicinity was *Echeveria retusa.*

The commonest competing species were *Valeriana scorpioides* and *Aegopogon tenellus*. Pollinating insects appeared to be thrips, flies, and a species of Hemiptera. In cultivation in the greenhouse at Ithaca, plants from the Sierra de Ozumatlán have flowered in June, November, December, and January.

My visits to the population at San Lorenzo were on Sept. 29 and Dec. 6, 1955. Plants had floral buds on the former date, but on Dec. 6 were abundantly in flower, though still with some floral buds and also with some flowers postanthesis or with immature fruits. The plants were growing in ash and organic matter in crevices in the lava about 1 km. southwest of San Lorenzo. According to Williams (1950), this lava is not more than a few thousand years old. Deposition of ash from Paricutín was less than 25 cm. in this area. Exposure of the plants was to the northeast, east-northeast, east, south, and southwest. The older plants must have been in existence during the period of Paricutín's eruptions and have been heavily showered with ash, since the site is only 17 km. from the cone of Paricutín. The presence of many large, dead plants in the western part of the population, where the slope faces southwest, suggests that the ash from Paricutín had caused damage. Most of the plants were in the open, exposed to the sun throughout the day, but some were shaded either by the lava itself or by trees of *Pinus montezumae*, *Quercus* (species unidentified), and *Prunus serotina* (subspecies not determined). The commoner competing plants were *Heterocentron roseum*, *Peperomia galioides*, unidentified species of mosses, *Selaginella*, *Polypodium*, *Agave*, and grasses. Another competitor was *Lopezia pubescens*. Nearby was *Echeveria retusa*. Thrips, beetles, and flies were common in the flowers and appeared to be agents of pollination. In cultivation in the greenhouse at Ithaca, plants from San Lorenzo have flowered in July, November, December, and January.

**Relationships.** The species obviously closely related to *Sedum griseum* is *S. bourgaei*. Herbarium specimens appear so similar that Fröderström (1930–1935) expressed doubt whether it "is an independent species or a cultivated variety of *S. bourgaei*." When living plants are available, several important distinctions are apparent. Significant differences exist in the characters listed in the following table, in which the data are for plants cultivated under similar conditions in the greenhouse at Ithaca:

| | n | n-obs. | $\bar{x}$ (mm.) | s (mm.) | n | n-obs. | $\bar{x}$ (mm.) | s (mm.) |
|---|---|---|---|---|---|---|---|---|
| | | | *S. bourgaei* | | | | *S. griseum* | |
| **Leaves** | | | | | | | | |
| Width* | 8 | 15 | 2 | .1 | 8 | 26 | 2.5 | .1 |
| Thickness** | 8 | 15 | 1 | .1 | 9 | 28 | 1.7 | .3 |
| **Petals** | | | | | | | | |
| Length of connate portion** | 7 | 13 | .1 | .16 | 7 | 17 | .4 | 0 |
| **Stamens** | | | | | | | | |
| Length of adnation of epipetalous filaments** | 5 | 10 | .6 | 0 | 4 | 12 | 1.7 | .5 |
| **Nectaries** | | | | | | | | |
| Width** | 8 | 14 | .3 | .06 | 8 | 19 | .99 | .1 |

In addition to the above differences, the leaves of *S. griseum* often are subglaucous. Those of *S. bourgaei* never are glaucous. The nectaries of *S. griseum* are yellow or white. Those of *S. bourgaei* are dark purple.

Since I have not had living plants of *Sedum guadalajaranum* available for cultivation and study, I am unable to compare satisfactorily *S. griseum* with that. On the basis of data for *S. guadalajaranum* derived from herbarium specimens and the literature, *S. griseum* differs from it in lacking tuberous roots and in having longer, broader leaves, stouter floral stems, longer petals, and yellow or creamy white nectaries. Probably *S. guadalajaranum* is less likely to be confused with *S. griseum* than with *S. bourgaei*.

The large shrubs of *Sedum frutescens*, with their stout trunks, are obviously different from *S. griseum*, though the two species may be closely related. Three significant differences between the two are indicated in the following table, in which the data are for plants cultivated under similar conditions:

| | n | n-obs. | $\bar{x}$ (mm.) | s (mm.) | n | n-obs. | $\bar{x}$ (mm.) | s (mm.) |
|---|---|---|---|---|---|---|---|---|
| | | | *S. frutescens* | | | | *S. griseum* | |
| **Leaves** | | | | | | | | |
| Length** | 8 | 40 | 31 | 3.9 | 9 | 28 | 17 | 2.8 |
| Width** | 8 | 40 | 6.2 | .4 | 8 | 26 | 2.5 | .1 |
| **Nectaries** | | | | | | | | |
| Width** | 2 | 13 | .4 | .3 | 8 | 19 | .99 | .1 |

## 14. *SEDUM OBCORDATUM* (figs. 45–48)

*Sedum obcordatum* and *S. stahlii* are the only two species of *Sedum* of the Trans-Mexican Volcanic Belt regularly with decussately opposite leaves. Both have yellow petals and divergent follicles. The leaves of *S. obcordatum* are flat, obcordate, and smooth; those of *S. stahlii* are terete, elliptic-oblong or globular, and hairy. The two species are not likely to be confused. Neither is *S. obcordatum* likely to be mistaken for any other species.

**Description.** Materials: 20 plants—8 from the Cofre de Perote and 12 from the peak of Orizaba. Measurements marked cult. are of plants cultivated in the greenhouse at Ithaca, N.Y. Those marked cult.—cf. are of plants cultivated in a cold frame at Ithaca.

Plants of *Sedum obcordatum* are subshrubs with stems cespitose, erect or ascending, much branched, glabrous, and 4–9 mm. in diameter; branches break off the main stems very easily; bark is gray and lustrous, cracking and peeling on older portions of stems; roots are woody and longer than stems. A slight difference between populations in length of stems with fruits is not significant.

| | $n$ | $n$-obs. | $\bar{x}$ (dm.) | $s$ (dm.) | $w$ (dm.) |
|---|---|---|---|---|---|
| Length of stems with fruits | | | | | |
| Cofre de Perote | 5 | 19 | 1.8 | .7 | .8–3.5 |
| Peak of Orizaba | 9 | 25 | 2 | 1.3 | .7–4.8 |

Leaves are decussately opposite, except sometimes spirally arranged upward on floral shoots, obcordate, obovate, or suborbicular, short-spurred, emarginate or broadly rounded at apices, and glaucous, appearing bluish. On the basis of measurements in the field, the leaves of plants on the peak of Orizaba are significantly wider than those of plants on the Cofre de Perote, but a difference in thickness is not significant, and no difference exists in length. In the greenhouse, a difference in length exists between the two populations, but this is not significant, and no difference exists in width. Although differences in both length and width of leaves occur among cultivated plants within both populations, further study is desirable to substantiate this observation. Leaves may continue to enlarge for a long time after initial expansion. In an experiment involving five leaves of a rapidly growing plant in the greenhouse,

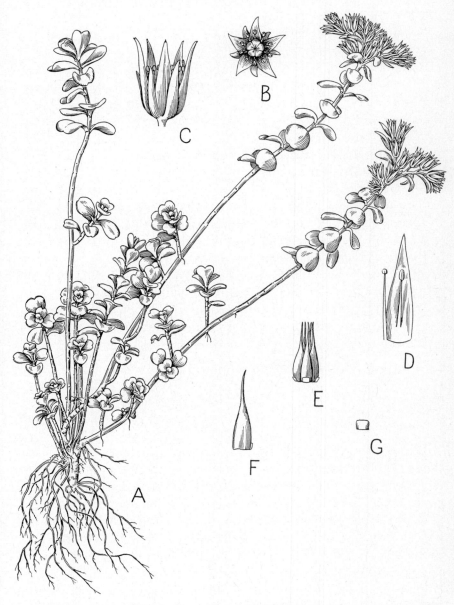

*Fig. 45.* Plant of *Sedum obcordatum* from the peak of Orizaba, cultivated in the greenhouse, Ithaca, N.Y.  A. Habit sketch (x .4).  B. Flower from above (x 1.6). C. Flower from side (x 1.6).  D. Petal and two stamens (x 2.4).  E. Pistils (x 2.4). F. Single pistil (x 3.2).  G. Nectary (x 4).

four leaves increased in width in three weeks and three leaves increased in length. All five leaves were remote from shoot apices and were primary leaves, presumably mature.

|  | n | n-obs. | x̄ (mm.) | s (mm.) | w (mm.) |
|---|---|---|---|---|---|
| **Length** | | | | | |
| Cofre de Perote | 5 | 19 | 21.4 | 2 | 16 −27 |
| Peak of Orizaba | 10 | 27 | 21.4 | 1.1 | 18 −24 |
| Cofre de Perote—cult. | 2 | 66 | 16.5 | 0 | 7 −26 |
| Peak of Orizaba—cult. | 5 | 145 | 17.9 | 1.6 | 7 −29 |
| Cofre de Perote—cult.—cf. | 6 | 229 | 14.6 | 1.6 | 7 −25 |
| Peak of Orizaba—cult.—cf. | 1 | 35 | 15.9 | — | 9 −23 |
| **Width** | | | | | |
| Cofre de Perote | 5 | 19 | 17.1 | 1.4 | 13 −23 |
| Peak of Orizaba | 10 | 27 | 19.7 | 2.2 | 13 −25 |
| Cofre de Perote—cult. | 2 | 66 | 13.9 | .2 | 6 −19 |
| Peak of Orizaba—cult. | 5 | 145 | 13.9 | 1.5 | 7 −21 |
| Cofre de Perote—cult.—cf. | 6 | 229 | 12.8 | 1.6 | 6 −21 |
| Peak of Orizaba—cult.—cf. | 1 | 35 | 14.6 | — | 9 −20 |
| **Thickness** | | | | | |
| Cofre de Perote | 5 | 16 | 2.1 | .3 | 1.2− 3 |
| Peak of Orizaba | 10 | 27 | 2 | .6 | 1 − 3.6 |
| —cult. | 1 | 3 | 1.6 | — | 1.5− 1.6 |

Inflorescences are terminal cymes of 1–5 cincinni. Stems with flowers elongate by the development of lateral shoots and often appear tortuous. Floral bracts are elliptical or obovate.

|  | n | n-obs. | x̄ | s | w |
|---|---|---|---|---|---|
| **No. of flowers per cyme** | | | | | |
| Cofre de Perote | 5 | 15 | 8 | — | 4–11 |
| Peak of Orizaba | 8 | 19 | 13 | — | 6–19 |
| —cult. | 1 | 2 | 20 | — | 17–24 |
| **Floral bracts—length** | | | | | |
| Peak of Orizaba | 7 | 18 | 14 mm. | 1.5 mm. | 10–17 mm. |
| **Floral bracts—width** | | | | | |
| Peak of Orizaba | 7 | 18 | 7.6 mm. | 0 mm. | 5–12 mm. |

Flowers are short-pedicellate, often 4-merous, rarely 6-merous.

|  | n | n-obs. | x̄ (mm.) | s (mm.) | w (mm.) |
|---|---|---|---|---|---|
| **Pedicels—length** | | | | | |
| Peak of Orizaba | 8 | 19 | 3.4 | 1 | 1 − 7 |
| —cult. | 1 | 3 | 2.3 | — | 2 − 2.6 |

| | n | n-obs. | x̄ (mm.) | s (mm.) | w (mm.) |
|---|---|---|---|---|---|
| Flowers—diameter | | | | | |
| Peak of Orizaba—cult. | 1 | 3 | 13 | — | 11 −16 |
| Torus—length | | | | | |
| Peak of Orizaba—cult. | 1 | 3 | .4 | — | .3− .5 |
| Cofre de Perote—cult.—cf. | 2 | 6 | .4 | .2 | .1− .8 |
| Peak of Orizaba—cult.—cf. | 5 | 15 | .7 | .3 | .4− 1.3 |

Sepals are oblanceolate-oblong or elliptic-oblong, sometimes spurred, obtuse, unequal, pale green, glaucous, persisting in withered condition around fruits. The sepals of two plants from the Cofre de Perote, cultivated in the cold frame, were significantly longer than those of five plants from the peak of Orizaba.

| | n | n-obs. | x̄ (mm.) | s (mm.) | w (mm.) |
|---|---|---|---|---|---|
| Length of longest sepals | | | | | |
| Peak of Orizaba | 8 | 19 | 11.5 | 0 | 8.9−15.1 |
| —cult. | 1 | 3 | 11.9 | — | 11.3−12.5 |
| Cofre de Perote—cult.—cf. | 2 | 6 | 11.6 | 1.2 | 9.5−13.7 |
| Peak of Orizaba—cult.—cf. | 5 | 15 | 8.4 | 1.1 | 6.5−12.6 |
| Width of longest sepals | | | | | |
| Peak of Orizaba | 8 | 19 | 3.4 | .5 | 2.3− 5.9 |
| —cult. | 1 | 3 | 2.6 | — | 2.3− 3 |

Petals are erect, lanceolate, acute or obtuse, mucronate-appendaged, carinate dorsally, yellow, glaucous and greenish at bases dorsally, partly imbricate in bud. The bases of the stamens alternating with the petals may hold these together. The slight cohesion of petals observed in the field possibly should be interpreted on this basis. Petals of a plant which flowered in the greenhouse were separate from each other, even at their bases.

| | n | n-obs. | x̄ (mm.) | s (mm.) | w (mm.) |
|---|---|---|---|---|---|
| Length | | | | | |
| Peak of Orizaba | 7 | 18 | 10.8 | 0 | 9.4−12.4 |
| —cult. | 1 | 3 | 12.2 | — | 12 −12.4 |
| Cofre de Perote—cult.—cf. | 2 | 6 | 11 | 1.2 | 9.2−12. |
| Peak of Orizaba—cult.—cf. | 5 | 15 | 8.7 | 1.8 | 6.5−12.1 |
| Length of connate portion | | | | | |
| Peak of Orizaba* | 7 | 18 | .6 | .3 | .3− 1.6 |
| —cult. | 1 | 3 | 0 | — | 0 |

| | $n$ | $n$-obs. | $\bar{x}$ (mm.) | $s$ (mm.) | $w$ (mm.) |
|---|---|---|---|---|---|
| **Width** | | | | | |
| Peak of Orizaba | 7 | 18 | 4.8 | .5 | 3.9– 6.7 |
| —cult. | 1 | 3 | 3.4 | — | 3.2– 3.8 |
| Cofre de Perote—cult.—cf. | 2 | 6 | 3.5 | .3 | 2.7– 4.2 |
| Peak of Orizaba—cult.—cf. | 5 | 15 | 3.1 | .7 | 2 – 4.5 |

Stamens have yellow filaments and anthers; pollen is well developed.

| | $n$ | $n$-obs. | $\bar{x}$ (mm.) | $s$ (mm.) | $w$ (mm.) |
|---|---|---|---|---|---|
| **Adnation of epipetalous filaments** | | | | | |
| Peak of Orizaba | 1 | 1 | 2.4 | — | 2.4 |
| —cult. | 1 | 3 | 1.4 | — | 1.2–1.5 |
| **Anthers—length** | | | | | |
| Peak of Orizaba | 5 | 11 | 1.4 | .1 | 1 –1.7 |
| —cult. | 1 | 3 | 1.3 | — | 1.2–1.4 |
| **Anthers—diameter** | | | | | |
| Peak of Orizaba—cult. | 1 | 3 | .7 | — | .6– .7 |

Nectaries are reniform or subquadrate, truncate, pale yellow or yellowish white, sometimes transparent.

| | $n$ | $n$-obs. | $\bar{x}$ (mm.) | $s$ (mm.) | $w$ (mm.) |
|---|---|---|---|---|---|
| **Length** | | | | | |
| Peak of Orizaba | 7 | 18 | .7 | .1 | .5–1.1 |
| —cult. | 1 | 3 | .6 | — | .6– .7 |
| Cofre de Perote—cult.—cf. | 2 | 6 | .7 | .1 | .5– .8 |
| Peak of Orizaba—cult.—cf. | 5 | 15 | .6 | .1 | .4– .8 |
| **Width** | | | | | |
| Peak of Orizaba | 7 | 18 | 1.5 | 0 | 1 –2.1 |
| —cult. | 1 | 3 | .8 | — | .7– .9 |
| Cofre de Perote—cult.—cf. | 2 | 6 | .8 | .1 | .6–1.1 |
| Peak of Orizaba—cult.—cf. | 5 | 15 | .5 | .1 | .2– .9 |

Pistils are erect, pale green, glaucous, without clear demarcation between ovary and style. One flower of a plant on the peak of Orizaba had three well-developed pistils, and a fourth, very much smaller than the others, was fused with a stamen and open below the apex, with the ovules exposed and an anther terminal.

| | $n$ | $n$-obs. | $\bar{x}$ | | $w$ | |
|---|---|---|---|---|---|---|
| **Length** | | | | | | |
| Peak of Orizaba | 1 | 1 | 6.4 mm. | | 6.4 | mm. |
| —cult. | 1 | 3 | 6.3 mm. | | 6.4–7.3 mm. | |

|                        | $n$ | $n$-obs. | $\bar{x}$ |     | $w$ |
|------------------------|-----|----------|-----------|-----|-----|
| No. of ovules per ovary |     |          |           |     |     |
| Peak of Orizaba        | I   | I        | 52        |     | 52  |
| —cult.                 | I   | 3        | 53        |     | 5I⁻54 |

Follicles are divergent, stramineous, with marginal lips broadest basally and narrowest apically. Inner and outer walls of immature follicles are somewhat viscid. Differences between populations in length of follicles, length of beaks, and width of lips are not significant.

|                  | $n$ | $n$-obs. | $\bar{x}$ (mm.) | $s$ (mm.) | $w$ (mm.) |
|------------------|-----|----------|-----------------|-----------|-----------|
| Length           |     |          |                 |           |           |
| Cofre de Perote  | 5   | 18       | 6.3             | .4        | 5.1–8.7   |
| Peak of Orizaba  | 9   | 25       | 6.4             | 1.2       | 4.3⁻9.4   |
| Length of beaks  |     |          |                 |           |           |
| Cofre de Perote  | 5   | 18       | 1.4             | 0         | 0  ⁻2.3   |
| Peak of Orizaba  | 9   | 25       | 1.3             | .5        | .4⁻2.8    |
| Width of lips    |     |          |                 |           |           |
| Cofre de Perote  | 5   | 18       | .3              | 0         | .2⁻ .4    |
| Peak of Orizaba  | 9   | 25       | .4              | .06       | .2⁻ .6    |

Seeds are fusiform, verrucose, brown, winged terminally, with the wings each about .3 mm. long. Differences between populations in dimensions of seeds are not significant.

|                  | $n$ | $n$-obs. | $\bar{x}$ (mm.) | $s$ (mm.) | $w$ (mm.) |
|------------------|-----|----------|-----------------|-----------|-----------|
| Length           |     |          |                 |           |           |
| Cofre de Perote  | 5   | 16       | 1.4             | .1        | 1.1–1.7   |
| Peak of Orizaba  | 6   | 23       | 1.3             | .1        | 1.1⁻1.7   |
| Diameter         |     |          |                 |           |           |
| Cofre de Perote  | 5   | 16       | .4              | 0         | .3⁻ .4    |
| Peak of Orizaba  | 6   | 23       | .3              | .02       | .2⁻ .4    |

**Variation.** *Sedum obcordatum* exhibits little variation. On the basis of study of wild plants, the populations on the Cofre de Perote and the peak of Orizaba differ significantly from each other in only one out of nine characters in which I compared them. The significant difference is in width of leaves, but this difference is not confirmed by plants cultivated in Ithaca. Other characters studied in the field were length of stems with fruits, length and thickness of leaves, and dimensions of both follicles and seeds. Since my visit to the Cofre de Perote was not at a time when the plants were in flower, I have been unable to compare wild plants in the two populations on the basis of floral characters. In addition, although I have had eighteen plants in cultivation in Ithaca, replicated both in greenhouse and cold frame, only eight have flowered, one in the greenhouse and seven in the cold frame. In the greenhouse, *S. obcordatum* has not grown well. In the cold frame, it does much better. Differences between two plants from the Cofre de Perote and five from the peak of Orizaba, which flowered in the cold frame, may be attributed to chance, except that the sepals of the plants from the Cofre de Perote were significantly longer.

Wild plants within populations differ in only nine out of twenty characters studied. Some of these differences may be the result of environmental modification, but differences in length and width of leaves may have a real, genetic basis, since these occur among plants of the same age, measured at the same time, and cultivated under similar conditions in the greenhouse and cold frame at Ithaca. Likewise, differences in the dimensions of sepals and petals and in the length of the tori and nectaries, observed among plants which flowered in the cold frame, may have a genetic basis. The easiest explanation of such possible heritable variation is by gene mutation. Since no other Crassulaceae occur associated with *Sedum obcordatum*, either on the Cofre de Perote or on the peak of Orizaba, interspecific hybridization appears to be an unlikely cause of this variation.

The rigorous conditions of life on the two high peaks inhabited by *Sedum obcordatum* subject the plants to drastic selection. Only those biotypes can survive which endure frequent frosts at night and the extreme desiccating effect of the strong winds prevalent at the high altitudes. One result of this selection might be a greater uniformity in the genetic constitutions of the populations of plants occurring in such places. My studies have revealed little variation in the two known populations of *S. obcordatum*.

**Nomenclature.** *Sedum obcordatum* R. T. Clausen, Bull. Torrey Club 68 (7): 474–475, fig. 1 (1941). Type locality: cliffs, alt. 3,812 m., Cofre de Perote. Type: E. K. Ball's collection no. 4,600 (US 1,793,671), collected on May 24, 1938. Two errors in the original description are leaves "alternate" and nectaries ".2" mm. long. Otherwise the information is in agreement with the more complete data which I have subsequently obtained from living plants.

**Distribution.** *Sedum obcordatum* is known only from the alpine region of the peak of Orizaba and the subalpine zone on the Cofre de Perote. Data for the two populations are summarized in the following table:

| Location | n-plants | Area (m.) | Alt. range (m.) | pH | Drainage |
|---|---|---|---|---|---|
| Cofre de Perote | > 50 | >500 x 80 | 3,810–3,890 | 6.8 | moderate |
| Peak of Orizaba | ab. 100 | 200 x 125 | 4,100–4,225 | 6.8–7.4 | good to excessive |

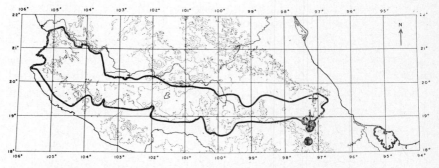

*Fig. 46.* Known distribution of *Sedum obcordatum* (+) and *S. stahlii* (•).

Dr. E. W. Nelson collected fragments of *Sedum obcordatum* on the Cofre de Perote in May, 1893. These are preserved in the United States National Herbarium. In May, 1938, E. K. Balls collected specimens in flower. He obtained these from crevices of cliffs at an elevation of 3,812 m. His collection includes the type of the species. My visit to this population was on Nov. 20, 1955. Conditions were not favorable for study, since a heavy rain was falling throughout the period of my visit, and the temperature of the air was 6.1°–6.7° C. Some of the plants had fruits, but no flowers. The plants were growing in volcanic ash and organic matter in crevices exposed to the northeast and east. Competing species included *Grimmia ovalis* (identified by Professor Albert Andrews), *Alchemilla vulcanica*, *Oxylobus arbutifolius*, and *Calamagrostis schiedeana*.

Liebmann (1844) mentioned the occurrence of *Sedum aureum* on precipices and dry cliffs on the peak of Orizaba at about 3,050 m. What that was I do not know, but the reported place of occurrence is considerably below where I have seen *S. obcordatum*. In September, 1907, Purpus collected *S. obcordatum* in the Barranca de Mala Cara on the peak of Orizaba. He collected further specimens there on March 3, 1908. These collections were the basis of a brief description prepared by Dr. Rose and preserved in the United States National Herbarium. Dr. Rose had a name for the species, but never published it. Had I known that when I published *S. obcordatum*, I would have used his specific epithet and assigned authorship to him. My visit to the Barranca de Mala Cara was on Oct. 24, 1955. The plants of *S. obcordatum* were in bud, flower, and fruit at that time. They were restricted to the western slope of the Barranca, facing east-southeast, and were rooted in volcanic ash in crevices of andesite-porphyry. Drainage was excessive. The plants either were exposed to the sun throughout the day or were in partial shade. Competing species included *Grimmia ovalis*, *Cerastium vulcanicum*, *Oxylobus arbutifolius*, *Gnaphalium vulcanicum*, *Senecio roseus*, and *Calamagrostis schiedeana*. The site was on the southeastern slope of the mountain, 30° east of south from the summit. At Ithaca, a plant flowered in the greenhouse in January, 1957, and

*Fig. 47.* Habitat of *Sedum obcordatum*, cliffs in the Barranca de Mala Cara, peak of Orizaba, Oct. 24, 1955.

Fig. 48. Sedum obcordatum on the southwestern slope of the Barranca de Mala Cara, peak of Orizaba, Oct. 24, 1955.

others in the cold frame in April, 1957, and in May and June, 1958.

**Relationships.** Sedum obcordatum and S. stahlii are the only stonecrops regularly with decussately opposite leaves inhabiting the Trans-Mexican Volcanic Belt. Both are subshrubs having yellow petals and divergent follicles with prominent lips. Despite these common characteristics, the two species are unlike in appearance. The leaves of S. stahlii are about as thick as broad and are hirtellous. Those of S. obcordatum are flat, much broader than thick, glabrous, and glaucous. The petals of S. obcordatum are longer than those of S. stahlii, and the seeds are longer and winged. Further consideration of these and other distinctions is included in the discussion of relationships under S. stahlii.

Sedum obcordatum may be distantly related to S. dendroideum. The possibility exists that both are descended from the same ancestral group, with S. obcordatum the more specialized. Some of the differences between them are listed in the following table, in which data for length of leaves are for plants cultivated under similar conditions in the greenhouse at Ithaca, N.Y., but data for other characters are for plants in the wild.

| | | S. obcordatum | | | | | S. dendroideum | |
|---|---|---|---|---|---|---|---|---|
| | n | n-obs. | x̄ (mm.) | s (mm.) | n | n-obs. | x̄ (mm.) | s (mm.) |
| Leaves | | | | | | | | |
| Length** | 7 | 211 | 17.5 | 1.3 | 17 | 51 | 46.7 | 4.9 |
| Sepals | | | | | | | | |
| Length | 8 | 19 | 11.5 | 0 | 4 | 12 | 5.6 | 0 |
| Petals | | | | | | | | |
| Length | 7 | 18 | 10.8 | 0 | 4 | 12 | 8.1 | 0 |
| Follicles | | | | | | | | |
| Length* | 14 | 43 | 6.3 | 1 | 5 | 25 | 3.8 | .4 |
| Seeds | | | | | | | | |
| Length* | 11 | 39 | 1.3 | .1 | 3 | 9 | .6 | .05 |

Obvious differences exist between the two species in shape and color of leaves, spatulate and bright green in *Sedum dendroideum*, obcordate and glaucous in *S. obcordatum*, and also in the position of the inflorescences, on axillary branches in *S. dendroideum*, but on terminal shoots, at least at first, in *S. obcordatum*.

*Sedum palmeri* and another species, a native of the Central Mexican Plateau, still undescribed, are both probably related to *S. obcordatum*. Since their leaves are borne spirally on the stems and their flowers are smaller than in *S. obcordatum*, they are easy to distinguish. Possibly these, as well as *S. dendroideum* and *S. obcordatum*, all had a common origin.

## 15. *SEDUM STAHLII* (figs. 49–50)

*Sedum stahlii* is easy to recognize by its thick, often globular leaves which are opposite and usually red or reddish. Otherwise only *S. obcordatum*, in the Trans-Mexican Volcanic Belt, regularly has opposite leaves, but the leaves of that are flat, obcordate, and glaucous, not terete, globular or elliptic-oblong, and hairy, as in *S. stahlii*.

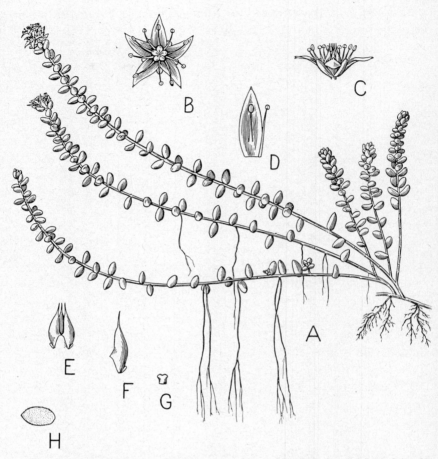

*Fig. 49.* Plant of *Sedum stahlii* from a slope near Acultzingo, cultivated in the greenhouse, Ithaca, N.Y. A. Habit sketch (x .4). B. Flower from above (x 1.6). C. Flower from side (x 1.6). D. Petal and two stamens (x 2.4). E. Pistils (x 2.4). F. Single pistil (x 3.2). G. Nectary (x 4). H. Leaf (x .8).

**Description.** Materials: 7 plants—2 from Maltrata, Vera Cruz, and 5 from the slope west of Acultzingo, Vera Cruz. Measurements marked cult. are of plants cultivated in the greenhouse at Ithaca, N.Y.

Plants of *Sedum stahlii* are subshrubs with stems much branched, spreading or trailing, reddish brown, puberulent, with hairs .03–.1 mm. long, frequently with aerial roots.

|  | $n$ | $n$-obs. | $\bar{x}$ | $s$ | $w$ |
|---|---|---|---|---|---|
| Height of stems with flowers |  |  |  |  |  |
| Maltrata—cult. | 1 | 1 | 1.6 dm. | — | 1.6    dm. |
| Acultzingo—cult. | 3 | 3 | 1.8 dm. | .4 dm. | 1.5–2.3 dm. |
| Height of stems with fruits |  |  |  |  |  |
| Maltrata | 2 | 6 | 1.2 dm. | .5 dm. | .7–1.9 dm. |
| Acultzingo | 5 | 15 | 1 dm. | .3 dm. | .6–1.8 dm. |
| Length of stems with flowers |  |  |  |  |  |
| Acultzingo—cult. | 1 | 10 | 3.3 dm. | — | 2.3–3.7 dm. |
| Diameter of stems with flowers |  |  |  |  |  |
| Acultzingo—cult. | 1 | 10 | 1.7 mm. | — | 1 –2   mm. |

Leaves are decussately opposite, rarely subopposite or even alternate, elliptic-oblong, elliptical, or globular, rounded at apices, terete in cross section, puberulent, lustrous usually suffused with red, detaching very easily.

|  | $n$ | $n$-obs. | $\bar{x}$ (mm.) | $s$ (mm.) | $w$ (mm.) |
|---|---|---|---|---|---|
| Length |  |  |  |  |  |
| Maltrata | 2 | 6 | 8.3 | 1 | 7– 9 |
| Acultzingo | 5 | 15 | 9.5 | 0 | 8–13 |
| Maltrata—cult. | 1 | 1 | 11 | — | 11 |
| Acultzingo—cult. | 4 | 48 | 11.7 | .8 | 9–14 |
| Width |  |  |  |  |  |
| Maltrata | 2 | 6 | 5.3 | .8 | 4– 6 |
| Acultzingo | 5 | 15 | 5.7 | 0 | 5– 8 |
| Maltrata—cult. | 1 | 1 | 6 | — | 6 |
| Acultzingo—cult. | 4 | 48 | 5.3 | .4 | 4– 6.5 |
| Thickness |  |  |  |  |  |
| Maltrata | 2 | 6 | 4.8 | 1.1 | 3– 6 |
| Acultzingo | 5 | 15 | 4.9 | .3 | 4– 7 |
| Maltrata—cult. | 1 | 1 | 5 | — | 5 |
| Acultzingo—cult. | 4 | 48 | 4.5 | .3 | 4– 5.5 |

Inflorescences are terminal cymes of 2–6, usually 3, cincinni.

|  | $n$ | $n$-obs. | $\bar{x}$ | $w$ |
|---|---|---|---|---|
| No. of flowers per cyme | 1 | 10 | 12 | 7–37 |

Flowers are short pedicellate, rarely 4- or 5-merous.

|  | $n$ | $n$-obs. | $\bar{x}$ (mm.) | $s$ (mm.) | $w$ (mm.) |
|---|---|---|---|---|---|
| Pedicels—length |  |  |  |  |  |
| Acultzingo—cult. | 1 | 12 | 1.2 | — | .6– 2 |

|                     | n | n-obs. | x̄ (mm.) | s (mm.) | w (mm.) |
|---------------------|---|--------|---------|---------|---------|
| Flowers—diameter    |   |        |         |         |         |
| Maltrata—cult.      | 1 | 1      | 13      | —       | 13      |
| Acultzingo—cult.    | 4 | 48     | 12.9    | .7      | 11 –15  |
| Torus—length        |   |        |         |         |         |
| Maltrata—cult.      | 1 | 1      | 1.4     | —       | 1.4     |
| Acultzingo—cult.    | 4 | 45     | 1.2     | .1      | .6–.1.6 |

*Fig. 50.* Floral stem of a plant of *Sedum stahlii* from the slope west of Acultzingo, cultivated in the greenhouse, Ithaca, N.Y., Feb. 25, 1957 (x 3.1).

Sepals are lanceolate, oblong-lanceolate, or ovate, acute, unequal, yellow-green, and puberulent.

|  | n | n-obs. | x̄ (mm.) | s (mm.) | w (mm.) |
|---|---|---|---|---|---|
| **Length** | | | | | |
| Maltrata—cult. | I | I | 3.1 | — | 3.1 |
| Acultzingo—cult. | 4 | 48 | 3.7 | .5 | 2.4–5.2 |
| **Width** | | | | | |
| Maltrata—cult. | I | I | 1.6 | — | 1.6 |
| Acultzingo—cult. | 4 | 48 | 1.8 | .1 | 1.3–2.2 |

Petals are elliptic-lanceolate, acute or acuminate, mucronate-
appendaged, canary-yellow, sometimes minutely connate basally.

|  | n | n-obs. | x̄ (mm.) | s (mm.) | w (mm.) |
|---|---|---|---|---|---|
| **Length** | | | | | |
| Maltrata—cult. | I | I | 6.7 | — | 6.7 |
| Acultzingo—cult. | 4 | 48 | 7.2 | .7 | 5.8–8.6 |
| **Width** | | | | | |
| Maltrata—cult. | I | I | 2.4 | — | 2.4 |
| Acultzingo—cult. | 4 | 48 | 2.4 | .1 | 2.1–2.7 |

Stamens have yellow filaments and anthers; pollen is well developed.

|  | n | n-obs. | x̄ (mm.) | s (mm.) | w (mm.) |
|---|---|---|---|---|---|
| **Adnation of epipetalous filaments** | | | | | |
| Maltrata—cult. | I | I | .8 | — | .8 |
| Acultzingo—cult. | 4 | 48 | 1.3 | .2 | .7–2.1 |
| **Anthers—length** | | | | | |
| Acultzingo—cult. | 4 | 20 | .9 | .1 | .7–1.1 |
| **Anthers—diameter** | | | | | |
| Acultzingo—cult. | 4 | 20 | .5 | .05 | .4–.6 |

Nectaries are subquadrate, rounded or concave at apex, deep
yellow or orange.

|  | n | n-obs. | x̄ (mm.) | s (mm.) | w (mm.) |
|---|---|---|---|---|---|
| **Length** | | | | | |
| Maltrata—cult. | I | I | .5 | — | .5 |
| Acultzingo—cult. | 4 | 48 | .69 | .03 | .6–.8 |
| **Width** | | | | | |
| Maltrata—cult. | I | I | .9 | — | .9 |
| Acultzingo—cult. | 4 | 48 | .7 | .05 | .6–1 |

Pistils are erect and yellow.

|  | n | n-obs. | $\bar{x}$ | s | w |
|---|---|---|---|---|---|
| Length |  |  |  |  |  |
| Maltrata—cult. | I | I | 4.8 mm. | — | 4.8     mm. |
| Acultzingo—cult. | 4 | 48 | 4.4 mm. | .5 mm. | 3.2– 5.4 mm. |
| No. of ovules per ovary |  |  |  |  |  |
| Maltrata—cult. | I | I | 18 | — | 18 |
| Acultzingo—cult. | 4 | 48 | 13 | — | 9 –18 |

Follicles are divergent.

|  | n | n-obs. | $\bar{x}$ (mm.) | s (mm.) | w (mm.) |
|---|---|---|---|---|---|
| Length |  |  |  |  |  |
| Maltrata | I | I | 2.5 | — | 2.5 |
| Acultzingo | 4 | 12 | 2.9 | .5 | 2 –4.2 |
| Length of beak |  |  |  |  |  |
| Maltrata | I | I | .7 | — | .7 |
| Width of lips |  |  |  |  |  |
| Maltrata | I | I | .4 | — | .4 |
| Acultzingo | 4 | 12 | .6 | .06 | .5– .8 |

Seeds are ovoid, finely papillose, brown.

|  | n | n-obs. | $\bar{x}$ (mm.) | w (mm.) |
|---|---|---|---|---|
| Length |  |  |  |  |
| Maltrata | I | I | .6 | .6 |
| Acultzingo | I | 3 | .6 | .6 |
| Diameter |  |  |  |  |
| Maltrata | I | I | .3 | .3 |
| Acultzingo | I | 3 | .3 | .3 |

**Variation.** Because *Sedum stahlii* presents no problems in classification, I have devoted little attention to it. Plants of my samples
from Maltrata and Acultzingo are very similar. No significant
differences exist between them. The species may not be genetically
uniform, however, since differences exist in fourteen characters
among four plants from Acultzingo, cultivated under similar conditions in the greenhouse. The variability in these characters suggests that *S. stahlii* may be more than a distinctive clone which
reproduces vegetatively.

**Nomenclature.** *Sedum stahlii* Solms, Sämereien bot. Gart.
Univ. Strassburg 1900: 4. Type locality: on limestone in the
Cañada Istapam near Tehuacán, Puebla. Type: cultivated in a

greenhouse at Strassbourg, originally obtained near Tehuacán by
Professor Ernst Stahl of Jena. Rehnelt published a further description in Die Gartenwelt 6: 316–317 (1902).

**Distribution.** *Sedum stahlii* occurs in the northeastern portion
of the Sierra Madre del Sur and on the adjacent slopes of the
Trans-Mexican Volcanic Belt. Usually it is on limestone, but
sometimes it grows on conglomerate if the pH is neutral or above.
Data for the two populations which I have observed are summarized in the following table:

| Location | n-plants | Area | Alt. range | pH | Drainage |
|---|---|---|---|---|---|
| Maltrata | 28 | 200 m. x 50 m. | 1,770–1,864 m. | 7.2–7.4 | excessive |
| Slope W of | | | | | |
| Acultzingo | >500 | 2 km. x 2 km. | 2,000–2,220 m. | 7 –7.4 | excessive |

Besides the occurrence at the type locality and at the two places
listed above, *Sedum stahlii* also occurs on rocky slopes, alt. 2,135–
2,440 m., at Esperanza, Carl Purpus (NY, US).

Professor Matuda collected *Sedum stahlii* at Maltrata on May 7,
1937 (NY). His specimens were with immature fruits. I saw the
species there on Nov. 6, 1955. At that time, a few old fruits still
persisted, but the plants were neither in flower nor with floral
buds. They were growing on limestone, exposed to the southeast,
and were competing with *S. dendroideum* ssp. *dendroideum*, *S. hemsleyanum*, and *S. lucidum*, all of which had floral buds. Evidently *S.
stahlii* flowers later in the winter than do the others. In the greenhouse at Ithaca, a plant from Maltrata produced a single flower
in February, 1958.

Dr. Miranda found *Sedum stahlii* on the declivity near Acultzingo
on Aug. 29, 1948. I visited that locality on Aug. 11 and Nov. 11,
1955. The plants were on the steep slope, facing east, west of
Acultzingo, and were on either limestone or conglomerate. They
were exposed to the sun except in the late afternoon. On Aug.
11, some old follicles still persisted, but most seeds had been shed.
Competing species included *Stevia* (? *pyrolaefolia*) and *Asphodelus
fistulosus*, but, except for *Sedum moranense*, no other Crassulaceae.
In the greenhouse at Ithaca, plants have flowered in February,
March, April, and May.

**Relationships.** Although *Sedum stahlii* and *S. obcordatum* are the
only two species of *Sedum* in the Trans-Mexican Volcanic Belt

regularly with decussately opposite leaves and both have yellow petals and divergent follicles with prominent lips, they are unlike in appearance and easy to distinguish. The leaves of *S. stahlii* are terete and puberulent; those of *S. obcordatum* are flat and glabrous. Some of the other differences are indicated in the following table, in which comparisons of dimensions of leaves, sepals, and petals are based on plants cultivated under similar conditions in the greenhouse at Ithaca. Comparisons of follicles and seeds are based on collections from wild plants.

| | | *S. stahlii* | | | | | *S. obcordatum* | | |
|---|---|---|---|---|---|---|---|---|---|
| | *n* | *n-obs.* | *x̄* (*mm.*) | *s* (*mm.*) | | *n* | *n-obs.* | *x̄* (*mm.*) | *s* (*mm.*) |
| Leaves | | | | | | | | | |
| Length* | 5 | 49 | 11.7 | .9 | | 7 | 211 | 17.5 | 1.3 |
| Width** | 5 | 49 | 5.3 | .4 | | 7 | 211 | 13.9 | 1.3 |
| Thickness | 5 | 49 | 4.5 | .4 | | 1 | 3 | 1.6 | — |
| Sepals | | | | | | | | | |
| Length | 5 | 49 | 3.7 | .6 | | 1 | 3 | 11.9 | — |
| Width | 5 | 49 | 1.8 | .1 | | 1 | 3 | 2.6 | — |
| Petals | | | | | | | | | |
| Length | 5 | 49 | 7.2 | .8 | | 1 | 3 | 12.2 | — |
| Width | 5 | 49 | 2.4 | .1 | | 1 | 3 | 3.4 | — |
| Follicles | | | | | | | | | |
| Length** | 5 | 13 | 2.8 | .5 | | 14 | 43 | 6.3 | 1 |
| Seeds | | | | | | | | | |
| Length** | 2 | 4 | .6 | 0 | | 11 | 39 | 1.3 | .1 |

The species which most resembles *Sedum stahlii* in appearance is *S. divergens* of the Coast Ranges and Cascade Mountains of western North America. That too has thick, decussately opposite leaves, yellow petals, and divergent follicles with prominent lips, but it differs in having the leaves both shorter and glabrous, the sepals shorter and connate basally, and the seeds larger and smooth. It flowers from July to October. If *S. stahlii* and *S. divergens* had a common origin, the separation must have occurred long ago.

Brown (1955) mentioned a cross, made by Dr. M. W. Morgan, of Richmond, Calif., between *Sedum morganianum* and *S. stahlii*. He reported that the hybrid had some characters of each. I have not seen this plant and have no further information about it.

## 16. *SEDUM LONGIPES* (figs. 51–56)

Plants of *Sedum longipes* are perennial, with fibrous roots, but no rootstocks. They have repent stems and elliptical. oblanceolate, or obovate leaves. The flowers, borne on slender pedicels, have petals which are pale green speckled with red and large nectaries which are dark red finely speckled with yellow. As in *S. botterii*, which also has large, red nectaries, the flowers are without cohesion of parts. The only species likely to be confused with *S. longipes* are the one next to be described. from the ravine of the Tiscalatengo River, with smaller leaves and flowers and with only one whorl of stamens per flower, and *S. clavifolium*, with branched rootstocks, basal leaves which are petiolate, then broadened and clasping basally, and smaller flowers with petals usually less than 4 mm. long.

**Description.** Materials: 14 plants—7 from the Sierra de Tepoztlán, Morelos; 5 from the Cerro Teresona, Toluca, Mexico; and 2 from cultivation, of unknown origin in the wild. Measurements marked cult. are of plants cultivated in the greenhouse at Ithaca, N.Y.

Plants of *Sedum longipes* are perennials, chamaephytes, with repent stems which are gray and finely papillose, 1.2–2.5 dm. long, commonly with filiform, brown, aerial roots.

| | *n* | *n-obs.* | $\bar{x}$ (mm.) | *s* (mm.) | *w* (mm.) |
|---|---|---|---|---|---|
| Diameter of stems with flowers | | | | | |
| Tepoztlán | 1 | 4 | 1.6 | — | 1.4–2.0 |
| —cult. | 2 | 10 | 1.9 | 0 | 1.6–2.3 |
| C. Teresona—cult. | 1 | 3 | 1.5 | — | 1 –2 |
| Origin unknown—cult. | 1 | 9 | 1.3 | — | 1 –1.7 |

Leaves are alternate, elliptical, oblanceolate, or obovate, rounded, papillose, especially on margins, sometimes finely speckled with red, often recurved. plane ventrally, convex dorsally. After the time of flowering, the old leaves wither and may be deciduous. The undeveloped leaves at that stage are very papillose and in dense rosettes. Differences among samples in the three dimensions of the leaves are not significant.

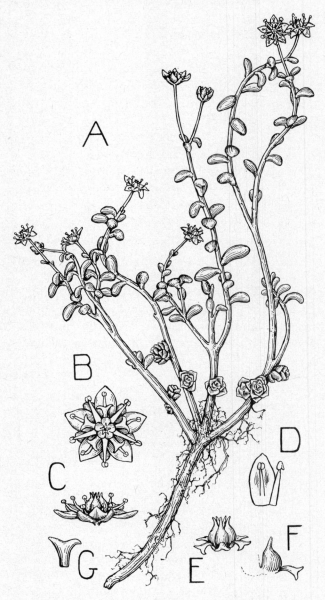

*Fig. 51.* Plant of *Sedum longipes* ssp. *longipes* cultivated in the greenhouse, Ithaca, N.Y.  A. Habit sketch (x 1.2). B. Flower from above (x 3.6).  C. Flower from side (x 3.6). D. Petal and two stamens (x 4.8).  E. Pistils (x 4.8). F. Single pistil (x 4.8).  G. Nectary (x 6).

|  | n | n-obs. | $\bar{x}$ (mm.) | s (mm.) | w (mm.) |
|---|---|---|---|---|---|
| Length |  |  |  |  |  |
| Tepoztlán | 7 | 42 | 10.2 | 2.4 | 4.9–15.4 |
| C. Teresona | 4 | 11 | 8 8 | 1.7 | 5.9–13.1 |
| Tepoztlán—cult. | 2 | 10 | 9 6 | 0 | 4.5–15 |
| C. Teresona—cult. | 1 | 3 | 10 3 | — | 9 –12 |
| Origin unknown—cult. | 2 | 14 | 8 3 | 2 | 5.5–15 |
| Width |  |  |  |  |  |
| Tepoztlán | 7 | 42 | 3.4 | .5 | 1.5– 4.9 |
| C. Teresona | 4 | 11 | 4.4 | .9 | 3.1– 5.5 |
| Tepoztlán—cult. | 2 | 10 | 4.5 | .7 | 2.5– 6.3 |
| C. Teresona—cult. | 1 | 3 | 6 | — | 5 – 7 |
| Origin unknown—cult. | 2 | 14 | 4.4 | .7 | 3.4– 6 |
| Thickness |  |  |  |  |  |
| Tepoztlán | 5 | 29 | 1.5 | .2 | 1 – 2.3 |
| C. Teresona | 3 | 10 | 1.3 | .7 | 1.1– 1.8 |
| Tepoztlán—cult. | 2 | 10 | 2.4 | .3 | 1.3– 4.1 |
| C. Teresona—cult. | 1 | 3 | 1.7 | — | 1.3– 2.2 |
| Origin unknown—cult. | 1 | 7 | 1.5 | — | 1.2– 1.9 |

Ten leaves of a plant in the Sierra de Tepoztlán. measured when fresh on Sept. 8, 1955, and again in dried condition on March 22, 1958, had shrunk significantly in width and somewhat, but not significantly, in length.

|  | $\bar{x}$ (mm.) | s (mm.) | w (mm.) |
|---|---|---|---|
| Length—fresh | 7.9 | 1.2 | 4.9–8.9 |
| —dried | 7.0 | 1 | 4.6–8.2 |
| Width—fresh | 3.2 | .3 | 2.7–3.6 |
| —dried | 2.9 | .3 | 2.5–3.4 |

Inflorescences are lax, terminal cymes.

|  | n | n-cfs. | $\bar{x}$ | w |
|---|---|---|---|---|
| No. of flowers per cyme |  |  |  |  |
| C. Teresona | 4 | 5 | 3 | 3–4 |
| Origin unknown—cult. | 1 | 7 | 3 | 3–4 |

Flowers are on filiform pedicels. Flowers of a cultivated plant of unknown origin are significantly smaller in diameter than those of the others.

| | n | n-obs. | x̄ (mm.) | s (mm.) | w (mm.) | |
|---|---|---|---|---|---|---|
| Pedicels—length | | | | | | |
| Tepoztlán | I | 4 | 8.5 | — | 5 | −11 |
| C. Teresona | 4 | 5 | 12.6 | .9 | 11 | −14 |
| Origin unknown—cult. | 2 | 9 | 16.8 | 3.8 | 9 | −22 |
| Flowers—diameter | | | | | | |
| Tepoztlán | I | 4 | 10 | — | 9 | −12 |
| C. Teresona | I | I | 12 | — | 12 | |
| Tepoztlán—cult. | 2 | 10 | 10.8 | 1.8 | 9 | −13 |
| C. Teresona—cult. | I | 3 | 11 | — | 10 | −12 |
| Origin unknown—cult. | I | 7 | 7.8 | — | 6 | −10 |
| Torus—length | | | | | | |
| Tepoztlán—cult. | 2 | 9 | .7 | 0 | .6− | .9 |
| C. Teresona—cult. | I | 2 | .6 | — | .5− | .7 |
| Origin unknown—cult. | I | 6 | .6 | — | .4− | .7 |

Sepals are lanceolate, elliptic-oblong, ovate-elliptical, or elliptical, acute, unequal in length, papillose at apex, pale green, sometimes sparsely speckled with red.

| | n | n-obs. | x̄ (mm.) | s (mm.) | w (mm.) |
|---|---|---|---|---|---|
| Length | | | | | |
| Tepoztlán | 2 | 8 | 3.8 | .1 | 3.3−4.2 |
| C. Teresona | 4 | 5 | 5 | .3 | 4.7−5.4 |
| Tepoztlán—cult. | 2 | 10 | 4.4 | I | 3.1−5.5 |
| C. Teresona—cult. | I | 3 | 4.4 | — | 4 −5.1 |
| Origin unknown—cult. | I | 7 | 4 | — | 3.4−4.9 |
| Length of spurs | | | | | |
| Tepoztlán | I | 4 | .7 | — | .6− .9 |
| C. Teresona | 4 | 5 | .7 | 0 | .6− .8 |
| Origin unknown—cult. | I | 7 | .4 | — | .3− .5 |
| Width | | | | | |
| Tepoztlán | 2 | 8 | 1.4 | .2 | 1.1−1.7 |
| C. Teresona | 4 | 5 | 1.9 | 0 | 1.8−2 |
| Tepoztlán—cult. | 2 | 10 | 1.7 | .2 | 1.4−2 |
| C. Teresona—cult. | I | 3 | 1.7 | — | 1.7−1.8 |
| Origin unknown—cult. | I | 7 | 1.7 | — | 1.5−2.1 |

Petals are lanceolate, ovate, or elliptic-oblong, acute, mucronate-appendaged, pale green, streaked or speckled with red, especially above middle. Those of a cultivated plant of unknown origin are shorter than those of the others.

| | $n$ | $n$-obs. | $\bar{x}$ (mm.) | $s$ (mm.) | $w$ (mm.) |
|---|---|---|---|---|---|
| **Length** | | | | | |
| Tepoztlán | 2 | 8 | 5.3 | 0 | 4.6–5.9 |
| C. Teresona | 4 | 5 | 5.4 | .23 | 5.2–5.6 |
| Tepoztlán—cult. | 2 | 10 | 5.4 | .7 | 4.3–6.5 |
| C. Teresona—cult. | 1 | 3 | 5.5 | — | 5.2–5.7 |
| Origin unknown—cult. | 1 | 7 | 4.1 | — | 3.8–4.5 |
| **Width** | | | | | |
| Tepoztlán | 2 | 8 | 2 | .1 | 1.6–2.3 |
| C. Teresona | 4 | 5 | 2.7 | .1 | 2.5–2.9 |
| Tepoztlán—cult. | 2 | 10 | 1.7 | .3 | 1.3–2.2 |
| C. Teresona—cult. | 1 | 3 | 2.4 | — | 2.3–2.5 |
| Origin unknown—cult. | 1 | 7 | 2.1 | — | 2 –2.2 |

Stamens have red, orange, or yellow anthers; pollen is well developed.

| | $n$ | $n$-obs. | $\bar{x}$ (mm.) | $s$ (mm.) | $w$ (mm.) |
|---|---|---|---|---|---|
| **Adnation of epipetalous filaments** | | | | | |
| Tepoztlán | 1 | 4 | 1 | — | .7–1.4 |
| Origin unknown—cult. | 1 | 7 | .7 | — | .4–1 |
| **Anthers—length** | | | | | |
| Tepoztlán | 1 | 1 | 1 | — | 1 |
| C. Teresona | 2 | 3 | 1.3 | 0 | 1.2–1.3 |
| Origin unknown—cult. | 1 | 6 | 1 | — | .7–1.3 |
| **Anthers—diameter** | | | | | |
| Origin unknown—cult. | 1 | 6 | .7 | — | .4– .9 |

Nectaries are obovate, two-lobed or lacerate, and dark red finely speckled with pale yellow.

| | $n$ | $n$-obs. | $\bar{x}$ (mm.) | $s$ (mm.) | $w$ (mm.) |
|---|---|---|---|---|---|
| **Length** | | | | | |
| Tepoztlán | 2 | 8 | 2 | 0 | 1.8–2.5 |
| C. Teresona | 4 | 5 | 1.8 | .1 | 1.7–1.9 |
| Tepoztlán—cult. | 2 | 10 | 2.2 | .2 | 1.3–2.7 |
| C. Teresona—cult. | 1 | 3 | 2 | — | 1.9–2.1 |
| Origin unknown—cult. | 1 | 7 | 2.1 | — | 2 –2.2 |
| **Width** | | | | | |
| Tepoztlán | 1 | 4 | 1.5 | — | 1.2–2 |
| C. Teresona | 4 | 5 | 1.9 | .1 | 1.8–2.1 |
| Tepoztlán—cult. | 2 | 9 | 1.6 | .2 | 1.4–1.9 |
| C. Teresona—cult. | 1 | 3 | 1.8 | — | 1.8 |
| Origin unknown—cult. | 1 | 7 | 1.7 | — | 1.5–1.8 |

Pistils are erect.

|  | n | n-obs. | x̄ | w |
|---|---|---|---|---|
| Length |  |  |  |  |
| Origin unknown—cult. | 1 | 7 | 2 mm. | 1.9– 2.1 mm. |
| No. of ovules per ovary |  |  |  |  |
| Tepoztlán—cult. | 2 | 9 | 19 | 13 –28 |
| C. Teresona—cult. | 1 | 3 | 31 | 24 –34 |
| Origin unknown—cult. | 1 | 7 | 19 | 14 –25 |

Follicles are erect, with marginal lips scarcely evident.

|  | n | n-obs. | x̄ (mm.) | w (mm.) |
|---|---|---|---|---|
| Length |  |  |  |  |
| Tepoztlán | 1 | 6 | 2 | 1.8–2.2 |
| Width of lips |  |  |  |  |
| Tepoztlán | 1 | 6 | .1 | 0 – .1 |

Seeds are elliptical, chestnut-brown, glabrous, finely ribbed longitudinally.

|  | n | n-obs. | x̄ (mm.) | w (mm.) |
|---|---|---|---|---|
| Length |  |  |  |  |
| Tepoztlán | 1 | 3 | .5 | .5–.6 |
| Diameter |  |  |  |  |
| Tepoztlán | 1 | 3 | .3 | .2–.3 |

**Variation.** Clearly two kinds of *Sedum longipes* occur, one exemplified by plants such as I have studied from Tepoztlán and the Cerro Teresona and the other a type which I have encountered only in cultivation. The latter produces many rosettes. These are prominent at the time when the plants are in flower, with the leaves spreading, 11–17 mm. long. A plant of the sort with large rosettes, cultivated in the greenhouse at Ithaca, had shorter petals than those of three plants of *S. longipes* from Tepoztlán and the Cerro Teresona, cultivated under the same conditions. Similarly, a plant cultivated in the patio of the Hotel Fausto in Ciudad Serdán, Puebla, had even shorter petals than the one in Ithaca. In this cultivated kind, the petals are either of the same length or shorter than the sepals, whereas the usual condition of *S. longipes* is for the petals to exceed the sepals. Since the rosette-bearing *S. longipes* is common in cultivation in eastern Mexico and since cultivated Crassulaceae usually are taken from the wild without modification, a reasonable deduction is that plants of this type are native somewhere in the Mexican highlands, but the area of occurrence still is unknown to botanists. If this is true, the plants deserve subspecific status. Accordingly, since some designation is necessary, I am supplying a name at the rank of subspecies. This will enable horticulturists to label plants in their collections, and also it will avoid the confusion which results from applying only a binomial to two different kinds of *S. longipes*.

*Fig. 52. Sedum longipes* ssp. *longipes* and ssp. *rosulare* side by side for comparison. The plant of ssp. *longipes* is from the Sierra de Tepoztlán; that of ssp. *rosulare* is the type of the subspecies. Photographed Dec. 5, 1956 (x .4).

### KEY TO SUBSPECIES

A. Rosettes, when present, usually with leaves compact; petals averaging
5.3–5.5 mm. long, longer than the sepals........ssp. *longipes*, p. 196

AA. Rosettes prominent, with leaves widely divergent; petals averaging
3.7–4.1 mm. long, equaling or shorter than the sepals...........
.............................................ssp *rosulare*, p. 199

## *Sedum longipes* ssp. *longipes*

**Nomenclature.** *Sedum longipes* Rose, Bull. N.Y. Bot. Gard. 3: 43 (1903). Type locality: mossy ledges of conglomerate, alt. 2,687 m., Sierra de Tepoztlán, Morelos. Type: C. G. Pringle's collection no. 8,049 (US 46,380), Feb. 8, 1899.

In the dry season, when *Sedum longipes* ssp. *longipes* is in flower, its new shoots form rosettes with the leaves closely compact, and its petals are longer than the sepals. These two characters easily distinguish it.

In cultivation, I have noted differences between two plants from the Sierra de Tepoztlán in the length and width of the sepals, petals, and nectaries, suggesting the possibility of genetic variation.

**Distribution.** *Sedum longipes* ssp. *longipes* occurs in the Trans-Mexican Volcanic Belt from the Sierra de Tepoztlán westward to the vicinity of Morelia, Michoacán. The altitudinal range is from 1,800–2,890 m., and the principal period of flowering extends from November to February, though plants have been collected in flower in September. Data for the two populations which I have studied are summarized in the following table:

| Location | n-plants | Area | Alt. range | pH | Drainage |
|---|---|---|---|---|---|
| Sierra de Tepoztlán | ab. 325 | > 2 km. x 20 m. | 1,800–2,310 m. | 5.6–6.8 | moderate to excessive |
| Cerro Teresona | > 25 | >50 m. x 30 m. | 2,890 m. | 5.4 | moderate |

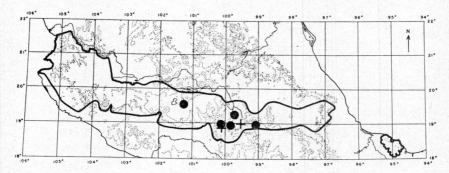

*Fig. 53.* Known distribution of *Sedum longipes* ssp. *longipes* (•) and *S. pentastamineum* (+).

Populations additional to the two studied by me and the discoverers of each are: Almoloya, District of Sultepec, George Hinton (NY, US); Luvianos, District of Temascaltepec, Hinton (NY, US); and near La Huerta, Morelia, Gerfroy Arsène (US).

Apparently Pringle was the first botanist to see *Sedum longipes*. He collected it in the Sierra de Tepoztlán on Feb. 8, 1899. I studied it there on Sept. 6, Sept. 13, Nov. 17, and Dec. 20, 1955. Although I searched for flowers on all trips, I did not see any until December. Habitats included cliffs of conglomerate, a boulder in a ravine inhabited also by *Polypodium pectinatum*, the bank of the railroad below El Parque, a wall of volcanic rock along a street on the north side of Tepoztlán, and moss on the bark of a tree. Exposure was to the south, southeast, southwest, or west-northwest. The only other species of Crassulaceae growing in association with *S. longipes* was *S. cremnophila*. Plants of the two species grew within 3 cm. of each other, but although they were in flower at the same time, I found no hybrids. *Sedum jaliscanum* and *S. oxypetalum* also occur in the Sierra de Tepoztlán, but nowhere close to *S. longipes*. Both flower in the wet season. *Sedum longipes* flowers in the dry season. *Sedum frutescens* likewise occurs in the Sierra de Tepoztlán, but not in association with *S. longipes*. It flowers late in the dry season, after *S. longipes* has begun to develop fruits. In the greenhouse at Ithaca, plants of *S. longipes* from the Sierra de Tepoztlán have flowered from January to March.

My family and I found *Sedum longipes* in the Cerro Teresona on the north side of Toluca on Nov. 23, 1955. The plants were near the crest of low cliffs, exposed to the west or northwest. Most were in bud, but a few flowers were in anthesis. The only competitors were mosses. Except for shade caused by the rocks in the early morning, the plants were exposed to the sun throughout the day. In the greenhouse, a plant from the Cerro Teresona has flowered in February.

**Relationships.** The species most closely related to *Sedum longipes* is one which occurs in the ravine of the Tiscalatengo River. A comparison of that with *S. longipes* is included in the next account. Likewise a comparison of *S. longipes* with *S. clavifolium* is included in the discussion of relationships of that species. Otherwise, *S. longipes* may be related to *S. batterii*. Although the two species are very unlike in general appearance, their flowers are remarkably similar, as shown in the accompanying photograph, fig. 54. In both, cohesion of floral parts is lacking, and the adnation

*Fig. 54.* Flowers of *Sedum botterii* (left) and *S. longipes* ssp. *longipes* (right), Feb. 15, 1957 (x 4.5).

of epipetalous stamens is slight. Both have large, red nectaries and greenish petals. Significant differences, based on plants cultivated under similar conditions, include the following:

|  | S. longipes | | | | S. botterii | | | |
|---|---|---|---|---|---|---|---|---|
|  | n | n-obs. | x̄ | s | n | n-obs. | x̄ | s |
|  |  |  | (mm.) | (mm.) |  |  | (mm.) | (mm.) |
| Leaves |  |  |  |  |  |  |  |  |
| Length** | 5 | 27 | 9 | 1.6 | 3 | 10 | 40.2 | 6.9 |
| Width** | 5 | 27 | 4.6 | .7 | 3 | 10 | 17.3 | 3.7 |
| Sepals |  |  |  |  |  |  |  |  |
| Length* | 4 | 20 | 4 | 1 | 3 | 19 | 7.7 | 2.7 |
| Petals |  |  |  |  |  |  |  |  |
| Length* | 4 | 20 | 5 | .3 | 3 | 19 | 8 | .2 |

If, instead of trying to relate *Sedum longipes* to other species of the Trans-Mexican Volcanic Belt, one tries to find a nearer relative elsewhere in the world, difficulty arises. Possibly that is why Dr. Rose considered placing it in a separate genus. No species of

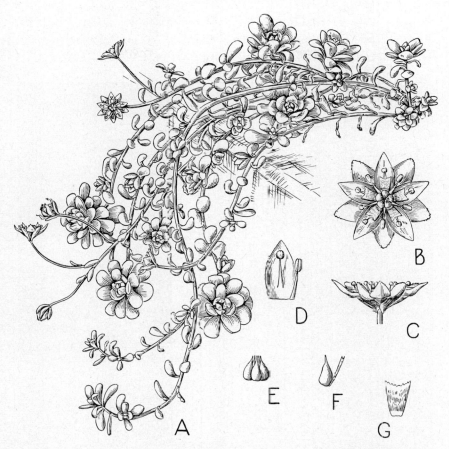

*Fig. 55.* Type plant of *Sedum longipes* ssp. *rosulare* cultivated in the greenhouse, Ithaca, N.Y.  A. Habit sketch (x .8).  B. Flower from above (x 2.4).  C. Flower from side (x 2.4).  D. Petal and two stamens (x 3.2).  E. Pistils (x 3.2).  F. Single pistil (x 4).  G. Nectary (x 4).

another region is closer to *S. longipes* than the ones already mentioned, which are native in the Trans-Mexican Volcanic Belt.

## *Sedum longipes* ssp. **rosulare**

Subspecies nova *Sedi longipedis* cum rosularibus conspicuis et multis, cum foliis divaricatis; flores minores quam ssp. *longipes* cum petalis 4.1 (3.8–4.5) mm. longis. Typus in Herbario Wiegand,

Universitatis Cornellianae, planta de cultu in Huauchinango, Puebla, culta in loco ad plantas colendas vitreis munito ad Ithaca, N.Y., 1954, Nov. 25, Robertus Clausenius n. Cu 1, est.

*Fig. 56.* Flower of type plant of *Sedum longipes* ssp. *rosulare* cultivated in the greenhouse, Ithaca, N.Y., Dec. 5, 1956 (x 13).

From the standpoint of habit of growth, the ssp. *rosulare* looks like a species different from ssp. *longipes.* It grows well in cultivation, making a mat of attractive rosettes. The ssp. *longipes,* on the other hand, does poorly in cultivation and appears straggling. Since the petals of ssp. *rosulare* are short, sometimes even shorter than the sepals or only equaling them, the flowers are smaller than those of ssp. *longipes.* The nectaries are less prominently two-lobed, but considerably variable.

When I first saw *Sedum longipes* ssp. *rosulare* in the market at Huauchinango in 1949, I thought that it was a distinct species.

After growing it for five years and seeing flowers, the relationship with *S. longipes* was evident, but it still appeared different. Detailed comparisons have revealed few characters for separation, however, and subspecific status seems proper. The possibility that ssp. *rosulare* is an interspecific hybrid does not seem likely since the pollen appears as good as in ssp. *longipes*, and the ovules appear to develop normally.

In Mexico, I have seen *Sedum longipes* ssp. *rosulare* in cultivation in the following places: Fortín de las Flores and Ohuapa, Vera Cruz; Huauchinango and Ciudad Serdán, Puebla; Amecameca, Puebla; and also elsewhere. The common name for it in Mexico is *"rosario."* No one seems to know where it is native.

## 17. *SEDUM PENTASTAMINEUM* (figs. 57–59)

Plants of *Sedum pentastamineum* are similar to those of *S. longipes*, but smaller, with rounder, petiolate leaves and with only a single whorl of stamens per flower. Few specimens are in herbaria. These are labeled as *S. longipes*. Since the name *pentastamineum* is proposed here for the first time, a brief description in Latin is provided before the usual description in English.

**Descriptio originalis.** *Sedum* **pentastamineum,** sp. nov., affine *Sedi longipedis*, sed minus, foliis fere orbicularibus, 4.8 ±2.7 mm. longis et 2.6 ±.9 mm. latis, floribus ca. 7 mm. in linea media, petalis 3.5 ±.3 mm. longis et staminibus quinquis. Typus in Herbario Wiegand, Universitatis Cornellianae, ab angustiis viarum fluminis Tiscalatengo, ca. 4 km. inter meridiem et occasum solis spectantibus ex Villa Guerrero, Mexico, collectio Roberti Clausenii, planta 7, 1956, Jan. 1, est.

**Description.** Materials: 7 plants, all from the ravine of the Tiscalatengo River about 4 km. northwest of Villa Guerrero, Mexico. Measurements marked cult. are of plants cultivated in the greenhouse at Ithaca, N.Y.

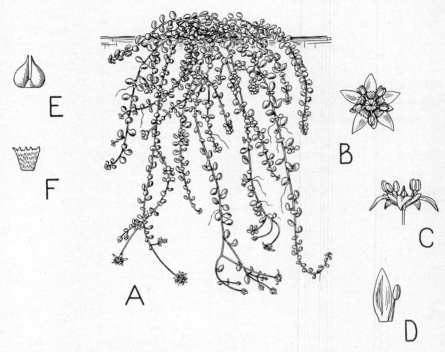

*Fig. 57.* Type plant of *Sedum pentastamineum,* cultivated in the greenhouse, Ithaca, N.Y. A. Habit sketch (x .5). B. Flower from above (x 2). C. Flower from side (x 2). D. Petal and one stamen (x 3). E. Torus and two pistils (x 4). F. Nectary (x 5).

Plants of *Sedum pentastamineum* are perennials, chamaephytes, with repent or pendulous stems which are pale pink, finely papillose, and with aerial roots .1–.5 mm. in diameter.

|  | n | n-obs. | x̄ | w |
|---|---|---|---|---|
| Length of stems—wild | 1 | 10 | 2.6 dm. | 1.8–3.3 dm. |
| —cult. | 1 | 5 | 1.7 dm. | 1.5–1.9 dm. |
| Diameter of stems—wild | 1 | 10 | 1 mm. | .9–1 mm. |
| —cult. | 1 | 7 | .8 mm. | .6–.9 mm. |

Leaves are alternate, subopposite, or opposite, elliptical, suborbicular, or orbicular, petiolate, short-spurred, rounded at apices, concave dorsally, papillose marginally, sometimes finely flecked with dark red. Differences in length, width, and thickness between wild and cultivated plants are not significant.

| | $n$ | $n$-obs. | $\bar{x}$ (mm.) | $s$ (mm.) | $w$ (mm.) |
|---|---|---|---|---|---|
| Length—wild | 7 | 34 | 4.8 | 1.2 | 2.4–7.9 |
| —cult. | 3 | 14 | 3 | .2 | 2.1–4.5 |
| Width—wild | 7 | 34 | 2.6 | .4 | 1.4–3.6 |
| —cult. | 3 | 14 | 2.1 | .6 | 1.2–3.6 |
| Thickness—wild | 6 | 27 | .5 | .1 | .3– .8 |
| —cult. | 3 | 14 | .6 | 0 | .4– .9 |

Inflorescences are lax, terminal or lateral cymes.

| | $n$ | $x$-obs. | $\bar{x}$ | $w$ |
|---|---|---|---|---|
| No. of flowers per cyme—cult. | 1 | 7 | 3 | 1–5 |

Flowers are on filiform pedicels.

| | $n$ | $n$-obs. | $\bar{x}$ (mm.) | $s$ (mm.) | $w$ (mm.) |
|---|---|---|---|---|---|
| Pedicels—length—wild | 1 | 10 | 14.6 | — | 10 –22 |
| —cult. | 3 | 14 | 16.1 | 1.4 | 5 –27 |
| Flowers—diameter—wild | 1 | 10 | 7 | — | 6 – 8 |
| —cult. | 3 | 13 | 7.7 | .5 | 6 –10 |
| Torus—length—cult. | 3 | 11 | 4 | .2 | .2– .7 |

Sepals are elliptical, elliptic-oblong, or lanceolate, with spurs
.1–.5 mm. long, obtuse at apices, nearly equal in size in each
flower, pale green.

| | $n$ | $n$-obs. | $\bar{x}$ (mm.) | $s$ (mm.) | $w$ (mm.) |
|---|---|---|---|---|---|
| Length—wild | 5 | 24 | 2.1 | .1 | 1.6–2.4 |
| —cult. | 3 | 13 | 2.3 | .4 | 1.3–3 |
| Width—wild | 5 | 24 | 1 | .1 | .8–1.4 |
| —cult. | 3 | 13 | 1 | .2 | .7–1.3 |

Petals are lanceolate or elliptic-lanceolate, acute, mucronate-
appendaged, pale green or yellowish white, streaked with purple
or red above middle.

| | $n$ | $n$-obs. | $\bar{x}$ (mm.) | $s$ (mm.) | $w$ (mm.) |
|---|---|---|---|---|---|
| Length—wild | 5 | 24 | 3.5 | 0 | 3.1–4.4 |
| —cult. | 3 | 13 | 3.8 | .1 | 3.1–4.4 |
| Width—wild | 5 | 24 | 1.3 | .3 | 1 –1.5 |
| —cult. | 3 | 13 | 1.2 | .1 | .9–1.5 |

Stamens are in one whorl, alternating with petals; anthers are yellow or orange; pollen is well developed.

|  | n | n-obs. | $\bar{x}$ (mm.) | w (mm.) |
|---|---|---|---|---|
| Anthers—length—wild | 1 | 2 | 1.2 | 1.2 |
| —cult. | 1 | 7 | .9 | .8–1.1 |
| Anthers—diameter—cult. | 1 | 7 | .5 | .4– .6 |

Nectaries are obovately subquadrate, laciniate, appearing dark red minutely speckled with pale yellow or translucent streaked with purple or pink.

|  | n | n-obs. | $\bar{x}$ (mm.) | s (mm.) | w (mm.) |
|---|---|---|---|---|---|
| Length—wild | 5 | 24 | 1.1 | .1 | .7–1.3 |
| —cult. | 3 | 13 | 1.3 | .2 | 1 –1.6 |
| Width—wild | 1 | 10 | 1.1 | — | .9–1.2 |
| —cult. | 3 | 13 | .9 | .2 | .4–1.3 |

Pistils are erect, with ovaries papillose and greenish white streaked with red.

|  | n | n-obs. | $\bar{x}$ | w |
|---|---|---|---|---|
| Length—cult. | 1 | 6 | 1.7 mm. | 1.6– 2 mm. |
| No. of ovules per ovary—cult. | 3 | 14 | 10 | 3 –15 |

Follicles and seeds were not available for study.

**Variation.** Of the four populations of *Sedum pentastamineum* known to me, I have studied one at the site in the wild and know the other three from herbarium specimens. Since data for living plants and herbarium specimens are not comparable, satisfactory comparisons of these populations are not possible. My impression from available evidence is that plants in the four populations are similar and that no further taxonomic subdivision is necessary.

Within the population in the ravine of the Tiscalatengo River, wild plants differed from each other in three out of eight characters studied. When cultivated under similar conditions in the greenhouse at Ithaca, N.Y., three of these same plants differed from each other in six out of thirteen characters studied. Only one of the six differences was the same as the three among the wild plants. That was width of leaves. The other two differences among wild plants, namely, length and thickness of leaves, disappeared in cultivation. Since the three cultivated plants flowered at different times in the greenhouse, differences among them in dimensions of floral parts are not necessarily proof that the plants are different genetically. Time of flowering might in some way affect the sizes of floral parts.

**Nomenclature.** *Sedum pentastamineum* Clausen, proposed as a species on p. 201. The type is my collection of Jan. 1, 1953, plant no. 7, from the ravine of the Tiscalatengo River about 4 km. northwest of Villa Guerrero, Mexico.

**Distribution.** I know *Sedum pentastamineum* only from the southern side of the central part of the Trans-Mexican Volcanic Belt. Data for the population which I have studied are as follows:

| Location | n-plants | Area (m.) | Alt. range (m.) | pH | Drainage |
|----------|----------|-----------|-----------------|-----|----------|
| Tiscalatengo Ravine | >70 | ab. 200 x 10 | 2,300–2,310 | 7.2 | moderate |

Other populations are at Ypericones (CU, NY), Tenayac (CU, Kew, NY, US), and Temascaltepec (NY, US), all in the District of Temascaltepec, Mexico, and discovered by George Hinton.

Carlos Palomé, men from Santa María, and I found plants of *Sedum pentastamineum* in the ravine of the Tiscalatengo River on Jan. 1, 1956. The plants had flowers in bud, preanthesis, anthesis, and postanthesis. They were growing on cliffs of andesite, exposed to the south, east, west, and northwest, in an area where pines were the dominant trees in the woods on either side of the ravine. The only other species of Crassulaceae associated with the *S. pentastamineum* was *Echeveria obtusifolia*. Farther upstream, the epiphytic *S. tortuosum* occurred and, perhaps 2 km. downstream, *S. oxypetalum* and the thick-leaved species which Edward Alexander intends to name.

**Relationships.** *Sedum pentastamineum* appears closely related to *S. longipes*. Possibly it is derived from that or from an ancestral population which was similar to that. Specialization has involved loss of one whorl of stamens and reduction in size, especially of leaves and floral parts. For purposes of comparison, data in the following table are for flowering plants cultivated under similar conditions in the greenhouse at Ithaca.

*Fig. 58.* Cultivated plants of *Sedum longipes* ssp. *longipes* (left) from the Sierra de Tepoztlán and *S. pentastamineum* (right) from the ravine of the Tiscalatengo River, Dec. 21, 1956 (x 1.4).

*Fig. 59.* Flowers of cultivated plants of *Sedum longipes* ssp *longipes* (below) from the Sierra de Tepoztlán and *S. pentastamineum* (above) from the ravine of the Tiscalatengo River, Dec. 21, 1956 (x 8).

| | | *S. pentastamineum* | | | | | *S. longipes* | |
|---|---|---|---|---|---|---|---|---|
| | *n* | *n-obs.* | *x̄* | *s* | *n* | *n-obs.* | *x̄* | *s* |
| Leaves | | | | | | | | |
| Length* | 3 | 14 | 3 mm. | .2 mm. | 5 | 27 | 9 mm. | 1.6 mm. |
| Width* | 3 | 14 | 2.1 mm. | .6 mm. | 5 | 27 | 4.6 mm. | .7 mm. |
| Thickness | 3 | 14 | .6 mm. | 0 mm. | 4 | 20 | 2 mm. | .4 mm. |
| Sepals | | | | | | | | |
| Length* | 3 | 13 | 2.3 mm. | .4 mm. | 4 | 20 | 4 mm. | 1 mm. |
| Width | 3 | 13 | 1 mm. | .2 mm. | 4 | 20 | 1.7 mm. | 0 mm. |
| Petals | | | | | | | | |
| Length | 3 | 13 | 3.8 mm. | .1 mm. | 4 | 20 | 5 mm. | .3 mm. |
| Width | 3 | 13 | 1.2 mm. | .1 mm. | 4 | 20 | 2 mm. | .3 mm. |
| Stamens | | | | | | | | |
| No. | 3 | 14 | 5 | — | 4 | 20 | 10 | — |
| Nectaries | | | | | | | | |
| Length** | 3 | 13 | 1.3 mm. | .2 mm. | 4 | 20 | 2.1 mm. | .2 mm. |
| Width* | 3 | 13 | .9 mm. | .2 mm. | 4 | 20 | 1.7 mm. | .1 mm. |

## 18. *SEDUM CLAVIFOLIUM* (figs. 60–62)

The diagnostic characteristics of *Sedum clavifolium* are the perennial habit, branched rhizomes, and rosettes of oblanceolate or spatulate leaves with long petioles which broaden basally and clasp the stems. The floral stems are erect or ascending and only a few centimeters high. The flowers are small, averaging 6 mm. in diameter, with greenish white petals and conspicuous, dark red nectaries which are finely speckled with yellow. The biennial species, next to be described, from the gorge of the Tenancingo River, differs in producing corms, as well as in having smaller seeds. Likewise, plants of *S. minimum* are biennials with corms, differing too in their white petals, each with a broad band of red below the middle. *Sedum longipes* and *S. pentastamineum*, both perennials, differ in having long, repent, aerial stems, no rhizomes, and larger flowers.

**Description.** Materials: 14 plants, all from the Cañada de Alcalican on the southwestern slope of Iztaccihuatl. Measurements marked cult. are of plants cultivated in the greenhouse at Ithaca, N.Y.

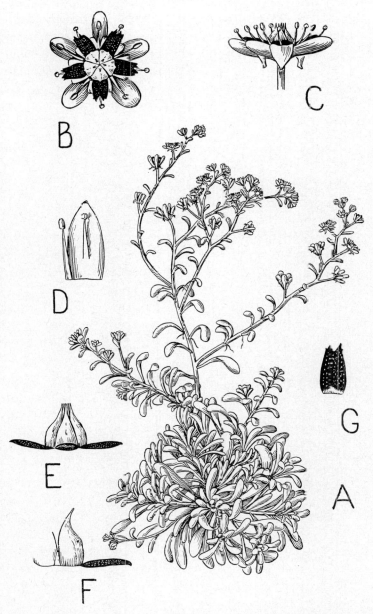

*Fig. 60.* Plant of *Sedum clavifolium* from Iztaccihuatl, cultivated in the greenhouse, Ithaca, N.Y. A. Habit sketch (x .6). B. Flower from above (x 3.6). C. Flower from side (x 3.6). D. Petal and two stamens (x 4.8). E. Pistils and nectaries (x 4.8). F. Single pistil and nectary (x 6). G. Nectary (x 5).

Plants of *Sedum clavifolium* are perennials, hemicryptophytes, with branched rhizomes 1.1–3.3 mm. in diameter, bearing ovate to oblong, blunt, scalelike, brownish leaves <1.4 mm. long, the branches terminating in cespitose rosettes of spatulate or oblanceolate, petiolate leaves; taproots are <4 cm. long. In cultivation, floral stems have attained a maximum length of 14 cm.

| | $n$ | $n$-obs. | $\bar{x}$ (mm.) | $s$ (mm.) | $w$ (mm.) |
|---|---|---|---|---|---|
| Height of stems with fruits—wild | 6 | 12 | 20 | 6.2 | 11.5–38 |

Leaves of rosettes are spatulate or oblanceolate, petiolate, with bases of petioles broadened and clasping the stems; brown bases of leaves persist on rootstocks; bases of leaves of floral stems are short-spurred, but neither broadened nor clasping. The leaves of plants cultivated in the greenhouse at Ithaca are highly significantly longer and significantly wider than those of wild plants.

| | $n$ | $n$-obs. | $\bar{x}$ (mm.) | $s$ (mm.) | $w$ (mm.) |
|---|---|---|---|---|---|
| Leaves of rosettes | | | | | |
| Length—wild | 12 | 21 | 11.2 | 3.7 | 4.7–18 |
| —cult. | 8 | 35 | 16.7 | 3.4 | 8.9–34 |
| Width—wild | 12 | 21 | 2.3 | .5 | .9– 4 |
| —cult. | 8 | 35 | 2.8 | .3 | 1.7– 5 |
| Thickness—wild | 9 | 17 | 1.2 | .1 | .9– 1.7 |
| —cult. | 8 | 35 | 1.4 | .2 | .9– 2.1 |

Inflorescences are cincinnal cymes. Seven plants, studied both in nature and in the greenhouse, had a highly significantly greater number of flowers in cultivation.

| | $n$ | $n$-obs. | $\bar{x}$ | $w$ |
|---|---|---|---|---|
| No. of flowers per cyme—wild | 10 | 13 | 2 | 1– 3 |
| —cult. | 8 | 35 | 6 | 2–14 |

Flowers are pedicellate.

| | $n$ | $n$-obs. | $\bar{x}$ (mm.) | $s$ (mm.) | $w$ (mm.) |
|---|---|---|---|---|---|
| Pedicels—length—wild | 10 | 13 | 4 | 1.2 | 2 – 7 |
| —cult. | 8 | 35 | 3.6 | 1.7 | .3–12 |
| Flowers—diameter—wild | 2 | 2 | 7.5 | .7 | 7 – 8 |
| —cult. | 6 | 23 | 6.3 | .6 | 5.1– 8 |
| Torus—length—cult. | 1 | 5 | .7 | — | .6– .8 |

*Fig. 61.* Flower of *Sedum clavifolium* from a plant cultivated in the green-house, Ithaca, N.Y., May 13, 1956 (x 15).

Sepals are clavate-oblanceolate or oblong, obtuse, green speckled with red. One flower had a petaloid sepal. Spurs of sepals of eight plants were highly significantly shorter in cultivation than in nature.

|  | n | n-obs. | x̄ (mm.) | s (mm.) | w (mm.) |
|---|---|---|---|---|---|
| Length—wild | 10 | 13 | 3.5 | 0 | 2.7–4 |
| —cult. | 8 | 35 | 3.4 | .8 | 2.4–7 |
| Length of spurs—wild | 10 | 13 | .9 | 0 | .6–1.2 |
| —cult. | 8 | 35 | .5 | .1 | .2– .8 |
| Width—wild | 10 | 13 | 1.5 | .1 | 1.3–1.9 |
| —cult. | 8 | 35 | 1.6 | .3 | 1.1–3 |

Petals are ovate, acute, mucronate-appendaged, before anthesis spreading, then recurved, greenish white streaked with red.

|  | n | n-obs. | x̄ (mm.) | s (mm.) | w (mm.) |
|---|---|---|---|---|---|
| Length—wild | 10 | 13 | 3.3 | .3 | 2.7–3.7 |
| —cult. | 8 | 35 | 3.1 | .3 | 2.4–4.1 |
| Width—wild | 10 | 13 | 1.9 | .2 | 1.4–2.2 |
| —cult. | 8 | 35 | 1.6 | 0 | 1.3–2.1 |

Stamens have yellow or orange anthers; pollen is well developed, the grains averaging .03 mm. in diameter. The validity of a highly significant difference in length of anthers between five wild and five cultivated plants is uncertain since only three of the five plants were duplicated in each sample.

|  | n | n-obs. | x̄ (mm.) | s (mm.) | w (mm.) |
|---|---|---|---|---|---|
| Adnation of epipetalous filaments—wild | 1 | 1 | 1.1 | — | 1.1 |
| —cult. | 1 | 4 | 1.2 | — | 1 –1.6 |
| Anthers—length—wild | 5 | 7 | 1 | .1 | .8–1.2 |
| —cult. | 5 | 11 | .7 | .1 | .6– .9 |
| Anthers—diameter—cult. | 4 | 9 | .4 | .1 | .3– .6 |

Nectaries are subquadrate, lacerate at apex, with two prominent teeth, dark red finely speckled with yellow.

|  | n | n-obs. | x̄ (mm.) | s (mm.) | w (mm.) |
|---|---|---|---|---|---|
| Length—wild | 10 | 13 | 1.8 | .2 | 1.4–2.3 |
| —cult. | 8 | 35 | 1.7 | .3 | 1.1–2.2 |
| Width—wild | 10 | 13 | .9 | .1 | .7–1.1 |
| —cult. | 8 | 35 | .9 | .1 | .6–1.3 |

Pistils are erect, yellow-green, heavily streaked with dark red dorsally and apically.

|  | n | n-obs. | x̄ |  | w |
|---|---|---|---|---|---|
| Length—wild | 1 | 1 | 2.5 mm. | 2.5 | mm. |
| —cult. | 1 | 4 | 2.3 mm. | 2.2– 2.5 mm. | |
| No. of ovules per ovary—cult. | 1 | 5 | 17 | 12 –22 | |

Follicles are erect, with lips of ventral margins .1–.2 mm. wide.

|  | n | n-obs. | x̄ (mm.) | s (mm.) | w (mm.) |
|---|---|---|---|---|---|
| Length—wild | 3 | 5 | 2.3 | 0 | 1.6–3.4 |
| Length of beaks—wild | 3 | 4 | .6 | .1 | .5– .8 |

Seeds are elliptic-oblong, with irregular longitudinal ridges, glabrous, and yellow-brown.

|              | n | n-obs. | $\bar{x}$ (mm.) | s (mm.) | w (mm.) |
|--------------|---|--------|-----------------|---------|---------|
| Length—wild  | 3 | 8      | 6               | .04     | .6–.7   |
| Diameter—wild | 3 | 8     | .3              | .04     | .3–.4   |

**Variation.** *Sedum clavifolium* varies little. Out of eighteen characters studied, wild plants differed in only two, namely length and width of leaves. Plants in cultivation did not differ in width of leaves, but continued to differ in length of leaves. In addition, plants in cultivation differed in six other characters. Since these cultivated plants did not flower simultaneously, study of them was necessary at different times of the year. It is uncertain how many of the differences have a real genetic basis and how many are seasonal expressions. The uniformity of characteristics among wild plants suggests slight or little genetic diversity. Pollen appears normal, seeds develop, and sexual as well as vegetative reproduction seems to occur.

**Nomenclature.** *Sedum clavifolium* Rose, Contr. U.S. Nat. Herb. 13 (9): 297 (1911). Type locality: rocks above the timber line, Iztaccihuatl. Type: collection no. 1,681 of C. A. Purpus (US 399,592), November, 1905.

**Distribution.** The only known locality for *Sedum clavifolium* is the western slope of Iztaccihuatl. Data for the population there are as follows:

| Location | n-plants | Area (m.) | Alt. range (m.) | pH | Drainage |
|----------|----------|-----------|-----------------|-----|----------|
| Iztaccihuatl | >50 | 20 x 21 | 3,700–3,721 | 5.4–5.8 | moderate to excessive |

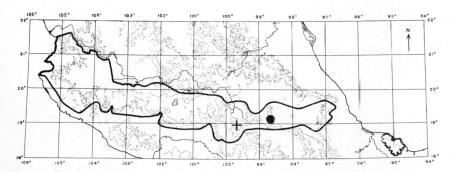

*Fig. 62.* Known distribution of *Sedum clavifolium* (•) and *S. corniferum* (+).

Carl Purpus found *Sedum clavifolium* on Iztaccihuatl in November, 1905. Possibly the population which I studied in 1955 is the one which he discovered, but that is uncertain, especially since Purpus designated the locality as above the timber line, whereas my plants were well below the timber line. Despite extensive search of cliffs both above and below the timber line on both sides of the Cañada de Alcalican, as well as in the Milpulco Valley and in the valley of its tributary, the Cañada de Texantilia, I found *S. clavifolium* at only one place. The plants were in partial shade on cliffs of conglomerate, facing east, east-northeast, and northeast, near and at the base of the Needle, one of the "Centinelas" on the northern side of the Cañada de Alcalican. The vegetational association on the slope below and beside these cliffs was a *Pinetum hartwegii. Echeveria secunda* and *Villadia batesii* were on the cliffs with the *Sedum,* and *S. minimum* was on the same slope within .5 km. *Penstemon gentianoides* was at the base of the cliffs, close to *S. clavifolium,* and *Ptychomitrium leibergii,* identified by Professor Andrews, was in crevices with it. *Sedum clavifolium* was in bud and anthesis on Sept. 4, 1955, and in fruit on Nov. 15, 1955. In the greenhouse at Ithaca, plants have flowered in every month of the year, but principally in the autumn and winter.

**Relationships.** The closest relative of *Sedum clavifolium* is a biennial species which occurs in the gorge of the Tenancingo River. A comparison of that with *S. clavifolium* is included under relationships in the next account. Likewise, a comparison with the biennial *S. minimum,* which has divergent follicles, appears in the account of that species. More closely related than *S. minimum* is *S. longipes,* also with large nectaries, but with a different habit of growth. *Sedum clavifolium* has rootstocks and short aerial stems; *S. longipes* lacks rootstocks, but has long, creeping stems. Other differences, all significant, are contrasted in the following table, in which data are for plants cultivated under similar conditions in the greenhouse at Ithaca.

|  | *S. clavifolium* | | | | | *S. longipes* | | |
|---|---|---|---|---|---|---|---|---|
|  | *n* | *n-obs.* | $\bar{x}$ (*mm.*) | *s* (*mm.*) | | *n* | *n-obs.* | $\bar{x}$ (*mm.*) | *s* (*mm.*) |
| Leaves |  |  |  |  |  |  |  |  |  |
| Length** | 8 | 35 | 16.7 | 3.4 | | 5 | 27 | 9 | 1.6 |

|  | S. clavifolium | | | | S. longipes | | |
|---|---|---|---|---|---|---|---|
|  | n | n-obs. | x̄ (mm.) | s (mm.) | n | n-obs. | x̄ (mm.) | s (mm.) |
| Pedicels |  |  |  |  |  |  |  |  |
| Length* | 8 | 35 | 3.6 | 1.7 | 2 | 9 | 16.3 | 3.8 |
| Nectaries |  |  |  |  |  |  |  |  |
| Length* | 8 | 35 | 1.7 | .3 | 4 | 20 | 2.1 | .2 |
| Width** | 8 | 35 | .9 | .1 | 4 | 20 | 1.7 | .1 |

In the foregoing comparison, the leaves of the rosettes of *Sedum
clavifolium* are compared with mature leaves of the stems of *S.
longipes*, since those of the rosettes of the latter are not fully expanded until after the stems have elongated. Were those employed
in the comparison, the difference in length of leaves between the
two species would be even greater than shown.

Elsewhere in the world, *Sedum correptum* of the Great Snowy
Mountains of Szechwan, China, and *S. surculosum* [*S. atlanticum*
(Ball) Maire] of the Atlas Mountains of northwestern Africa
somewhat resemble *S. clavifolium* in general appearance and habit
of growth. According to Fröderström (1930–1935), *S. correptum*
has solitary flowers on long, slender pedicels, only one whorl of
stamens per flower, sepals much smaller than the petals, narrowly
spatulate nectaries, two ovules per ovary, and narrowly winged
seeds. *Sedum surculosum* likewise has slender pedicels and small
sepals, but four to five flowers per cyme, the floral parts in whorls
of five to seven, yellow petals, and three to four ovules per ovary.
Whether or not these species are more closely related to each
other than to other species is uncertain. An eventual resolution of
this problem must depend on data of different sorts. Not only
must these species be compared minutely with each other, but they
must also be appraised in context with the other species of *Sedum*
in the geographical areas where they occur. On the basis of my
experience in the Trans-Mexican Volcanic Belt, *S. clavifolium* appears more similar to the species of the gorge of the Tenancingo
River and to *S. longipes* than it does to either *S. correptum* or *S.
surculosum*. Resemblances among these species may be coincidental
results of adjustment to similar environmental conditions. This
opinion is not definite, however. More attention to the topic is
necessary.

## 19. *SEDUM CORMIFERUM* (fig. 63)

When plants of *Sedum cormiferum* and *S. clavifolium* are cultivated under similar conditions, they resemble each other. In nature, they grow in different environments and appear dissimilar. *Sedum cormiferum* is biennial, with corms; *S. clavifolium* is perennial, with rootstocks. This is the obvious distinction between them. Because the name *cormiferum* is used here for the first time, a brief description in Latin is provided before the detailed description in English.

**Descriptio originalis.** *Sedum* **cormiferum,** sp. nov., affine *Sedi clavifolii,* sed bienne, cum cormis, foliis et sepalis majoribus, floribus pluribus et seminibus parvioribus, .46 ±.05 mm. longis. Typus in Herbario Wiegand, Universitatis Cornellianae, ab angustiis viarum fluminis Tenancingo, ca. 4 km. inter ortum brumalem et meridiem spectantibus ex Villa Guerrero, Mexico, collectio Roberti Clausenii, planta 4, 1955, Julio 27, est.

**Description.** Materials: 51 plants, all from a small ravine tributary to the gorge of the Tenancingo River about 4 km. south-southeast of Villa Guerrero, Mexico. Measurements marked cult. are of plants cultivated in the greenhouse at Ithaca, N.Y.

Plants of *Sedum cormiferum* are biennials, geophytes, each producing in the first year, in the rainy season, several elliptical or ovoid leaves and a subterranean corm; leaves wither in the dry season, but a new set of spatulate or oblanceolate, petiolate leaves and erect or ascending floral stems develop in the second rainy season, after which the corms shrivel and the plants die. Floral stems are papillose, reddish brown or green streaked with red, sometimes branched. A floral stem of a plant in cultivation became fasciated and attained a width of 5 mm. One plant in cultivation had fifteen floral stems. In nature the number usually is one.

| | $n$ | $n$-obs. | $\bar{x}$ (mm.) | $s$ (mm.) | $w$ (mm.) | |
|---|---|---|---|---|---|---|
| Corms—diameter | | | | | | |
| At end of first growing season—wild | 29 | 29 | 3.5 | .9 | 2 | — 5 |
| When plants are in flower—wild | 1 | 1 | 7 | — | 7 | |
| When plants are in fruit—wild | 6 | 6 | 2.6 | 1.6 | .8– | 4.4 |
| Height of stems | | | | | | |
| With flowers—wild | 4 | 4 | 74 | 19 | 57 | −102 |
| —cult. | 1 | 1 | 85 | — | 85 | |
| With fruits—wild | 6 | 6 | 41 | 7.3 | 32 | — 53 |

Leaves of seedlings are elliptical, ovoid, or orbicular, withering at the end of the first rainy season; leaves in the second rainy season are oblanceolate or spatulate and petiolate. The leaves of two plants in cultivation were significantly longer than those of seven plants in nature.

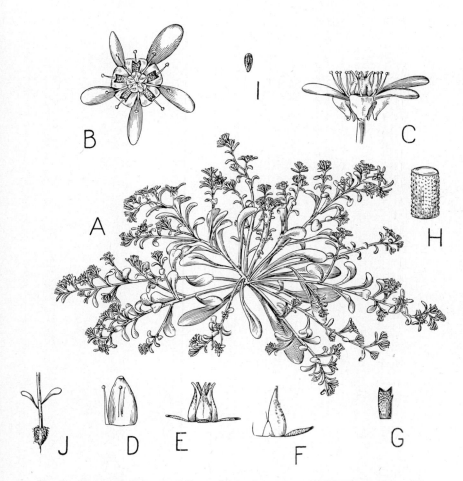

*Fig. 63.* Plant of *Sedum corniferum* from the gorge of the Tenancngo River, cultivated in the greenhouse, Ithaca, N.Y. A. Habit sketch (x .5). B. Flower from above (x 2.7). C. Flower from side (x 2.7). D. Petal and two stamens (x 3.6). E. Pistils and nectaries (x 3.6). F. Single pistil and nectary (x 4.5). G. Nectary (x 4.5). H. Portion of floral stem (x 4.5). I. Seed (x 9). J. Corm and base of floral stem (x .5).

|  | n | n-obs. | $\bar{x}$ (mm.) | s (mm.) | w (mm.) |
|---|---|---|---|---|---|
| **Length** |  |  |  |  |  |
| Of seedlings—wild | 11 | 11 | 24.3 | 5.5 | 16 −32 |
| Of plants with flowers—wild | 7 | 9 | 28.2 | 12.7 | 16 −59 |
| —cult. | 2 | 8 | 46.2 | 0 | 38 −61 |
| **Width** |  |  |  |  |  |
| Of seedlings—wild | 11 | 11 | 6.4 | 1.1 | 5 − 8 |
| Of plants with flowers—wild | 1 | 3 | 5.7 | — | 5 − 6 |
| —cult. | 2 | 8 | 8.7 | 2.3 | 6 −12 |
| **Thickness** |  |  |  |  |  |
| Of seedlings—wild | 11 | 11 | 1 | 0 | 1 |
| Of plants with flowers—wild | 1 | 3 | 1 | — | 1 |
| —cult. | 2 | 8 | 1.9 | .5 | 1.2− 2.8 |

Inflorescences are cymes of 1–3 cincinni.

|  | n | n-obs. | $\bar{x}$ | w |
|---|---|---|---|---|
| No. of flowers per cyme—wild | 20 | 24 | 8 | 4−12 |
| —cult. | 5 | 22 | 13 | 5−27 |

Flowers are on dark red pedicels.

|  | n | n-obs. | $\bar{x}$ (mm.) | s (mm.) | w (mm.) |
|---|---|---|---|---|---|
| Pedicels—length—wild | 1 | 3 | 6.6 | — | 6 − 8 |
| —cult. | 2 | 8 | 3.8 | .5 | 2.6− 4.8 |
| Flowers—diameter—cult. | 2 | 8 | 8.7 | .7 | 7 −11 |
| Torus—length—cult. | 3 | 15 | .7 | .2 | .4− 1 |

Sepals are clavate-oblanceolate, spurred, rounded or truncate at apices, sometimes six in number.

|  | n | n-obs. | $\bar{x}$ (mm.) | s (mm.) | w (mm.) |
|---|---|---|---|---|---|
| Length—wild | 21 | 29 | 4.5 | .9 | 2.9−7.3 |
| —cult. | 5 | 23 | 4.8 | .4 | 3.6−8.5 |
| Length of spurs—wild | 1 | 3 | .7 | — | .2−1 |
| —cult. | 2 | 8 | .7 | .1 | .5−1.2 |
| Width—wild | 21 | 29 | 1.8 | .5 | 1 −3.2 |
| —cult. | 5 | 23 | 1.6 | .3 | 1.1−2.8 |

Petals are lanceolate or ovate, hooded, eventually reflexed, rarely four or six, pale green or greenish white, sparsely streaked with pink near margins, sometimes pink basally.

|  | n | n-obs. | x̄ (mm.) | s (mm.) | w (mm.) |
|---|---|---|---|---|---|
| Length—wild | 21 | 29 | 3.1 | .1 | 1.4–4.1 |
| —cult. | 3 | 13 | 3.3 | .1 | 2.9–4 |
| Width—wild | 21 | 29 | 2.4 | .05 | .7–2 |
| —cult. | 3 | 13 | 2.6 | 0 | 1.4–1.9 |

Stamens are rarely seven or twelve; anthers are yellow; pollen is well developed, the grains .015–.02 mm. in diameter.

|  | n | n-obs. | x̄ (mm.) | s (mm.) | w (mm.) |
|---|---|---|---|---|---|
| Adnation of epipetalous filaments—wild | 1 | 1 | .5 | — | .5 |
| —cult. | 2 | 3 | .5 | c | .3–.7 |
| Length of epipetalous filaments—cult. | 1 | 5 | 1.9 | — | 1.5–2.3 |
| Anthers—length—wild | 18 | 24 | .9 | .2 | .5–1.2 |
| —cult. | 1 | 1 | .5 | — | .5 |

Nectaries are oblong, emarginate, sometimes serrate or doubly emarginate, appearing dark red speckled with pale yellow or pale yellow heavily speckled with dark red.

|  | n | n-obs. | x̄ (mm.) | s (mm.) | w (mm.) |
|---|---|---|---|---|---|
| Length—wild | 21 | 29 | 1.6 | 0 | 1.2–2 |
| —cult. | 5 | 23 | 1.9 | .3 | 1.3–2.4 |
| Width—wild | 21 | 29 | .8 | .1 | .7–1 |
| —cult. | 5 | 23 | .9 | .03 | .6–1 |

Pistils are erect, rarely six in number.

|  | n | n-obs. | x̄ | s | w |
|---|---|---|---|---|---|
| Length—cult. | 2 | 8 | 2 mm. | 0 mm. | 1.7–2.8 mm. |
| No. of ovules per ovary—cult | 4 | 18 | 24 | — | 18–31 |

Follicles are erect, with marginal lips only .1 mm. wide.

|  | n | n-obs. | x̄ (mm.) | s (mm.) | w (mm.) |
|---|---|---|---|---|---|
| Length—wild | 24 | 24 | 2.4 | .3 | 1.7–2.9 |
| Length of beaks—wild | 24 | 24 | .5 | .1 | .3–.7 |

Seeds are pyriform, alveolate, glabrous, brown.

|  | n | n-obs. | x̄ (mm.) | s (mm.) | w (mm.) |
|---|---|---|---|---|---|
| Length—wild | 24 | 60 | .46 | 0 | .4–.5 |
| Diameter—wild | 24 | 60 | .2 | .01 | .1–.3 |

**Variation.** Few differences exist among plants of *Sedum cormiferum*. Plants which I studied in the field differed in length of leaves and in length and width of sepals. Of plants in cultivation in Ithaca, two differed in width of leaves, and five differed in width of sepals and in length and width of nectaries.

Because plants of *Sedum cormiferum* are biennial, those studied in the field could not be propagated and restudied after culture in Ithaca. For that reason, the sample studied in Ithaca comprised plants different from those studied in the field. As a result, the differences already noted among wild and cultivated plants may in part or in whole indicate genetic differences between the two samples. On the basis of this evidence, the plants in the population may not be uniform genetically. Possibly mutations have occurred.

**Nomenclature.** *Sedum cormiferum* Clausen, proposed as a species on p. 216. The type is my collection of July 27, 1955, plant no. 4, from the gorge of the Tenancingo River about 4 km. south-southeast of Villa Guerrero, Mexico.

**Distribution.** I have seen *Sedum cormiferum* only in the gorge of the Tenancingo River south-southeast of Villa Guerrero. Data for the population there are as follows:

| Location | n-plants | Area (m.) | Alt. range (m.) | pH | Drainage |
|---|---|---|---|---|---|
| Tenancingo Gorge | 772 | 170 x 10 | 1,860–1,900 | 5.8–6.6 | moderate |

Edward Alexander, of the New York Botanical Garden, first brought *Sedum cormiferum* to my attention. He had found it in July, 1946, probably in the lower part of the gorge of the Tiscalatengo River, east of Rancho Santo Tobías and only about 2 km. from the site where I found it in 1955. My trips to study it were on July 27, Aug. 15, Oct. 10 and 28, and Dec. 21. Plants were in flower in July and August and had mature follicles on Oct. 10. They were growing on banks of conglomerate, on both sides of a small ravine, exposed to the east, northeast, or west, on the west side of the gorge of the Tenancingo River. No other Crassulaceae were in intimate association with plants of *S. cormiferum*, that is, growing within a meter of them, but only a few meters away were *S. frutescens*, *S. hemsleyanum*, and an unidentified species of *Echeveria*. These other species all flower in the dry season, when the fruits of *S. cormiferum* are mature. Plants of other families, competing with *S. cormiferum*, included: *Asterella echinella, Selaginella lepidophylla, Ophioglossum crotalophoroides* ssp. *crotalophoroides, Adiantum concinnum, Cheilanthes aurantiaca, Russelia jaliscensis, Nissolia hintonii,* and *Muhlenbergia diversiglumis.* On the basis of counts in two quadrats, each 2 m. square, situated in centers of concentration of *Sedum cormiferum,* the density was 57 plants per square meter. In one of these quadrats, 38 per cent of the plants were in flower; the rest were seedlings. In the greenhouse at Ithaca, plants have flowered in every month from December to May and also in August. Two plants persisted for three years, but after producing flowers in the third year, they withered and died.

**Relationships.** *Sedum cormiferum* appears similar to *S. clavifolium*. It has corms and generally is biennial. *Sedum clavifolium* has rhizomes and is perennial. Other differences, all highly significant and, except for seeds, noted from plants cultivated under similar conditions in the greenhouse at Ithaca, are as follows:

| | | | *S. cormiferum* | | | | *S. clavifolium* | |
|---|---|---|---|---|---|---|---|---|
| | n | n-obs. | $\bar{x}$ | s | n | n-obs. | $\bar{x}$ | s |
| Leaves | | | | | | | | |
| Length** | 2 | 8 | 46.2 mm. | 0 mm. | 8 | 35 | 16.7 mm. | 3.4 mm. |
| Width** | 2 | 8 | 8.7 mm. | 2.3 mm. | 8 | 35 | 2.8 mm. | .3 mm. |
| Flowers | | | | | | | | |
| No. per cyme** | 4 | 16 | 12 | — | 4 | 16 | 6 | — |
| Sepals | | | | | | | | |
| Length** | 5 | 23 | 4.8 mm. | .4 mm. | 8 | 35 | 3.4 mm. | .8 mm. |
| Seeds | | | | | | | | |
| Length** | 24 | 60 | .46 mm. | 0 mm. | 3 | 8 | .6 mm. | .04 mm. |
| Diameter** | 24 | 60 | .2 mm. | .01 mm. | 3 | 8 | .3 mm. | .04 mm. |

## 20. *SEDUM VERSADENSE* (fig. 64)

Plants of *Sedum versadense* are chamaephytes. The leaves are spatulate or obovate, truncate or rounded apically, concave ventrally, and on erect or decumbent stems which are 1–7 cm. long. Unlike the condition of most species of the Trans-Mexican Volcanic Belt, the leaves are hairy, in this respect resembling only

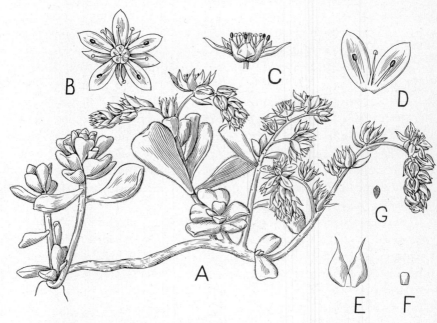

*Fig. 64.* Portion of a plant of *Sedum versadense* from the gorge of the Tenancingo River, cultivated in the greenhouse, Ithaca, N.Y. A. Habit sketch (x .8). B. Flower from above (x 1.6). C. Flower from side (x 1.6). D. Two petals and three stamens (x 2.4). E. Two pistils and torus (x 3.2). F. Nectary (x 4). G. Seed (x 8).

those of *S. hemsleyanum*, *S. ebracteatum*, *S. griseum*, and *S. stahlii*. The last-named species has opposite, terete leaves, yellow petals, and divergent follicles. *Sedum versadense* has alternate leaves which are broader than thick, white or pale pink petals, and erect follicles. *Sedum hemsleyanum* and *S. ebracteatum*, similarly with white petals and erect follicles, have their leaves in dense, basal rosettes, not raised on aerial stems, and carpels with distinctive, basal concavities in which the nectaries are borne. *Sedum griseum* sometimes has its leaves sparingly hirtellous, but the plants are shrubs with linear leaves.

**Description.** Materials: 3 plants, 1 from each of the following sources: gorge of the Tenancingo River about 4 km. south-southeast of Villa Guerrero, Mexico; New York Botanical Garden, via C. Lansing Seymour, probably originally from Versada, Oaxaca; and New York Botanical Garden, via Charles Uhl, probably from the summit above San Miguel, Tenango, Oaxaca. Measurements marked cult. are of plants cultivated in the greenhouse at Ithaca, N.Y. Since only one plant is involved from each source, the column $n$ is omitted from the following tables.

Plants of *Sedum versadense* are perennials, chamaephytes, with primary stems hirtellous, gray, erect or decumbent, 1–7 cm. long; floral stems are terminal, erect, glabrous upward, 3–20 cm. long. Roots are white. The habit of growth is intermediate between that of a subshrub and an herb. After bearing fruits, the stems for the most part wither and die. New growth usually is from axillary shoots near the bases of old stems, but sometimes shoots arise from the median portions of the old floral stems. These root if the floral stems come to rest on the ground. Later, the basal portions of the old stems die, and the new shoots function as new plants. In this way, a plant may spread and give rise to new individuals. The stems of the plant from the gorge of the Tenancingo River are more decumbent than the others. This is shown in figure 64.

Leaves of primary stems are obovate or spatulate, cuneate basally, truncate or rounded, and varying from apiculate to emarginate apically, concave ventrally, convex dorsally, hirtellous, green, red apically and marginally (Tenancingo Gorge) or red dorsally (San Miguel). Leaves upward on floral stems are much smaller than others, short-spurred, and oblanceolate-elliptical. Dimensions below are of mature leaves of primary stems.

| | n-obs. | $\bar{x}$ (mm.) | w (mm.) |
|---|---|---|---|
| Length | | | |
| Tenancingo Gorge | 10 | 18.4 | 16 –23 |
| —cult. | 6 | 27 | 22 –32 |
| Versada—cult. | 1 | 14 | 14 |
| San Miguel—cult. | 2 | 16.5 | 7 –26 |
| Width | | | |
| Tenancingo Gorge | 10 | 10.1 | 9 –13 |
| —cult. | 6 | 14.6 | 12 –17 |
| Versada—cult. | 1 | 10 | 10 |
| San Miguel—cult. | 2 | 8.5 | 4 –13 |
| Thickness | | | |
| Tenancingo Gorge | 10 | 3.6 | 3.2– 4.1 |
| —cult. | 6 | 3.7 | 3.5– 4.6 |
| San Miguel—cult. | 2 | 2.5 | 1 – 4 |

Inflorescences are cymes of 2–5 cincinni with the distal portions having unopened buds recurved. Floral bracts are prominent, similar to leaves of stems just below cymes.

| | n-obs. | $\bar{x}$ | w |
|---|---|---|---|
| No. of flowers per cyme | | | |
|   Tenancingo Gorge—cult. | 13 | 13 | 1–36 |
|   Versada—cult. | 2 | 12 | 12–13 |
|   San Miguel—cult. | 1 | 39 | 39 |

Flowers are on pedicels 2–3 mm. long, rarely 4- or 6-merous.

| | n-obs. | $\bar{x}$ (mm.) | w (mm.) |
|---|---|---|---|
| Flowers—diameter | | | |
|   Tenancingo Gorge—cult. | 6 | 13.2 | 11 –14 |
|   Versada—cult. | 1 | 12 | 12 |
|   San Miguel—cult. | 3 | 10.7 | 10 –11 |
| Torus—length | | | |
|   Tenancingo Gorge—cult. | 3 | .8 | .6– 1 |

Sepals are very unequal, oblanceolate-elliptical or oblong, acute or abruptly apiculate, green suffused with red. Dimensions cited are of the longest sepals of the flowers studied.

| | n-obs. | $\bar{x}$ (mm.) | w (mm.) |
|---|---|---|---|
| Length | | | |
|   Tenancingo Gorge—cult. | 8 | 7 | 5.5–8.1 |
|   Versada—cult. | 1 | 5 | 5 |
|   San Miguel—cult. | 1 | 5 | 5 |
| Width | | | |
|   Tenancingo Gorge—cult. | 8 | 2.8 | 2.2–3.6 |
|   San Miguel—cult. | 1 | 2.2 | 2.2 |

Petals are oblanceolate-elliptical or elliptical, mucronately apiculate, pinkish white, pink in bud.

| | n-obs. | $\bar{x}$ (mm.) | w (mm.) |
|---|---|---|---|
| Length | | | |
|   Tenancingo Gorge—cult. | 8 | 5.6 | 4.5–6.6 |
|   Versada—cult. | 1 | 5 | 5 |
|   San Miguel—cult. | 1 | 5 | 5 |
| Length of connate portion | | | |
|   Tenancingo Gorge—cult. | 8 | .2 | 0 – .4 |
| Width | | | |
|   Tenancingo Gorge—cult. | 8 | 2.4 | 2 –2.8 |
|   San Miguel—cult. | 1 | 2 | 2 |

Stamens have white filaments and red anthers; pollen is well developed.

|  | n-obs. | x̄ (mm.) | w (mm.) |
|---|---|---|---|
| Adnation of epipetalous filaments | | | |
| Tenancingo Gorge—cult. | 8 | .6 | .3– .8 |
| Anthers—length | | | |
| Tenancingo Gorge—cult. | 11 | .9 | .5–1.2 |
| Anthers—diameter | | | |
| Tenancingo Gorge—cult. | 6 | .6 | .5– .6 |

Nectaries are subquadrate, emarginate, white.

|  | n-obs. | x̄ (mm.) | w (mm.) |
|---|---|---|---|
| Length | | | |
| Tenancingo Gorge—cult. | 8 | .5 | .4–.7 |
| Versada—cult. | 1 | .2 | .2 |
| San Miguel—cult. | 1 | .4 | .4 |
| Width | | | |
| Tenancingo Gorge—cult. | 8 | .4 | .4–.6 |
| Versada—cult. | 1 | .4 | .4 |
| San Miguel—cult. | 1 | .5 | .5 |

Pistils are erect, white, gibbous ventrally.

|  | n-obs. | x̄ | w |
|---|---|---|---|
| Length | | | |
| Tenancingo Gorge—cult. | 5 | 3.4 mm. | 3 – 3.7 mm. |
| Versada—cult. | 1 | 3 mm. | 3 mm. |
| San Miguel—cult. | 1 | 3.4 mm. | 3.4 mm. |
| No. of ovules per ovary | | | |
| Tenancingo Gorge—cult. | 3 | 50 | 44 –54 |

Follicles are erect and brown.

|  | n-obs. | x̄ (mm.) | w (mm.) |
|---|---|---|---|
| Length | | | |
| Tenancingo Gorge—cult. | 6 | 2.3 | 1.6–2.6 |

Seeds are elliptical, reticulate, and brown.

|  | n-obs. | x̄ (mm.) | w (mm.) |
|---|---|---|---|
| Length | | | |
| Tenancingo Gorge—cult. | 6 | .4 | .4 |
| Diameter | | | |
| Tenancingo Gorge—cult. | 6 | .2 | .1–.2 |

**Variation.** With samples of only one plant per population, no information is available concerning variation within populations. Among populations, my three plants show variation. The flowers of the plant from above San Miguel are smaller than those of the other two plants. On the basis of present evidence, the difference in size of flowers could be a chance variation or a genetic difference at the level of either individuals or populations. Until adequate samples are available, that problem will be unsettled, as will the infraspecific classification.

**Nomenclature.** *Sedum versadense* C. H. Thompson, Trans. Acad. Sci. St. Louis 20: 23, pl. 12 (1911). Type locality: Versada, halfway between El Parián and Tomellín, Oaxaca. Type: a collection of William Trelease ("Missouri Botanical Garden"), February, 1905. I have studied an isotype (US 399,714).

A synonym is:

1947. *Sedum chontalense* Alexander, Cact. Succ. Jour. 19: 51, fig. 34. Type locality: cliff on summit above San Miguel, Tenango, in the mountains west of Tehuantepec, Oaxaca. Type: collected by T. Mac-Dougall ("NY," according to Alexander) in the winter of 1938–1939. I have seen the type in the greenhouse (NY), but not the dried specimen. This plant may be genetically distinct from the type of *S. versadense*, but an interpretation of its taxonomic status requires adequate samples of the populations from which both types originated.

**Distribution.** (fig. 66, p. 234). *Sedum versadense* occurs in two areas in the Sierra Madre del Sur and in the gorge of the Tenancingo River on the southern slope of the Trans-Mexican Volcanic Belt. I have seen it in the field only in the gorge of the Tenancingo River; from there I have the following data:

| Location | n-plants | Area (cm.) | Alt. (m.) | pH | Drainage |
|---|---|---|---|---|---|
| Tenancingo Gorge | 1 | ab. 10 x 10 | 1,920 | 6.8 | moderate |

Edward Alexander, of the New York Botanical Garden, found *Sedum versadense* near Villa Guerrero, Mexico, at the time that he found *S. cormiferum* in 1946. Although I made five trips to the gorge of the Tenancingo River, I saw *S. versadense* only on the last, on Dec. 27, 1955, and then a single plant. It was on a boulder of andesite, on the east side of the gorge, exposed to the west, in the shade of shrubs and trees of unidentified species of Fabaceae. No other Crassulaceae were in close association, but in the same gorge were *S. cormiferum, S. frutescens, S. hemsleyanum*, and a species of *Echeveria*. Plants propagated by cuttings from the plant in the Tenancingo River have flowered in February, March, and April.

**Relationships.** Of the species of the Trans-Mexican Volcanic Belt, *Sedum hemsleyanum* and *S. ebracteatum* appear most closely related to *S. versadense*. Since comparisons will be more satisfactory after descriptive data for these have been presented, each is compared with *S. versadense* in the discussion of its relationships. Together, these three species are not close to any other species of the Trans-Mexican Volcanic Belt, but they may all be derived from species which were shrubs with flat leaves. Of those already discussed, *S. quevae*, though itself specialized, may be derived from the same ancestral group, as may be *S. oxypetalum. Sedum versadense* differs from *S. quevae* in lacking tubers or peeling bark and in having lower stature, hairy stems and leaves, and shorter petals and seeds. Based on plants cultivated under similar conditions, the difference between the two species in length of petals, 5.4 mm. in *S. versadense* and 6.9 in *S. quevae*, is significant.

Of species outside of the Trans-Mexican Volcanic Belt, none appear to be close to *Sedum versadense*. Its relationship seems to be with other species of the Mexican highlands.

## 21. *SEDUM HEMSLEYANUM* (figs. 65 and 66)

The distinctive features of *Sedum hemsleyanum* are dense basal rosettes of puberulent leaves, oblong or lanceolate leaves on the floral stems, paniculate cymes of 1–24 cincinni, white petals, and erect pistils with prominent, basal concavities on the dorsal sides. The species of the Trans-Mexican Volcanic Belt most like *S. hemsleyanum* is *S. ebracteatum*. That has wider, ovate or elliptical leaves which are cordate basally on the floral stems.

**Description.** Materials: 24 plants—2 from Río Blanco, Vera Cruz; 4 from Maltrata, Vera Cruz; and 18 from the gorge of the

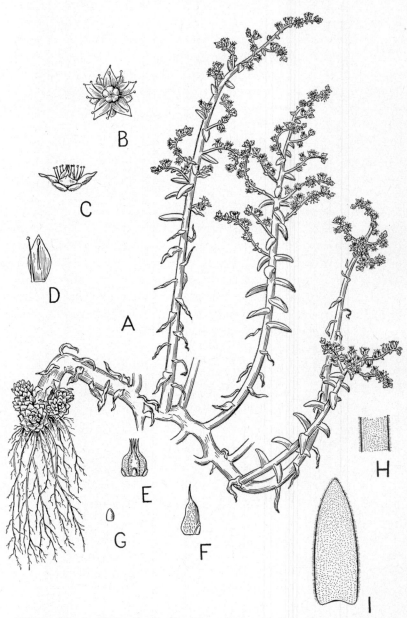

*Fig. 65.* Plant of *Sedum hemsleyanum* from the gorge of the Tenancingo River, cultivated in the greenhouse, Ithaca, N.Y.  A. Habit sketch (x .4).  B. Flower from above (x 1.6).  C. Flower from side (x 1.6).  D. Petal and two stamens (x 2.4).  E. Pistils (x 2.4).  F. Single pistil (x 3.2).  G. Nectary (x 4).  H. Portion of floral stem (x 1.6).  I. Leaf of floral stem (x 1.6).

Tenancingo River about 4 km. south-southeast of Villa Guerrero, Mexico. Measurements marked cult. are of plants cultivated under similar conditions in the greenhouse at Ithaca, N.Y.

Plants of *Sedum hemsleyanum* are perennials through the development, near the bases of the floral stems, of secondary shoots with the leaves in dense rosettes which take root and perpetuate the individuals and also hemicryptophytes, each plant producing 1–8 floral stems, these usually puberulent and streaked with purple. In cultivation, floral stems have attained a length of 5.9 dm.

| | $n$ | $n$-obs. | $\bar{x}$ (dm.) | $s$ (dm.) | $w$ (dm.) |
|---|---|---|---|---|---|
| Floral stems—height | | | | | |
| Río Blanco | 1 | 3 | 2.2 | — | 1.8–2.8 |
| Maltrata | 4 | 13 | 1.8 | .3 | .5–3.3 |
| Tenancingo Gorge | 1 | 5 | 3.1 | — | 2.7–3.6 |
| Río Blanco—cult. | 2 | 2 | 1.6 | 1.7 | .4–2.8 |
| Maltrata—cult. | 2 | 2 | 3.1 | .4 | 2.9–3.4 |
| Tenancingo Gorge—cult. | 11 | 11 | 2.3 | 1.2 | .3–3.8 |

Leaves of rosettes are oblanceolate-oblong or obovate, puberulent; those of floral stems oblanceolate-oblong, oblong, lanceolate, or linear-lanceolate, puberulent, sometimes suffused with purple. The leaves of the floral stems of two plants at Río Blanco were significantly thicker than those of four plants at Maltrata and three in the Tenancingo Gorge. All dimensions below are of leaves of floral stems.

| | $n$ | $n$-obs. | $\bar{x}$ (mm.) | $s$ (mm.) | $w$ (mm.) |
|---|---|---|---|---|---|
| Length | | | | | |
| Río Blanco | 2 | 7 | 32 | 0 | 27 –37 |
| Maltrata | 4 | 13 | 25 | 7.8 | 3 –37 |
| Tenancingo Gorge | 6 | 21 | 31 | 9.2 | 5 –59 |
| Río Blanco—cult. | 2 | 6 | 31 | 20.3 | 4 –56 |
| Maltrata—cult. | 2 | 6 | 23 | 0 | 2? –27 |
| Tenancingo Gorge—cult. | 11 | 33 | 27 | 3 | 7 –40 |
| Width | | | | | |
| Río Blanco | 2 | 7 | 10 | 1.9 | 7 –13 |
| Maltrata | 4 | 13 | 7 | 1 | 5 – 9 |
| Tenancingo Gorge | 6 | 21 | 8 | 1.9 | 4 –12 |
| Río Blanco—cult. | 2 | 6 | 9 | 3.7 | 6 –13 |
| Maltrata—cult. | 2 | 6 | 9 | 1.6 | 7 –11 |
| Tenancingo Gorge—cult. | 11 | 33 | 9 | 1.2 | 6 –12 |

|  | $n$ | $n$-obs. | $\bar{x}$ (mm.) | $s$ (mm.) | $w$ (mm.) |
|---|---|---|---|---|---|
| Thickness |  |  |  |  |  |
| Río Blanco | 2 | 7 | 4.5 | .1 | 4 − 5 |
| Maltrata | 4 | 13 | 3.5 | 0 | 3 − 4 |
| Tenancingo Gorge | 3 | 4 | 3.5 | .6 | 3 − 4 |
| Río Blanco—cult. | 1 | 3 | 1.9 | — | 1.5− 2.3 |

Inflorescences are cymes of 1–24 cincinni.

Flowers are sessile, with pungent odor.

|  | $n$ | $n$-obs. | $\bar{x}$ (mm.) | $w$ (mm.) |
|---|---|---|---|---|
| Flowers—diameter |  |  |  |  |
| Río Blanco | 1 | 1 | 9 | 9 |
| Tenancingo Gorge | 1 | 5 | 8.6 | 8 − 9 |
| Río Blanco—cult. | 1 | 3 | 10.7 | 10 −11 |
| Tenancingo Gorge—cult. | 1 | 1 | 9 | 9 |
| Torus—length |  |  |  |  |
| Río Blanco—cult. | 1 | 3 | .5 | .4− .7 |
| Tenancingo Gorge—cult. | 1 | 1 | .5 | .5 |

Sepals are ovate or elliptical, acute or obtuse, puberulent. In cultivation, those of two plants from Río Blanco and of two plants from Maltrata were significantly longer than those of eleven plants from the Tenancingo Gorge.

|  | $n$ | $n$-obs. | $\bar{x}$ (mm.) | $s$ (mm.) | $w$ (mm.) |
|---|---|---|---|---|---|
| Length |  |  |  |  |  |
| Río Blanco | 1 | 1 | 4.2 | — | 4.2 |
| Tenancingo Gorge | 1 | 5 | 2.5 | — | 2.4–2.6 |
| Río Blanco—cult. | 2 | 7 | 4.5 | 0 | 2.9–8 |
| Maltrata—cult. | 2 | 6 | 3.9 | .4 | 2.8–4.5 |
| Tenancingo Gorge—cult. | 11 | 33 | 3.3 | .4 | 2.3–4.4 |
| Width |  |  |  |  |  |
| Río Blanco | 1 | 1 | 2.4 | — | 2.4 |
| Tenancingo Gorge | 1 | 5 | 1.6 | — | 1.4–1.9 |
| Río Blanco—cult. | 2 | 7 | 2.8 | 0 | 2.3–3.9 |
| Maltrata—cult. | 2 | 6 | 2.5 | 0 | 2.4–2.8 |
| Tenancingo Gorge—cult. | 11 | 33 | 2.3 | .3 | 1.7–3.2 |

Petals are ovate or lanceolate, acute or obtuse, mucronate-appendaged, rarely four, white, green on dorsal keel above middle, sometimes finely speckled with purple centrally. One petal of a plant at Río Blanco was two-lobed apically.

|  | n | n-obs. | x̄ (mm.) | s (mm.) | w (mm.) |
|---|---|---|---|---|---|
| **Length** | | | | | |
| Río Blanco | 1 | 2 | 6.2 | — | 6.2–6.3 |
| Tenancingo Gorge | 15 | 54 | 4.9 | .4 | 4 –6 |
| Río Blanco—cult. | 2 | 7 | 6.2 | .8 | 5.5–7.6 |
| Maltrata—cult. | 2 | 6 | 6.3 | 0 | 5.4–6.7 |
| Tenancingo Gorge—cult. | 11 | 33 | 5.4 | .5 | 4.2–6.7 |
| **Width** | | | | | |
| Río Blanco | 1 | 2 | 3 | — | 2.4–3.6 |
| Tenancingo Gorge | 1 | 5 | 2.5 | — | 2.3–2.8 |
| Río Blanco—cult. | 1 | 3 | 3 | — | 2.8–3.2 |

Stamens have anthers papillose and red or sometimes yellow. Pollen of some plants is well developed, of others abortive.

|  | n | n-obs. | x̄ (mm.) | s (mm.) | w (mm.) |
|---|---|---|---|---|---|
| **Adnation of epipetalous filaments** | | | | | |
| Tenancingo Gorge | 2 | 9 | 1.5 | .2 | 1.2–2 |
| Río Blanco—cult. | 1 | 3 | 1.9 | — | 1.6–2.1 |
| Tenancingo Gorge—cult. | 1 | 3 | 1.7 | — | .9–2.1 |
| **Anthers—length** | | | | | |
| Tenancingo Gorge | 10 | 25 | .8 | .03 | .7– .9 |
| Río Blanco—cult. | 2 | 6 | .9 | 0 | .8–1 |
| Maltrata—cult. | 2 | 6 | .9 | 0 | .8–1 |
| Tenancingo Gorge—cult. | 11 | 33 | .8 | .03 | .7–1.1 |
| **Anthers—diameter** | | | | | |
| Río Blanco—cult. | 2 | 6 | .5 | 0 | .5– .6 |
| Maltrata—cult. | 2 | 6 | .5 | 0 | .5– .6 |
| Tenancingo Gorge—cult. | 11 | 33 | .5 | .03 | .4– .7 |

Nectaries are subquadrate or lanceolate-oblong and pale yellow or sometimes white.

|  | n | n-obs. | x̄ (mm.) | s (mm.) | w (mm.) |
|---|---|---|---|---|---|
| **Length** | | | | | |
| Río Blanco | 1 | 1 | .8 | — | .8 |
| Tenancingo Gorge | 1 | 5 | .7 | — | .6– .8 |
| Río Blanco—cult. | 2 | 7 | .9 | .05 | .8–1 |
| Maltrata—cult. | 2 | 6 | 1 | .04 | .8–1.1 |
| Tenancingo Gorge—cult. | 11 | 33 | .9 | .1 | .6–1.3 |
| **Width** | | | | | |
| Río Blanco | 1 | 1 | .5 | — | .5 |
| Tenancingo Gorge | 1 | 5 | .7 | — | .5– .8 |
| Río Blanco—cult. | 1 | 3 | .4 | — | .3– .5 |

Pistils are erect with ovaries white or green, speckled with red, warty, concave basally on dorsal sides. A pistil of a plant at Río Blanco was clearly inrolled, with one side of the carpel inside the other, making the ovary open. Other pistils had the margins of the carpels meeting, but only weakly united.

|  | $n$ | $n$-obs. | $\bar{x}$ | $w$ |
|---|---|---|---|---|
| Length |  |  |  |  |
| Río Blanco—cult. | I | 3 | 5.3 mm. | 4.8– 5.8 mm. |
| No. of ovules per ovary |  |  |  |  |
| Río Blanco—cult. | I | 3 | 38 | 32 –45 |
| Tenancingo Gorge—cult. | I | 3 | 38 | 24 –45 |

Follicles are erect.

|  | $n$ | $n$-obs. | $\bar{x}$ (*mm.*) | $w$ (*mm.*) |
|---|---|---|---|---|
| Length |  |  |  |  |
| Tenancingo Gorge—cult. | I | 10 | 3.8 | 2.8–4.9 |

Seeds are pyriform, glabrous, with irregular, longitudinal ridges, obscurely reticulate, brown.

|  | $n$ | $n$-obs. | $\bar{x}$ (*mm.*) | $w$ (*mm.*) |
|---|---|---|---|---|
| Length |  |  |  |  |
| Tenancingo Gorge—cult. | I | 10 | .6 | .6 |
| Diameter |  |  |  |  |
| Tenancingo Gorge—cult. | I | 10 | .2 | .2 |

**Variation.** The three populations of *Sedum hemsleyanum* which I have studied are similar, except that in cultivation the sepals of plants from Río Blanco and Maltrata were significantly longer than those of plants from the gorge of the Tenancingo River and that the leaves of two plants at Río Blanco were significantly thicker than those of plants at the other two localities. They are best included in the same species without special subspecific designations, although small genetic differences probably exist among them.

Within populations, wild plants differed in four characters. In the greenhouse at Ithaca, plants of the same population differed in six characters. These suggest genetic variation. The easiest explanation for the origin of the variation, if it is genetic, is by gene mutations. If interspecific hybridization has been a factor, it probably has not involved species presently associated with *Sedum hemsleyanum* at the sites investigated. At Maltrata, for example, *S. dendroideum* ssp. *dendroideum*, *S. lucidum*, and *S. stahlii* grow intermixed with *S. hemsleyanum*, yet no obvious hybrids are there. Similarly, in the gorge of the Tenancingo River, hybridization does not occur with *S. cormiferum*, *S. frutescens*, or *S. versadense*. Hybridization has more likely involved different biotypes of *S. hemsleyanum*.

Reproduction may be both vegetative and by seeds. The only plant from which I obtained seeds had good pollen and appeared to be sexually fertile.

**Nomenclature.** *Sedum "Hemsleanum"* Rose, Bull. N.Y. Bot. Gard. 3: 41 (1903). Rose (No. Am. Flora 22: 58, 1905) corrected the spelling of the specific epithet to *hemsleyanum*. Type locality: dry banks of hills near Oaxaca, alt. 1,677 m. Type: collection no. 6,042 of C. G. Pringle (US 865,461), November, 1894. Hemsley (1879–1888, p. 396) listed this as species no. 12, without a name. He cited Bourgeau's collection no. 1,182 from Cuernavaca and F. Mueller's no. 322 from Orizaba.

Synonyms are:

1905. *Sedastrum Hemsleyanum* Rose, No. Am. Flora 22: 58.
1905. *Sedastrum Painteri* Rose, No. Am. Flora 22: 58. Type locality: near Cuernavaca. Type: collection no. 796 of J. N. Rose and J. H. Painter (US 592,134), Sept. 18, 1903.
1911. (? *Sedastrum pachucense* C. H. Thompson), Trans. Acad. Sci. St. Louis 20: 21, pl. 10 (1911). Type locality: among rocks and low shrubs on the mountain sides above Pachuca, Hidalgo. Type: a collection of C. H. Thompson, August, 1910, cited by him as in the herbarium of the Missouri Botanical Garden. My interpretation is based on the original description and Thompson's plate 10. When I visited the slopes above Pachuca in March, 1949, I did not see plants of the sort which Thompson described. The narrow leaves of the floral stems and small flowers of *Sedastrum pachucense* are in agreement with *Sedum hemsleyanum*, but the glabrous condition of the floral stems and their leaves, plus the tolerance of frost, suggests that it may be different. Pending further study, I doubtfully include it as a synonym of *Sedum hemsleyanum*.
1921. *Sedum pachucense* (C. H. Thompson) Praeger, Jour. Roy. Hort. Soc. 46: 128.
1930. *Sedum Painteri* (Rose) Berger, in Engler's Nat. Pflanzenfam., ed. 2, 18 a: 445.

Rose had a manuscript name, which he never published, for a collection of C. A. Purpus (US), 1907, from the Barranca de Tenampa, Vera Cruz. Plants of that collection are most suggestive of the type of *S. painteri*, but their leaves are remarkably short, 4–10 mm. long.

**Distribution.** *Sedum hemsleyanum* occurs primarily in the Sierra Madre del Sur and sparingly in the Trans-Mexican Volcanic Belt. I have studied it at three localities as follows:

| Location | n-plants | | Area (m.) | Alt. range (m.) | pH | Drainage |
|---|---|---|---|---|---|---|
| Río Blanco | ab. 10 | ab. | 2 x 2 | ab. 1,340 | 7.4 | moderate |
| Maltrata | ab. 20 | | 50 x 30 | 1,784–1,814 | — | excessive |
| Tenancingo Gorge | >471 | | >200 x 500 | 1,860–2,000 | 6.4–7.2 | moderate to poor |

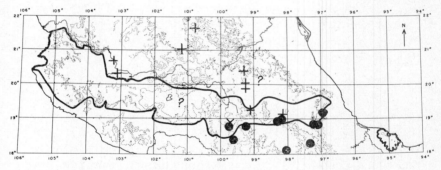

*Fig. 66.* Known distribution in the Trans-Mexican Volcanic Belt and adjacent regions of *Sedum hemsleyanum* (•), *S. ebracteatum* (+), and *S. versadense* (x).

Other localities where *Sedum hemsleyanum* occurs in the Trans-Mexican Volcanic Belt and the discoverers of each are: the Barranca de Tenampa, Vera Cruz, Carl Purpus (US); Batán, vicinity of Puebla, Gerfroy Arsène (US); Cerro Tepoxuchil, vicinity of Puebla, Gerfroy Arsène (US); Atlixco, Puebla, discoverer unknown (NY); and ravine near Cuernavaca, Joseph Rose and Joseph Painter (NY, US). Additional localities in the Sierra Madre del Sur include Orizaba, Frederick Mueller (NY), near Ciudad Mendoza, Vera Cruz, observed by me, but not collected; Tehuacán, Carl Purpus (NY); Iguala Canyon, Guerrero, Joseph Rose (NY); ravine, Campo-Morado-Otatlán, alt. 1,200 m., District of Mina,

Guerrero, George Hinton *et al.* (CU); between Petlalcingo and Acatlán, Edward Nelson (NY, US); Sierra de San Felipe, Casiano Conzatti (NY); and hills near Oaxaca, Cyrus Pringle (NY, US). The only population known from the Central Mexican Plateau is the one which Thompson named *Sedastrum pachucense*, from the slope above Pachuca. Its taxonomic status is doubtful.

Marcelino López, my son Eric, and I found *Sedum hemsleyanum* on limestone on the south side of the trail 20 m. above the bridge at Río Blanco, on Nov. 9, 1955. The plants had floral buds at the time of our visit. Only one flower was expanded. The plants grew in partial shade, exposed to the west. Other Crassulaceae in the vicinity were *Echeveria nuda*, *Kalanchoe pinnata*, and *S. dendroideum* ssp. *praealtum*, all without floral buds or flowers on Nov. 9. *Epidendrum ibaguense* was a common competing species, showy because of its orange-red flowers. In the greenhouse at Ithaca, two plants of *S. hemsleyanum* from Río Blanco have flowered in December, January, and March.

I saw *Sedum hemsleyanum* about .5 km. west-southwest of the center of Maltrata on Nov. 6, 1955. The plants there were in bud on that date, growing on limestone, exposed to the southeast. They were associated with *S. dendroideum* ssp. *dendroideum* and *S. lucidum*, both likewise with floral buds, and with *S. stahlii*. At Ithaca, two plants of *S. hemsleyanum* from Maltrata have flowered in January.

Edward Alexander discovered a population of *Sedum hemsleyanum* near Villa Guerrero in 1946. I studied the species on cliffs on both sides of the gorge of the Tenancingo River, about 4 km. south-southeast of Villa Guerrero, on July 27, Aug. 15, Oct. 10 and 28, and Dec. 21 and 27 of 1955. The plants had floral buds in October and were in anthesis in December. They were on cliffs of conglomerate, shaded for most of the day, exposed to the east, southeast, or west. A tree shading those cliffs was *Myriocarpa brachystachys*. A grass common on the cliffs was *Oplismenus cristatus*. The only member of the Crassulaceae intimately associated with *S. hemsleyanum* was a species of *Echeveria*. Elsewhere in the gorge were *S. cormiferum*, in fruit when *S. hemsleyanum* was in flower, and *S. frutescens* which apparently flowers when *S. hemsleyanum* is in fruit. *Sedum versadense*, also in the same gorge, probably blooms when the main period of flowering of *S. hemsleyanum* is past. I saw no

plants which had the appearance of interspecific hybrids and be-
lieve that the chances for hybridization in the Tenancingo Gorge
are slight. In cultivation at Ithaca, plants from there have flowered
in the greenhouse in December, January, and February.

**Relationships.** The only species closely related to *Sedum hemsleyanum* in the Trans-Mexican Volcanic Belt is *S. ebracteatum*. The
leaves of the floral stems of that are wider. A comparison is included
in the section on relationships under *S. ebracteatum*. Otherwise, *S.
versadense* is the next most closely related species. That has erect or
decumbent secondary shoots with the leaves above the level of the
ground, not in dense basal rosettes. Other differences between *S.
hemsleyanum* and *S. versadense* are indicated in the following table,
in which all data are for plants cultivated under similar conditions
in the greenhouse at Ithaca.

| | | *S. hemsleyanum* | | | | *S. versadense* | | |
|---|---|---|---|---|---|---|---|---|
| | $n$ | $n$-obs. | $\bar{x}$ (mm.) | $s$ (mm.) | $n$ | $n$-obs. | $\bar{x}$ (mm.) | $s$ (mm.) |
| Sepals | | | | | | | | |
| Length* | 15 | 46 | 3.6 | .2 | 3 | 10 | 6.6 | 1.8 |
| Nectaries | | | | | | | | |
| Length** | 15 | 46 | .9 | .1 | 3 | 10 | .5 | .2 |
| Follicles | | | | | | | | |
| Length | 1 | 10 | 3.8 | — | 1 | 6 | 2.3 | — |
| Seeds | | | | | | | | |
| Length | 1 | 10 | .6 | — | 1 | 6 | .4 | — |

Reference. Clausen, R. T. (1943).

## 22. *SEDUM EBRACTEATUM* (fig. 67)

*Sedum ebracteatum* is similar to *S. hemsleyanum*, but has broader
leaves on the floriferous branches. These leaves average >11 mm.
wide, compared with <10 mm. in *S. hemsleyanum*. Like the latter,
it is herbaceous, with musky-scented white flowers in paniculate
cymes, short secondary shoots bearing leaves in dense rosettes,
and ovaries with basal concavities on the dorsal sides. No other
species of the Trans-Mexican Volcanic Belt is likely to be confused with it.

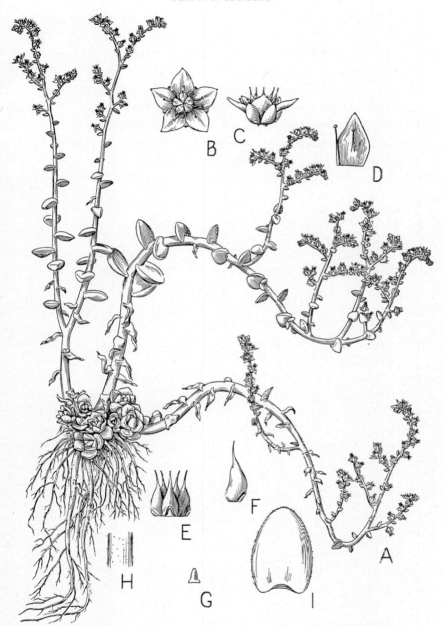

*Fig. 67.* Plant of *Sedum ebracteatum* ssp. *ebracteatum* from Guadalupe, D.F., cultivated in the greenhouse, Ithaca, N.Y. A. Habit sketch (x .4). B. Flower from above (x 1.6). C. Flower from side (x 1.6). D. Petal and two stamens (x 2.4). E. Pistils (x 2.4). F. Single pistil (x 3.2). G. Nectary (x 4). H. Portion of floriferous branch showing pubescence (x 1.6). I. Leaf of floriferous branch (x 1.6).

**Description.** Materials: 5 plants—3 from cliffs on the north side of Guadalupe, D.F., and 2 from a canyon in the Sierra Madre Oriental southwest of Ciudad Victoria, Tamaulipas. Measurements marked cult. are of plants cultivated under similar conditions in the greenhouse at Ithaca, N.Y.

Plants of *Sedum ebracteatum* are perennials, hemicryptophytes, developing short, secondary shoots near the bases of the floriferous branches, with the leaves puberulent and in dense rosettes. Each plant produces 1–7 floriferous branches per season. These are either erect or tortuously decumbent; often they are puberulent and streaked with purple.

| | $n$ | $n$-obs. | $\bar{x}$ (dm.) | $w$ (dm.) |
|---|---|---|---|---|
| Floriferous branches—height | | | | |
| Guadalupe—cult. | 1 | 2 | 2.1 | 1.7–2.5 |

Leaves of rosettes are suborbicular to spatulate-oblong, obtuse or rounded apically, puberulent; those of floriferous branches are ovate to oblong, cordate basally, subacute to obtuse apically, puberulent, sometimes speckled with purple. In cultivation, the leaves of a plant from Guadalupe were thicker than those of a plant from near Ciudad Victoria. The same plant from Guadalupe, studied both in the field and in cultivation, had highly significantly thicker leaves in the greenhouse, where moisture was more evenly distributed throughout the year. All dimensions below are of leaves of floriferous branches.

| | $n$ | $n$-obs. | $\bar{x}$ (mm.) | $s$ (mm.) | $w$ (mm.) |
|---|---|---|---|---|---|
| Length | | | | | |
| Guadalupe | 2 | 6 | 20 | 0 | 17 –25 |
| —cult. | 1 | 11 | 23 | — | 11 –42 |
| Victoria—cult. | 1 | 2 | 20 | — | 10 –30 |
| Width | | | | | |
| Guadalupe | 2 | 6 | 14.3 | 2.6 | 12 –17 |
| —cult. | 1 | 11 | 15.3 | — | 8 –28 |
| Victoria—cult. | 1 | 2 | 11 | — | 9 –13 |
| Thickness | | | | | |
| Guadalupe | 2 | 6 | 2.7 | 0 | 2.4– 3.7 |
| —cult. | 1 | 11 | 4.9 | — | 4.1– 6 |
| Victoria—cult. | 1 | 2 | 3.5 | — | 3 – 4 |

Inflorescences are paniculate cymes of 1–18 cincinni. Because of the manner in which the floriferous branches become further branched, the delimitation of what constitutes an inflorescence is somewhat arbitrary.

Flowers are sessile, with musky odor.

| | n | n-obs. | $\bar{x}$ (mm.) | s (mm.) | w (mm.) |
|---|---|---|---|---|---|
| Flowers—diameter | | | | | |
| Guadalupe—cult. | 2 | 6 | 12 | 1 | 10 −13 |
| Victoria—cult. | 1 | 1 | 13 | — | 13 |
| Torus—length | | | | | |
| Guadalupe—cult. | 1 | 2 | 1.35 | — | 1.3– 1.4 |

Sepals are ovate, acute or obtuse, often minutely puberulent, sometimes speckled with red.

| | n | n-obs. | $\bar{x}$ (mm.) | s (mm.) | w (mm.) |
|---|---|---|---|---|---|
| Length | | | | | |
| Guadalupe | 2 | 6 | 3.6 | 0 | 3 −3.9 |
| —cult. | 2 | 7 | 3.3 | 0 | 3 −4 |
| Victoria—cult. | 1 | 2 | 4.3 | — | 3.6–5 |
| Width | | | | | |
| Guadalupe | 2 | 6 | 2.4 | .4 | 1.8–3.6 |
| —cult. | 2 | 7 | 2.8 | .2 | 2 −3.4 |
| Victoria—cult. | 1 | 2 | 2.3 | — | 2 −2.6 |

Petals are ovate or elliptic-ovate, connate for .1–.3 mm., recurved apically, acute, mucronate-appendaged, white, often pale green medially, sometimes with a few red streaks dorsally.

| | n | n-obs. | $\bar{x}$ (mm.) | s (mm.) | w (mm.) |
|---|---|---|---|---|---|
| Length | | | | | |
| Guadalupe | 2 | 6 | 6.1 | .5 | 5.5–6.6 |
| —cult. | 2 | 6 | 5.7 | .4 | 5 −6.5 |
| Victoria—cult. | 1 | 1 | 7 | — | 7 |
| Width | | | | | |
| Guadalupe | 2 | 6 | 3.2 | .4 | 2.7–3.7 |
| —cult. | 2 | 6 | 3.6 | .3 | 3 −4.1 |
| Victoria—cult. | 1 | 1 | 3.4 | — | 3.4 |

Stamens have anthers papillose and yellow or reddish. Pollen is mostly well developed, the grains about .06 mm. in diameter.

| | n | n-obs. | x̄ (mm.) | s (mm.) | w (mm.) |
|---|---|---|---|---|---|
| **Adnation of epipetalous filaments** | | | | | |
| Guadalupe | 1 | 1 | 1.8 | — | 1.8 |
| —cult. | 2 | 3 | 1.2 | 0 | 1.1–1.4 |
| Victoria—cult. | 1 | 1 | 2 | — | 2 |
| **Anthers—length** | | | | | |
| Guadalupe | 2 | 2 | .7 | .4 | .5–1 |
| —cult. | 1 | 3 | .9 | — | .7–1 |
| **Anthers—diameter** | | | | | |
| Guadalupe—cult. | 1 | 2 | .7 | — | .7 |

Nectaries are ovate or ovate-oblong, truncate or obtusely bi-dentate, pale yellow or white.

| | n | n-obs. | x̄ (mm.) | s (mm.) | w (mm.) |
|---|---|---|---|---|---|
| **Length** | | | | | |
| Guadalupe | 2 | 6 | .9 | .1 | .7–1.1 |
| —cult. | 2 | 4 | .8 | 0 | .6–1.2 |
| Victoria—cult. | 1 | 1 | .8 | — | .8 |
| **Width** | | | | | |
| Guadalupe | 2 | 6 | .6 | .05 | .6– .7 |
| —cult. | 2 | 4 | .6 | 0 | .6– .7 |
| Victoria—cult. | 1 | 1 | .4 | — | .4 |

Pistils are erect with divergent styles; ovaries are verrucose, pale green speckled with red, with basal concavities on dorsal sides.

| | n | n-obs. | x̄ (mm.) | s (mm.) | w (mm.) |
|---|---|---|---|---|---|
| **Length** | | | | | |
| Guadalupe—cult. | 2 | 3 | 4.6 | 0 | 3.9– 5 |
| Victoria—cult. | 1 | 1 | 6 | — | 6 |
| **No. of ovules per ovary** | | | | | |
| Guadalupe—cult. | 1 | 2 | 23 | — | 22 –24 |

Follicles are erect and pale brown.

| | n | n-obs. | x̄ (mm.) | w (mm.) |
|---|---|---|---|---|
| **Length** | | | | |
| Guadalupe | 1 | 1 | 4 | 4 |

Seeds are pyriform, glabrous and finely reticulate, brown.

| | n | n-obs. | $\bar{x}$ (mm.) | w (mm.) |
|---|---|---|---|---|
| Length | | | | |
| Guadalupe | 1 | 4 | .60 | .60 |
| —cult. | 1 | 4 | .62 | .60–.70 |
| Diameter | | | | |
| Guadalupe | 1 | 4 | .30 | .29–.33 |
| —cult. | 1 | 4 | .25 | .20–.33 |

**Variation.** *Sedum ebracteatum* primarily is a species of the Central Mexican Plateau. It occurs at only a few places in the Trans-Mexican Volcanic Belt. At Guadalupe, where I have studied it, the population is small, probably a surviving remnant from the past.

Besides the five plants which were the basis for the above descriptive data, I have cultivated ten others, mostly from horticultural sources and of unknown origin in the wild, and I have also studied herbarium specimens from fourteen additional localities. These indicate greater variation within the species than do my small samples, but they do not permit a satisfactory interpretation of its significance since most of the cultivated plants cannot be associated with wild populations and since herbarium specimens scarcely are adequate samples of populations from which they were collected. Most distinctive is the collection of George Hinton, no. 14,933, from Chilacayote, Michoacán, with large leaves, the largest 10.5 cm. long. Whether Hinton's specimens illustrate an average condition of the population at Chilacayote is uncertain. Also unknown is the possibility that they may be a response to a different environmental condition and really similar genetically to plants from elsewhere. The ssp. *grandifolium*, based on Hinton's collection, is of doubtful status, though maintained here, since the chance that it is valid is about as good as the reverse.

The leaves of the floriferous branches of a plant from near Ciudad Victoria were thinner than those of a plant from Guadalupe. Three cultivated plants, two of unknown origin, have produced some 4-merous flowers. One had floriferous branches to 4 dm. high and small sepals, 1.8–2.6 mm. long. Such differences may indicate genetic diversity within the species and suggest that study of populations on the Central Mexican Plateau and elsewhere will be interesting as well as necessary for a clear understanding of the variation of the species.

KEY TO SUBSPECIES

A. Leaves of floriferous branches .4–5 cm. long, ovate to oblong, puberulent with simple hairs.................ssp. *ebracteatum*, p. 242

AA. Leaves of floriferous branches 2.5–10.5 cm. long, mostly ellipticoblong, prominently ciliate and pubescent with hairs which are sometimes branched....................ssp. *grandifolium*, p. 244

## *Sedum ebracteatum* ssp. *ebracteatum*

**Nomenclature.** *Sedum ebracteatum* A.P. DC., Mém. Fam. Crass., p. 37, pl. 6, fig. B (1828). De Candolle's diagnosis is based on drawings copied from Mociño's unpublished Flora of Mexico. Type locality: not designated, but presumably somewhere in Mexico. Type: de Candolle's pl. 6, fig. B. Probably de Candolle never saw the plant which was the basis for the drawings.

Synonyms are:

1878. *Sedum incertum* Hemsley, Diag. Pl. Nov. 1: 11. Type locality: Valley of Mexico. Type: Bourgeau's collection of Nov. 9, 1899. I have studied a photograph of the type which is preserved in the herbarium at Kew and also an isotype (US 48,492).

1887. *Sedum chapalense* S. Watson, Proc. Am. Acad. 22: 411. Type locality: Chapala, Jalisco. Type: E. Palmer's collection no. 726 (GH), Oct. 27–Nov. 3, 1886.

1894. *Sedum cordifolium* Sessé et Mociño, Flora Mexicana, ed. 2, p. 117. Type locality: near the city of Mexico. Type: location uncertain.

1905. *Sedastrum ebracteatum* (DC.) Rose, No. Am. Flora 22: 59.

1905. *Sedastrum rubricaule* Rose, No. Am. Flora 22: 59. Type locality: Concepción del Oro, Zacatecas. Type: collection no. 386 of E. Palmer (US 397,895), Nov. 22, 1902.

1905. *Sedastrum chapalense* (S. Watson) Rose, No. Am. Flora 22: 59.

1905. *Sedastrum incertum* (Hemsley) Rose, No. Am. Flora 22: 59.

1921. *Sedum rubricaule* (Rose) Praeger, Jour. Roy. Hort. Soc. 46: 132.

1935. (? *Sedum barrancae* M. E. Jones), Contr. West. Bot. 18: 37. Type locality: wet, loose soil under cliffs, Barranca de Guadalajara. Type: collection no. 27,845 of M. E. Jones (Pomona College, sheet no. 191,717), Nov. 17, 1935. The status of the population in the Barranca de Guadalajara needs to be checked by study of plants in the field. The possibility exists that it is *S. hemsleyanum.*

1935. *Sedum ebracteatum* var. *rubricaule* (Rose) Fröderström, Act. Hort. Goth. 10 (App.): 73.

The leaves of the floriferous branches of ssp. *ebracteatum* never attain the size of the largest leaves of ssp. *grandifolium*, and the pubescence always is of simple hairs. The probability of genetic diversity within the subspecies is attested by the lengthy list of synonyms.

**Distribution.** *Sedum ebracteatum* ssp. *ebracteatum* is widely distributed on the Central Mexican Plateau, and it also occurs at several localities in the Trans-Mexican Volcanic Belt, at altitudes at the level of the plateau, and in both Sierra Madre Oriental and Occidental, as well as on the Northern Mexican Plateau. Data for the only population which I have studied are as follows:

| Location | n-plants | Area (m.) | Alt. range (m.) | pH | Drainage |
|----------|----------|-----------|-----------------|-----|----------|
| Guadalupe | ab. 15 | 5 x 1 | 2,335–2,336 | 5.2 | excessive |

Populations in the Trans-Mexican Volcanic Belt, known to me from herbarium specimens only, and the discoverers of each are: Puebla, discoverer unknown (NY); Valley of Mexico, E. Bourgeau (US); and near Jesús del Monte, vicinity of Morelia, Gerfroy Arsène (US), the identification of the last doubtful. Localities on the Central Mexican Plateau include: near Dublán, Hidalgo, Joseph Rose (NY, US); near Tula, Hidalgo, Cyrus Pringle (NY, US, Vt); km. 172 on the Mexico-Laredo highway, Mezquital Valley, Hidalgo, discoverer unknown (Mexu); Guanajuato, A. Dugés (US); Santa María del Río, San Luis Potosí, Edward Palmer (NY, US); Chapala, Jalisco, Edward Palmer (GH); and (? Barranca de Guadalajara, Marcus Jones [Pomona College]). Other localities are Concepción del Oro, District of Mazapil, Zacatecas, on the Northern Mexican Plateau, Edward Palmer (NY, US, Vt); Tobar Mining Camp, Tepehuanes, Durango, in the Sierra Madre Occidental, Edward Palmer (US); and the canyon southwest of Ciudad Victoria, Tamaulipas, in the Sierra Madre Oriental, J. L. Edwards (CU).

Bourgeau collected *Sedum ebracteatum* ssp. *ebracteatum* in the Valley of Mexico in 1866. He did not cite a precise locality, but one of the possible places is Guadalupe. Pringle (NY, US) collected it there on Oct. 20, 1902, and I studied it there on April 2, 1949, and Oct. 14, 1955. The first hill, just north of Guadalupe, where *S. ebracteatum* occurs, is known as Campanario. Many people and domestic animals traverse this hill. The *Sedum* appears to be restricted to a small area of cliffs of dacite, near a cave, where most of the plants are difficult to reach. Exposure is to the south, but projecting rocks shade the site both in early morning and in late afternoon. Plants were in anthesis at the time of my visit in October. No other Crassulaceae were in the vicinity, but *Tagetes tenuifolia* was abundant and much in evidence because of its showy orange-yellow heads of florets. In the greenhouse at Ithaca, plants of *S. ebracteatum* from Guadalupe have flowered in December and January and also in June and July.

## *Sedum ebracteatum* ssp. *grandifolium*

**Nomenclature.** *Sedum ebracteatum* DC. ssp. *grandifolium* R. T. Clausen, Cact. Succ. Jour. 18: 61, fig. 53 (1946). Type locality: Chilacayote, 17° 45″ N, 100° 42″ W, alt. 1,500 m., District of Mina, Guerrero. Type: collection no. 14,933 of G. B. Hinton (CU), Nov. 30, 1939.

The diagnostic features of ssp. *grandifolium* are the large leaves on the floriferous branches, sometimes as long as 10.5 cm., and the occasional presence of branched hairs on the stems, pedicels, and leaves. Subspecies *grandifolium* is known only from the type locality, and that is my only record of *S. ebracteatum* in the Sierra Madre del Sur.

**Relationships.** *Sedum ebracteatum* is most closely related to *S. hemsleyanum*. Occasionally the two species are confused, but usually *S. ebracteatum* is distinguished by the broader leaves of the floriferous branches. This difference is shown in the following table, in which the data are for plants cultivated under similar conditions. The only two plants from which I obtained seeds in cultivation differed in the diameter of these. This difference also is shown.

| | *S. ebracteatum* | | | | *S. hemsleyanum* | | | |
|---|---|---|---|---|---|---|---|---|
| | n | n-obs. | $\bar{x}$ (mm.) | s (mm.) | n | n-obs. | $\bar{x}$ (mm.) | s (mm.) |
| Leaves of floriferous branches | | | | | | | | |
| Width* | 2 | 13 | 14.6 | 0 | 15 | 45 | 8.7 | 1.6 |
| Seeds | | | | | | | | |
| Diameter | 1 | 4 | .25 | — | 1 | 10 | .2 | — |

*Sedum ebracteatum* and *S. versadense* are easy to separate. The former has the leaves of the secondary branches in dense, basal rosettes; the latter has the secondary branches elongate by the time the plants are in flower. Two other differences, based on plants cultivated under similar conditions, are the following:

| | *S. ebracteatum* | | | | *S. versadense* | | | |
| | $n$ | $n$-obs. | $\bar{x}$ (mm.) | $s$ (mm.) | $n$ | $n$-obs. | $\bar{x}$ (mm.) | $s$ (mm.) |
|---|---|---|---|---|---|---|---|---|
| Sepals | | | | | | | | |
| Length* | 3 | 9 | 3.5 | 0 | 3 | 10 | 6.6 | 1.8 |
| Nectaries | | | | | | | | |
| Length* | 3 | 5 | .8 | 0 | 3 | 10 | .5 | .2 |

Outside the Trans-Mexican Volcanic Belt, the species nearest to *Sedum ebracteatum* is *S. glabrum* of the Northern Mexican Plateau. That is glabrous, with thicker, subglaucous leaves which are plane ventrally and convex dorsally. I have seen it in the wild near Saltillo, and I have also cultivated it at Ithaca. Plants in the population near Saltillo are distinctive, but exploration in the area between there and Concepción del Oro, Zacatecas, might reveal populations intermediate between the two species.

Reference. Clausen, R. T. (1943).

## 23. *SEDUM GRANDIPETALUM* (figs. 68–69)

Only two species of stonecrops native in the Trans-Mexican Volcanic Belt are herbs with yellow flowers. These are *Sedum grandipetalum* and *S. greggii*. Primarily they differ in size, *S. grandipetalum* being larger in most dimensions. The combination of glabrous, falcate, lanceolate leaves, separate sepals, yellow petals which are glaucous dorsally, reniform nectaries, and divergent follicles without prominent marginal lips separate *S. grandipetalum* from all other species.

**Description.** Materials: 14 plants, all from a ravine on the

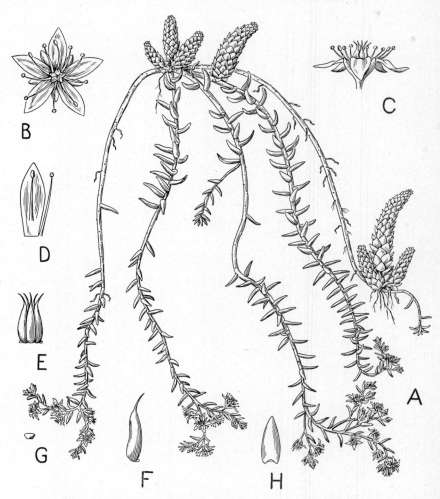

*Fig. 68.* Plant of *Sedum grandipetalum* from the Nevado de Colima, cultivated in the greenhouse, Ithaca, N.Y.  A. Habit sketch (x .4).  B. Flower from above (x 1.6).  C. Flower from side (x 1.6).  D. Petal and two stamens (x 2.4).  E. Pistils (x 2.4).  F. Single pistil (x 3.2).  G. Nectary (x 4).  H. Single leaf (x .8).

northwestern slope of the Nevado de Colima. Measurements marked cult. are of plants cultivated in the greenhouse at Ithaca, N.Y.

Plants of *Sedum grandipetalum* are perennials, chamaephytes, sometimes epiphytes, with prostrate or pendulous floriferous branches, perennating from lateral branches which arise near the bases of the floriferous ones and are well developed at the time of flowering, with the leaves suborbicular, papillose on margins, and densely imbricate. Stems are glabrous.

| | n | n-obs. | $\bar{x}$ | s | w |
|---|---|---|---|---|---|
| Roots—diameter—wild | 14 | 16 | 3 mm. | 1.6 mm. | 1 —9 mm. |
| Floriferous branches—length—wild | 13 | 42 | 2.7 dm. | .6 dm. | 1.1–4.1 dm. |
| —cult. | 7 | 19 | 2.3 dm. | .5 dm. | 1.1–3 dm. |

Leaves of floriferous branches are lanceolate, elliptic-lanceolate, or linear-lanceolate, falcate, at bases two-spurred and clasping stems, obtuse apically, glaucous, sometimes slightly papillose on margins.

| | n | n-obs. | $\bar{x}$ (mm.) | s (mm.) | w (mm.) |
|---|---|---|---|---|---|
| Length—wild | 12 | 35 | 13.6 | 1.8 | 9 —21 |
| —cult. | 7 | 19 | 11 | 2.2 | 7.5–16 |
| Width—wild | 12 | 35 | 4.8 | .8 | 3.5– 8 |
| —cult. | 1 | 3 | 5 | — | 4 – 6 |
| Thickness—cult. | 1 | 3 | 2.2 | — | 1.6– 2.8 |

Ten leaves, measured in fresh condition on Dec. 12, 1955, and again in dried condition on July 6, 1958, had shrunk in both length and width, but not significantly in either dimension.

| | $\bar{x}$ (mm.) | s (mm.) | w (mm.) |
|---|---|---|---|
| Length—fresh | 12.1 | 2.1 | 10 —16 |
| —dried | 10.5 | 1.7 | 8.3–14 |
| Width—fresh | 4.9 | .7 | 4 – 6 |
| —dried | 4.5 | .8 | 4– 5.5 |

Inflorescences are cymes of 2 or 3 cincinni.

| | n | n-obs. | $\bar{x}$ | w |
|---|---|---|---|---|
| No. of flowers per cyme—wild | 13 | 42 | 12 | 1–27 |
| —cult. | 1 | 3 | 16 | 11–22 |

Flowers are pedicellate, rarely 4- or 6-merous.

| | n | n-obs. | $\bar{x}$ | s | w |
|---|---|---|---|---|---|
| Pedicels—length—wild | 11 | 37 | 2.4 | .9 | .8– 5.8 |
| Flowers—diameter—wild | 11 | 37 | 13.7 | 1.4 | 10 —18 |
| —cult. | 6 | 18 | 13.8 | .5 | 11 —16 |
| Torus—length—cult. | 1 | 3 | .56 | — | .5– .6 |

Sepals are lanceolate or elliptic-oblong, usually sessile, but rarely with spurs .1–.2 mm. long, obtuse, pale green and glaucous. The sepals of each flower are unequal in size. Dimensions below are of the largest sepals per flower.

| | n | n-obs. | $\bar{x}$ (mm.) | s (mm.) | w (mm.) |
|---|---|---|---|---|---|
| Length—wild | 11 | 37 | 5.3 | .9 | 3.6–8.8 |
| —cult. | 6 | 18 | 5.1 | .4 | 3.1–8.4 |
| Width—wild | 11 | 37 | 2.3 | .3 | 1.7–3.3 |
| —cult. | 1 | 3 | 2.1 | — | 1.9–2.3 |

Ten sepals, measured in fresh condition on Dec. 12, 1955, and again in dried condition on July 6, 1958, had shrunk significantly in both length and width.

| | $\bar{x}$ (mm.) | s (mm.) | w (mm.) |
|---|---|---|---|
| Length—fresh | 5.5 | .7 | 4.5–6.5 |
| —dried | 4.7 | .6 | 3.9–5.7 |
| Width—fresh | 2.5 | .4 | 2 –2.9 |
| —dried | 2 | .4 | 1.4–2.8 |

Petals are elliptical or elliptic-lanceolate, acute or obtuse, minutely mucronate-appendaged, yellow, glaucous dorsally. The petals are not connate, though the bases of the filaments alternating with them may hold them together.

| | n | n-obs. | $\bar{x}$ (mm.) | s (mm.) | w (mm.) |
|---|---|---|---|---|---|
| Length—wild | 11 | 37 | 7.7 | .9 | 5.8–9.4 |
| —cult. | 6 | 18 | 7.2 | .2 | 6.1–9.3 |
| Width—wild | 11 | 37 | 3.4 | .5 | 2.5–4.3 |
| —cult. | 2 | 6 | 2.6 | .3 | 2.3–2.9 |

Stamens have yellow anthers; pollen is well developed.

| | n | n-obs. | $\bar{x}$ (mm.) | s (mm.) | w (mm.) |
|---|---|---|---|---|---|
| Adnation of epipetalous filaments—wild | 11 | 37 | 1.4 | .2 | .8–2.1 |
| —cult. | 6 | 18 | 1.3 | .3 | .4–2.1 |
| Anthers—length—wild | 7 | 19 | 1.1 | .1 | .9–1.5 |
| —cult. | 1 | 3 | .9 | — | .8–1 |
| Anthers—diameter—cult. | 1 | 1 | .5 | — | .5 |

Nectaries are reniform or reniform-obovate, emarginate, pale yellow or white, translucent.

|  | n | n-obs. | x̄ (mm.) | s (mm.) | w (mm.) |
|---|---|---|---|---|---|
| Length—wild | 11 | 37 | .5 | .1 | .2– .7 |
| —cult. | 6 | 18 | .5 | .1 | .3– .7 |
| Width—wild | 11 | 37 | .8 | .1 | .6–1 |
| —cult. | 6 | 18 | .7 | .1 | .5–1.1 |

Pistils are erect and yellow.

|  | n | n-obs. | x̄ | w |
|---|---|---|---|---|
| Length—cult. | 1 | 3 | 5.2 mm. | 5.2 mm. |
| No. of ovules per ovary—cult. | 1 | 3 | 17 | 15 –19 |

Follicles are divergent and pale brown.

The one well-developed seed which I obtained from a wild plant is elongate-pyriform, longitudinally wrinkled, glabrous, dark brown, .9 mm. long and .3 mm. in diameter.

**Variation.** The above descriptive data for plants on the Nevado de Colima are in general agreement with the details of Fröderström's original description, based on a dried specimen from the crest of La Bufa. Most of the leaves of the floriferous branches of the type are missing. For that reason, an accurate appraisal of dimensions from that specimen is impossible. Fröderström interpreted the dry carpels as connate, but careful dissection of fresh carpels has convinced me that these really are attached to a small torus which extends upward among the bases of the carpels, thus giving the appearance that they are connate. In addition, Fröderström noted the length of the nectaries as .9 mm., which might be the result of an error in measuring. Of the fifty-five nectaries which I measured, the largest were .7 mm. long and the average length .5 mm., with a standard deviation of .1 mm. for wild specimens.

Wild plants differed from each other in thirteen out of fourteen characters studied. In cultivation, only six of these differences were evident, suggesting the probability that some of the other differences in the wild were environmental modifications.

The only other *Sedum* associated with *S. grandipetalum* on the Nevado de Colima was *S. tortuosum*. Both species were in flower at the time of my visit, but I saw no hybrids. Neither did I find any hybrids between *Villadia batesii*, which also was in flower there at the same time, and either species of *Sedum*. The practical explanation for any genetic variation in the populations of *Sedum* is gene mutation.

**Nomenclature.** *Sedum grandipetalum* Fröderström, Act. Hort. Goth. 10 (App.): 52 (1936). Type locality: among mosses in crevices of rocky precipice, Real Alto, crest of La Bufa, 2,500 m., Jalisco. Type: collection of Ynez Mexia, no. 1,625 (NY), Feb. 2, 1927.

**Distribution.** The range of *Sedum grandipetalum* is in the western part of the Trans-Mexican Volcanic Belt. I know it from only three localities and have studied it at but one of these.

| Location | n-plants | Area (m.) | Alt. range (m.) | pH | Drainage |
|---|---|---|---|---|---|
| Nevado de Colima | ab. 300 | ab. 100 x 20 | 2,500–2,540 | 6.6–6.8 | poor to good |

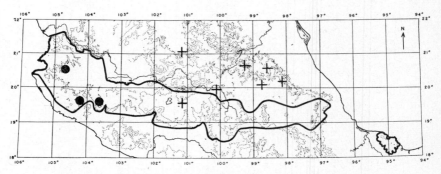

*Fig. 69.* Known distribution of *Sedum grandipetalum* (•) and *S. greggii* (+).

The other populations are in a ravine, alt. 2,400–2,600 m., about 24 km. southeast of Autlán, Jalisco, Rogers McVaugh, no. 10,275 (Univ. of Mich.), and on the crest of La Bufa, Ynez Mexia, no. 1,625 (NY, US).

Carl Reiche (Mexu) discovered *Sedum grandipetalum* on the Nevado de Colima in December, 1913. Subsequently, Rogers McVaugh collected it there on March 29, 1949, and I studied it there on Dec. 10, 1955. The plants were in a ravine about 2 km. south-southeast of El Isote and about 5 km. southeast of Jazmín, on the northwestern slope, in an area where trees of *Abies* and *Pinus* were common. The plants of *S. grandipetalum* were growing on cliffs or boulders of andesite and on the trunks of trees of *Quercus* (species not identified). Exposure was to the northwest, southwest, south, and east. All plants were in partial shade. They were at the height of flowering at the time of my visit. In cultivation in the greenhouse at Ithaca, plants have flowered from December to May. The only other Crassulaceae associated with *S. grandipetalum* on the Nevado de Colima were *S. tortuosum*, sometimes epiphytic on the same trees, and *Villadia batesii*, both in flower at the same time. I found seedlings of *S. grandipetalum* and also a reddish larva feeding on the leaves of one plant.

**Relationships.** *Sedum grandipetalum* appears like a large edition of *S. greggii*. The two species are similar morphologically. For a comparison, see the section on relationships under *S. greggii*. Other herbaceous species of the Trans-Mexican Volcanic Belt either have white petals and ovaries with basal concavities dorsally or are biennials with corms or have large, dark red nectaries. Possibly both *S. humifusum* of the Central Mexican Plateau and *S. compactum* of the Sierra Madre del Sur are more closely related—though to *S. greggii*—than are any of the other species of the volcanic belt. *Sedum humifusum* has the leaves and sepals prominently ciliate and the flowers solitary; *S. compactum* has tiny flowers with white petals. Other possible relatives are a species of which I have not yet published the name, of the Sierra Madre Oriental, with oblong leaves <6.3 mm. long, sepals <4 mm. long, and nectaries <.5 mm. long; *S. cockerellii* of the Southern Rocky Mountains and Northern Mexican Plateau, with white petals and oblanceolate or spatulate leaves; and *S. lanceolatum* which ranges from the western Great Plains to the Pacific mountain system, with foriferous branches <2 dm. long and leaves <15 mm. long. Possibly these species to the north evolved from the same stock which gave rise to *S. grandipetalum*. If that be true, this whole group of species may have had a long history in North America independent of other groups of species in Asia, Europe, and Africa.

## 24. *SEDUM GREGGII* (fig. 70)

Plants of *Sedum greggii* are perennial herbs with dense, basal rosettes of papillose leaves and with slender, floriferous branches

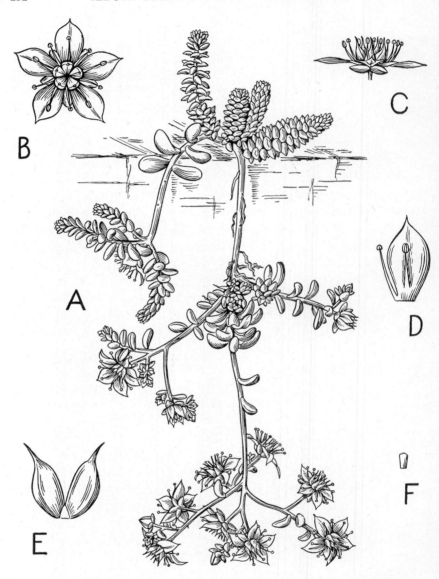

*Fig. 70.* Plant of *Sedum greggii* from the Cerro Azul, cultivated in the greenhouse, Ithaca, N.Y.  A. Habit sketch (x 1.1).  B. Flower from above (x 2.2).  C. Flower from side (x 2.2).  D. Petal and two stamens (x 3.4).  E. Two pistils and torus (x 4.5).  F. Nectary (x 5.6).

bearing cymes of 1–18 yellow flowers. Except for being smaller, plants of *S. greggii* are similar in appearance to *S. grandipetalum*. The leaves of *S. humifusum* of the Central Mexican Plateau are prominently ciliate, and the flowers solitary. The flowers of *S. compactum* of the Sierra Madre del Sur are tiny with white petals. *Sedum lanceolatum* of western, temperate North America, another species with yellow flowers, has lanceolate or elliptic-oblong leaves, lanceolate sepals and petals, and nectaries which are broader than long.

**Description.** Materials: 14 plants—11 from the Cerro Azul southeast of Morelia, Michoacán; 1 from north-northwest of Huauchinango, Puebla; 1 from Real del Monte, Hidalgo; and 1 from the Barranca de Marmoles, Hidalgo. Measurements marked cult. are of plants cultivated in the greenhouse at Ithaca, N.Y.

Plants of *Sedum greggii* are perennials, chamaephytes, with erect, decumbent, or pendulous floriferous branches, these sometimes twice branched, always with short, secondary shoots near their bases and bearing dense rosettes of obovate, elliptical, or oblanceolate, obtuse, papillose leaves. Stems are glabrous.

| | n | n-obs. | $\bar{x}$ (cm.) | s (cm.) | w (cm.) |
|---|---|---|---|---|---|
| Height | | | | | |
| Huauchinango | 1 | 2 | 10 | — | 5 –15 |
| Real del Monte | 1 | 2 | 4 | — | 2.5– 5.5 |
| Cerro Azul—cult. | 1 | 1 | 2 | — | 2 |
| Floriferous branches—length | | | | | |
| Cerro Azul—cult. | 3 | 7 | 6.3 | 3.4 | 2.7–14 |
| Huauchinango—cult. | 1 | 2 | 13 | — | 11.1–15 |
| Real del Monte—cult. | 1 | 2 | 7.5 | — | 7 – 8 |
| Barranca de Marmoles—cult. | 1 | 4 | 7.1 | — | 4.7–10 |

Leaves of floriferous branches are rarely opposite, divergent or reflexed, obovate, oblanceolate, or elliptical, sessile, rounded at apices, papillose, sometimes speckled with red. Dimensions below are of leaves of floriferous branches except for the wild plants in the Cerro Azul, and these are of leaves on the elongate, primary stems.

|  | $n$ | $n$-obs. | $\bar{x}$ (mm.) | $s$ (mm.) | $w$ (mm.) |
|---|---|---|---|---|---|
| Length |  |  |  |  |  |
| Cerro Azul | 11 | 65 | 5.3 | 2.3 | 2.8–10.3 |
| Huauchinango | 1 | 2 | 6.2 | — | 3 – 9.5 |
| Cerro Azul—cult. | 3 | 9 | 6 | 0 | 3.1– 9 |
| Huauchinango—cult. | 1 | 2 | 11 | — | 10 –12 |
| Real del Monte—cult. | 1 | 2 | 7.3 | — | 6.7– 7.9 |
| Barranca de Marmoles—cult. | 1 | 5 | 8.3 | — | 6.7–12 |
| Width |  |  |  |  |  |
| Cerro Azul | 11 | 65 | 2.4 | .2 | 1.7– 3.4 |
| Huauchinango | 1 | 2 | 2.1 | — | 1.2– 3 |
| Cerro Azul—cult. | 1 | 3 | 3.5 | — | 3.1– 4.1 |
| Huauchinango—cult. | 1 | 2 | 3.5 | — | 3 – 4 |
| Barranca de Marmoles—cult. | 1 | 2 | 4.5 | — | 4 – 5 |
| Thickness |  |  |  |  |  |
| Cerro Azul | 11 | 65 | 1.3 | .2 | .9– 1.9 |
| Huauchinango | 1 | 2 | 1.4 | — | .8– 2 |
| Cerro Azul—cult. | 1 | 3 | 2.5 | — | 2 – 3.2 |
| Huauchinango—cult. | 1 | 2 | 1.7 | — | 1.5– 2 |
| Barranca de Marmoles—cult. | 1 | 2 | 1.7 | — | 1.4– 2 |

Inflorescences are cymes of 1–4 cincinni. Sometimes vegetative shoots with small rosettes of leaves develop instead of flowers.

|  | $n$ | $n$-obs. | $\bar{x}$ | $w$ |
|---|---|---|---|---|
| No. of flowers per cyme |  |  |  |  |
| Huauchinango | 1 | 2 | 4 | 1– 8 |
| Real del Monte | 1 | 2 | 10 | 3–18 |
| Cerro Azul—cult. | 1 | 3 | 4 | 2– 6 |
| Huauchinango—cult. | 1 | 2 | 9 | 3–15 |
| Barranca de Marmoles—cult. | 1 | 1 | 1 | 1 |

Flowers are pedicellate, sometimes 4-merous.

|  | $n$ | $n$-obs. | $\bar{x}$ (mm.) | $s$ (mm.) | $w$ (mm.) |
|---|---|---|---|---|---|
| Pedicels—length |  |  |  |  |  |
| Huauchinango | 1 | 2 | 1.3 | — | .6– 2 |
| Real del Monte | 1 | 2 | 1.7 | — | .5– 3 |
| Cerro Azul—cult. | 1 | 2 | 4.4 | — | 3 – 5.9 |
| Huauchinango—cult. | 1 | 3 | 2.4 | — | 1 – 5 |
| Barranca de Marmoles—cult. | 1 | 1 | 5 | — | 5 |
| Flowers—diameter |  |  |  |  |  |
| Huauchinango | 1 | 2 | 9.5 | — | 9 –10 |
| Real del Monte | 1 | 2 | 9.5 | — | 9 –10 |
| Cerro Azul—cult. | 3 | 9 | 13.3 | 1.4 | 7 –18 |
| Huauchinango—cult. | 1 | 3 | 10 | — | 10 –11 |

|  | n | n-obs. | x̄ (mm.) | s (mm.) | w (mm.) |
|---|---|---|---|---|---|
| Real del Monte—cult. | I | 2 | 14.5 | — | 13 –16 |
| Barranca de Marmoles—cult. | I | 4 | 13 | — | 11 –15 |
| Torus—length |  |  |  |  |  |
| Cerro Azul—cult. | I | 3 | .8 | — | .7– .9 |

Sepals are elliptical, either not spurred or with spurs .2–.4 mm. long, obtuse, papillose on margins, sometimes speckled with red. The sepals of a 4-merous flower of a cultivated plant from the Cerro Azul were spirally arranged, with the inner two yellow on the adaxial sides and green on the abaxial sides.

|  | n | n-obs. | x̄ (mm.) | s (mm.) | w (mm.) |
|---|---|---|---|---|---|
| Length |  |  |  |  |  |
| Huauchinango | I | 2 | 2.2 | — | 2 –2.5 |
| Real del Monte | I | I | 3.5 | — | 3.5 |
| Cerro Azul—cult. | 3 | 9 | 3.3 | o | 1.7–4.9 |
| Huauchinango—cult. | I | 3 | 2.8 | — | 2.6–3.2 |
| Real del Monte—cult. | I | 2 | 7.4 | — | 7.1–7.7 |
| Barranca de Marmoles—cult. | I | 5 | 3.6 | — | 2.4–5 |
| Width |  |  |  |  |  |
| Huauchinango | I | 2 | I | — | .8–1.2 |
| Real del Monte | I | 2 | 1.6 | — | 1.5–1.8 |
| Cerro Azul—cult. | I | 3 | 2.3 | — | 1.7–2.7 |
| Huauchinango—cult. | I | 3 | 1.4 | — | 1.2–1.9 |
| Barranca de Marmoles—cult. | I | 2 | 2.6 | — | 2.2–3 |

Petals are elliptical or ovate, rarely connate for .1–.5 mm., acute, mucronate-appendaged, sulphur yellow, sometimes speckled with red toward apices on dorsal keels.

|  | n | n-obs. | x̄ (mm.) | s (mm.) | w (mm.) |
|---|---|---|---|---|---|
| Length |  |  |  |  |  |
| Huauchinango | I | I | 5 | — | 5 |
| Real del Monte | I | I | 5 | — | 5 |
| Cerro Azul—cult. | 3 | 9 | 6.5 | .9 | 4.1–9.7 |
| Huauchinango—cult. | I | 3 | 5.5 | — | 5 –5.8 |
| Real del Monte—cult. | I | 2 | 6.4 | — | 6.2–6.6 |
| Barranca de Marmoles—cult. | I | 5 | 5.6 | — | 4.2–7.8 |
| Width |  |  |  |  |  |
| Huauchinango | I | I | 2.2 | — | 2.2 |
| Real del Monte | I | I | 2 | — | 2 |
| Cerro Azul—cult. | I | 3 | 3.9 | — | 3.3–5 |
| Huauchinango—cult. | I | 3 | 2.5 | — | 2.2–2.8 |
| Barranca de Marmoles—cult. | I | 2 | 2.9 | — | 2.8–3 |

Stamens have yellow anthers; pollen is mostly well developed.

| | $n$ | $n$-obs. | $\bar{x}$ (mm.) | $s$ (mm.) | $w$ (mm.) |
|---|---|---|---|---|---|
| Adnation of epipetalous filaments | | | | | |
| Huauchinango | I | I | .5 | — | .5 |
| Cerro Azul—cult. | 3 | 9 | .9 | .3 | .3–1.5 |
| Huauchinango—cult. | I | 3 | I | — | I |
| Real del Monte—cult. | I | 2 | .4 | — | .2– .6 |
| Barranca de Marmoles—cult. | I | 4 | .8 | — | .6– .9 |
| Anthers—length | | | | | |
| Cerro Azul—cult. | I | 3 | .8 | — | .7– .8 |
| Huauchinango—cult. | I | 2 | I | — | I |
| Anthers—diameter | | | | | |
| Cerro Azul—cult. | I | 3 | .48 | — | .4– .5 |

Nectaries are subquadrate, obovate, or oblong, truncate, yellow.

| | $n$ | $n$-obs. | $\bar{x}$ (mm.) | $s$ (mm.) | $w$ (mm.) |
|---|---|---|---|---|---|
| Length | | | | | |
| Huauchinango | I | I | .7 | — | .7 |
| Real del Monte | I | I | .4 | — | .4 |
| Cerro Azul—cult. | 3 | 9 | .6 | o | .6–.7 |
| Huauchinango—cult. | I | 3 | .5 | — | .4–.7 |
| Real del Monte—cult. | I | 2 | .85 | — | .8–.9 |
| Barranca de Marmoles—cult. | I | 4 | .5 | — | .4–.7 |
| Width | | | | | |
| Huauchinango | I | I | .4 | — | .4 |
| Real del Monte | I | I | .3 | — | .3 |
| Cerro Azul—cult. | 3 | 9 | .4 | .02 | .3–.5 |
| Huauchinango—cult. | I | 3 | .4 | — | .4 |
| Real del Monte—cult. | I | 2 | .45 | — | .4–.5 |
| Barranca de Marmoles—cult. | I | 4 | .4 | — | .3–.5 |

Pistils are erect and greenish yellow. Two flowers of a cultivated plant from the Cerro Azul had eight pistils each. A pistil of another plant from the same source bore an anther on one side and an undeveloped style on the other.

| | $n$ | $n$-obs. | $\bar{x}$ | $w$ | |
|---|---|---|---|---|---|
| Length | | | | | |
| Huauchinango | I | I | 3.5 mm. | 3.5 | mm. |
| Real del Monte | I | I | 3.5 mm. | 3.5 | mm. |
| Cerro Azul—cult. | I | 3 | 3.8 mm. | 3.4– 4.1 mm. | |
| Huauchinango—cult. | I | 3 | 3 mm. | 2.7– 3.2 mm. | |
| Barranca de Marmoles—cult. | I | I | 2.4 mm. | 2.4 | mm. |
| No. of ovules per ovary | | | | | |
| Cerro Azul—cult. | I | 3 | 43 | 40 –46 | |

Follicles are divergent and brown.

|  | n | n-obs. | $\bar{x}$ (mm.) | s (mm.) | w (mm.) |
|---|---|---|---|---|---|
| Length |  |  |  |  |  |
| Cerro Azul—cult. | 2 | 4 | 2 | .4 | 1.7–2.3 |
| Barranca de Marmoles—cult. | 1 | 2 | 2.5 | — | 2.3–2.8 |

The one well-developed seed which I have had for study (Barranca de Marmoles—cult.) was ellipsoid, glabrous, finely reticulate, with the longitudinal ribbing more prominent than the transverse, brown, .5 mm. long and .2 mm. in diameter.

**Variation.** I know only one small population of *Sedum greggii* in the Trans-Mexican Volcanic Belt. Although I visited that twice, once in September and again in December, the plants were not in flower on either occasion. Only three of five plants, brought from there and cultivated in the greenhouse, have flowered. Differences among the averages of characteristics of these and of three plants, each from a different locality on the Central Mexican Plateau, are minor. The large sepals of two flowers of a cultivated plant from Real del Monte apparently were abnormal—at least they far exceeded the size recorded for the same plant in the field in 1949.

Wild plants in the Cerro Azul differed in the three dimensions of the leaves. That some of these differences, perhaps all, should be attributed to the environment is indicated by the fact that the leaves of plant no. 11, compared with the others studied, were longest in the wild, but shortest in cultivation. The condition of the plants at time of study and the influence of the environment are both important in affecting the sizes of structures.

**Nomenclature.** *Sedum greggii* Hemsley, Diag. Pl. Nov. 1: 12 (1878). Type locality: "cliff border," Real del Monte, Hidalgo. Type: collection no. 635 of J. Gregg, March 22, 1849, reported to be in the herbarium at Kew. I have studied isotypes (GH, NY). A synonym is:

1903. *Sedum diversifolium* Rose, Bull. N.Y. Bot. Gard. 3: 44 (1903). Type locality: near Tultenango, Mexico. Type: a plant which flowered in the greenhouse of the Department of Agriculture in Washington in December, 1901, J. N. Rose's no. 248 (US 399,922). Rose and Hay had collected this in the wild on July 13, 1901. Rose did not indicate how to distinguish his species from *S. greggii*. The condition of the bases of the sepals, used by Fröderström (1930–1935), is not a satisfactory basis for separation.

**Distribution.** *Sedum greggii* is widely distributed on the Central Mexican Plateau, and it also occurs in the Trans-Mexican Volcanic Belt at one or more localities. Data for the populations which I have visited are as follows:

| Location | n-plants | Area (m.) | Alt. range (m.) | pH | Drainage |
|---|---|---|---|---|---|
| Cerro Azul | 147 | 6 x 5 | 2,090–2,100 | 6.4–6.8 | moderate |
| Huauchinango | — | — | 1,300 ± | — | moderate |
| Real del Monte | — | — | 2,745 | 7.5 | good |
| Barranca de Marmoles | — | — | 2,300 | — | — |

In 1903, Rose and Painter (Mexu) collected *Sedum greggii* at Santa Fe. Whether or not that is the locality in the Federal District, adjacent to Tacubaya, is unclear to me. Otherwise, known localities for *S. greggii* are on the Central Mexican Plateau: Huauchinango, Puebla, Clausen and Edwards no. 7,473 (CU); Real del Monte, Hidalgo, J. Gregg no. 635 (GH, NY); above Metzquititlán, Hidalgo, H. E. Moore, Jr., no. 2,487 (BH); Barranca de Marmoles, Hidalgo, R. Clausen no. 7,532 (CU); near Tultenango, Mexico, Rose and Hay; and Guanajuato, A. Dugés (GH).

Gerfroy Arsène (US 1,001,507) discovered *Sedum greggii* near Jesús del Monte, southeast of Morelia, in January, 1910. I studied it near there on Sept. 22, 1955, on a cliff of conglomerate on the south side of the Río Los Filtros, .2 km. east of its junction with Agua Sarca, at the western base of the Cerro Azul. Exposure was to the north-northeast and north-northwest. The plants of *Sedum* were in shade for much of the day, not only because of the exposure, but because of adjacent trees and shrubs. These included *Berberis* (? *lanceolata*) and *Ilex tolucana*. A liverwort common on the cliff was *Reboulia hemisphaerica* (identification by Professor Andrews). The only species of Crassulaceae associated with *S. greggii* near Jesús del Monte was an *Echeveria* with thick, spine-tipped leaves. This looks like *E. agavoides*. As the *Sedum,* it was not in flower at the time of my visit in September or on the occasion of my second visit on Dec. 2. In the greenhouse, plants of *S. greggii* from the Cerro Azul have flowered from January to May, but the *Echeveria* has not flowered in two and a half years of culture.

**Relationships.** *Sedum greggii* is most closely related tc *S. grandi-petalum*, from which it differs in being smaller in most dimensions. Significant differences include the following; data are for plants cultivated under similar conditions in the greenhouse at Ithaca.

| | | S. greggii | | | | S. grandipetalum | |
|---|---|---|---|---|---|---|---|
| *n* | *n-obs.* | $\bar{x}$ | *s* | *n* | *n-obs.* | $\bar{x}$ | *s* |
| **Floriferous** | | | | | | | |
| **branches** | | | | | | | |
| Length* | 3 | 7 | .6 dm. | .3 dm. | 7 | 19 | 2.3 dm. | .5 dm. |
| **Leaves** | | | | | | | |
| Length** | 3 | 9 | 6 mm. | o mm. | 7 | 19 | 11 mm. | 2.2 mm. |
| **Nectaries** | | | | | | | |
| Width** | 3 | 9 | .4 mm. | .02 mm. | 6 | 18 | .7 mm. | .1 mm. |

Other species related to *Sedum greggii* are *S. humifusum* of the Central Mexican Plateau, with prominently ciliate leaves and sepals and solitary flowers, and *S. compactum* of the Sierra Madre del Sur, with tiny white flowers. Probably these and *S. grandipetalum* are more closely related to *S. greggii* than are species occurring elsewhere in the world.

## 25. *SEDUM MORANENSE* (figs. 71–74)

*Sedum moranense* is the only stonecrop of the Trans-Mexican Volcanic Belt with the leaves of the floriferous branches closely set in several spiral ranks. The plants are subshrubs with decumbent stems and with small, ovate or lanceolate leaves which are almost as thick as wide, short-spurred, and obtuse. The petals are white, and the follicles divergent with prominent, marginal lips. Species which superficially resemble *S. moranense* are *S. parvum* of the Northern Mexican Plateau and Sierra Madre Oriental, with yellow petals; *S. liebmannianum* of the Sierra Madre del Sur, of which the enlarged bases of the withered leaves are white and persistent; and *S. cupressoides* of the Sierra Madre del Sur, with tiny, imbricate leaves and yellow petals.

**Description.** Materials: 36 plants—15 from the northeastern

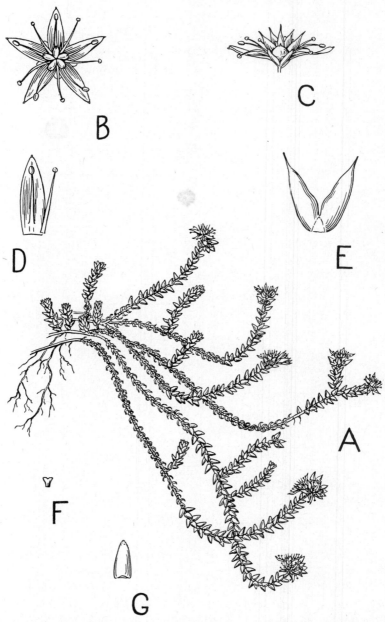

*Fig. 71.* Plant of *Sedum moranense* from near Las Vigas, Vera Cruz, cultivated in the greenhouse, Ithaca, N.Y.  A. Habit sketch (x .6).  B. Flower
from above (x 2.4).  C. Flower from side (x 2.4).  D. Petal and two stamens
(x 3.6).  E. Two pistils and torus (x 4.8).  F. Nectary (x 6).  G. Leaf (x 2.4).

slope of the Cofre de Perote, southeast of Las Vigas, Vera Cruz; 6 from the steep slope west of Acultzingo, Vera Cruz; 5 from the northwestern base of Mt. Malinche, Tlaxcala; 5 from the Sierra de las Cruces, Mexico; 3 from the Cerro Teresona, Toluca, Mexico; 1 from near km. 253 on the Pan-American Highway 1 km. north of El Salto, Hidalgo; and 1 from a slope 35 km. east of San Luis Potosí, in the state of the same name. Measurements marked cf. are of plants cultivated in an experiment in a cold frame at Ithaca, N.Y.; those marked gh. are of plants in a similar experiment in a greenhouse.

Plants of *Sedum moranense* are decumbent, much-branched sub-shrubs, chamaephytes; stems are glabrous, green when young, becoming brown and dark red, commonly producing aerial roots. Replicates of six plants from Las Vigas, cultivated simultaneously in the greenhouse and cold frame, were highly significantly taller in the greenhouse.

| | $n$ | $\bar{x}$ (cm.) | $s$ (cm.) | $w$ (cm.) |
|---|---|---|---|---|
| Height | | | | |
| El Salto | 1 | 8.5 | — | 5–12 |
| San Luis Potosí | 1 | 8.5 | — | 8– 9 |
| Las Vigas—cf. | 6 | 6 | .9 | 5– 7 |
| Acultzingo—cf. | 2 | 7.5 | .7 | 7– 8 |
| Malinche—cf. | 3 | 7.3 | 3.5 | 5–10 |
| Sierra de las Cruces—cf. | 4 | 6.7 | 1.5 | 5– 8 |
| Toluca—cf. | 2 | 6 | 1.4 | 5– 7 |
| El Salto—cf. | 1 | 8 | — | 8 |
| San Luis Potosí—cf. | 1 | 7 | — | 7 |
| Las Vigas—gh. | 6 | 8.7 | 1.7 | 6–11 |
| Acultzingo—gh. | 2 | 6 | 2.8 | 4– 8 |
| Malinche—gh. | 1 | 9 | — | 9 |
| Sierra de las Cruces—gh. | 5 | 7 | 1.2 | 6– 9 |
| El Salto—gh. | 1 | 6 | — | 6 |
| San Luis Potosí—gh. | 1 | 8 | — | 8 |

Leaves are divergent, closely set in several, usually five or six, spiral ranks, ovate or lanceolate, short-spurred, obtuse or truncate, sometimes papillose, green, frequently red-tipped. The dimensions of leaves vary with the amount of available light. For example, a plant on the lava near Las Vigas, growing in the shade of a rock, had highly significantly longer leaves than twelve other plants growing in the open. If this plant is omitted from the sample, differences in length of leaves among the other twelve plants are not significant. Unless the exposure of each leaf is experimentally controlled, differences in samples do not necessarily indicate genetic variation.

| | n | n-obs. | $\bar{x}$ (mm.) | s (mm.) | w (mm.) |
|---|---|---|---|---|---|
| Length | | | | | |
| Las Vigas | 13 | 71 | 3.6 | .4 | 2.8–6.5 |
| Acultzingo | 6 | 10 | 3.9 | .5 | 3 –4.9 |
| Malinche | 4 | 8 | 4.3 | 0 | 3.6–5.9 |
| Sierra de las Cruces | 5 | 15 | 4.3 | .9 | 3 –6.6 |
| Toluca | 1 | 2 | 4.9 | — | 4.7–5.2 |
| El Salto | 1 | 2 | 2.7 | — | 2.5–3 |
| San Luis Potosí | 1 | 2 | 2.7 | — | 2 –3.5 |
| Las Vigas—cf. | 6 | 39 | 4 | .5 | 3 –6.7 |
| Acultzingo—cf. | 1 | 4 | 3.8 | — | 3.2–4 |
| Malinche—cf. | 2 | 8 | 3.8 | .7 | 3.2–4.7 |
| Toluca—cf. | 1 | 4 | 5.4 | — | 4.8–5.8 |
| El Salto—cf. | 1 | 4 | 4.1 | — | 4 –4.2 |
| San Luis Potosí—cf. | 1 | 25 | 3.9 | — | 3.4–4.6 |
| Las Vigas—gh. | 4 | 16 | 4.7 | .5 | 3.2–6 |
| Malinche—gh. | 1 | 4 | 3.2 | — | 3.2–3.3 |
| Toluca—gh. | 1 | 4 | 3.1 | — | 2.5–3.4 |
| El Salto—gh. | 1 | 4 | 5 | — | 4.6–5.3 |
| San Luis Potosí—gh. | 1 | 4 | 3.8 | — | 3.2–4.2 |
| Width | | | | | |
| Las Vigas | 13 | 71 | 1.9 | 0 | 1.2–2.4 |
| Acultzingo | 6 | 10 | 2 | .1 | 1.7–2.2 |
| Malinche | 4 | 8 | 2.3 | 0 | 2 –2.7 |
| Sierra de las Cruces | 5 | 15 | 2.5 | 0 | 2.2–2.8 |
| Toluca | 1 | 2 | 2.3 | — | 2.2–2.5 |
| El Salto | 1 | 2 | 1.3 | — | 1.2–1.5 |
| San Luis Potosí | 1 | 2 | 1.6 | — | 1.2–2 |
| Las Vigas—cf. | 6 | 39 | 1.9 | .1 | 1.4–2.4 |
| Acultzingo—cf. | 1 | 4 | 2.2 | — | 2.1–2.4 |
| Malinche—cf. | 2 | 8 | 2.3 | .5 | 1.6–2.6 |
| Toluca—cf. | 1 | 4 | 2.4 | — | 2.3–2.5 |
| El Salto—cf. | 1 | 4 | 2.2 | — | 2.1–2.3 |
| San Luis Potosí—cf. | 1 | 25 | 2.1 | — | 1.6–2.5 |
| Las Vigas—gh. | 4 | 16 | 1.9 | .1 | 1.7–2.2 |
| Malinche—gh. | 1 | 4 | 1.8 | — | 1.7–1.9 |
| Toluca—gh. | 1 | 4 | 1.9 | — | 1.7–2.1 |
| El Salto—gh. | 1 | 4 | 2.1 | — | 2 –2.2 |
| San Luis Potosí—gh. | 1 | 4 | 2.2 | — | 2 –2.4 |

|                       | n | n-obs. | x̄ (mm.) | s (mm.) | w (mm.) |
|-----------------------|---|--------|----------|---------|---------|
| Thickness             |   |        |          |         |         |
| El Salto              | I | I      | ·5       | —       | ·5      |
| San Luis Potosí       | I | 2      | .6       | —       | .5– .8  |
| Las Vigas—cf.         | I | 15     | 1·4      | —       | I  –1·7 |
| San Luis Potosí—cf.   | I | 25     | 1·5      | —       | 1·3–1·7 |
| Las Vigas—gh.         | I | 4      | 1·3      | —       | 1·2–1·3 |

Inflorescences are cymes, usually of a single cincinnus, but sometimes two-parted.

|                       | n | n-obs. | x̄ | w     |
|-----------------------|---|--------|----|-------|
| No. of flowers per cyme |   |      |    |       |
| Las Vigas             | I | 8      | 3  | 2– 5  |
| El Salto              | I | 2      | 4  | 1– 7  |
| San Luis Potosí—cf.   | I | 9      | 5  | 3– 8  |
| Las Vigas—gh.         | I | 4      | 11 | 10–12 |
| El Salto—gh.          | I | I      | 10 | 10    |

Flowers are either sessile or on very short pedicels .1–1 mm. long, rarely 6- or 7-merous.

|                       | n | n-obs. | x̄ (mm.) | w (mm.)  |
|-----------------------|---|--------|----------|----------|
| Flowers—diameter      |   |        |          |          |
| El Salto              | I | 2      | 7·5      | 7 – 8    |
| Las Vigas—cf.         | I | 7      | 8·7      | 7 –11    |
| San Luis Potosí—cf.   | I | 16     | 13·4     | 10 –16   |
| Las Vigas—gh.         | I | 4      | 10       | 8 –11    |
| El Salto—gh.          | I | I      | 9        | 9        |
| San Luis Potosí—gh.   | I | 4      | 13·5     | 12 –15   |
| Torus—length          |   |        |          |          |
| Las Vigas—gh.         | I | I      | ·9       | ·9       |

Sepals are ovate or lanceolate, of different sizes in the same flower, with short spurs .1–.9 mm. long, obtuse, green, more or less scarious-margined, sometimes red at apices or speckled with red. All measurements are of the longest sepal in each flower. On the basis of experiments in both cold frame and greenhouse, the plant from San Luis Potosí has longer, wider sepals than those of plants from other populations.

| | n | n-obs. | x̄ (mm.) | s (mm.) | w (mm.) |
|---|---|---|---|---|---|
| **Length** | | | | | |
| Las Vigas | 12 | 39 | 2.4 | .1 | 1.9–3.4 |
| Acultzingo | 4 | 4 | 2.6 | .3 | 2.4–3 |
| Malinche | 2 | 3 | 2.4 | .3 | 2.1–2.7 |
| Toluca | 1 | 2 | 2.6 | — | 2.5–2.7 |
| El Salto | 1 | 2 | 2.4 | — | 2.2–2.6 |
| Las Vigas—cf. | 6 | 31 | 2.7 | 0 | 1.9–3.9 |
| Acultzingo—cf. | 1 | 4 | 3 | — | 2.8–3.2 |
| Malinche—cf. | 2 | 8 | 2.3 | .2 | 2 –2.6 |
| Toluca—cf. | 1 | 4 | 2.8 | — | 2.6–3.1 |
| El Salto—cf. | 1 | 4 | 2.4 | — | 2.2–2.7 |
| San Luis Potosí—cf. | 1 | 17 | 3.9 | — | 3.7–4.1 |
| Las Vigas—gh. | 4 | 16 | 2.6 | .06 | 2.4–3 |
| Malinche—gh. | 1 | 4 | 2.2 | — | 2.1–2.3 |
| Toluca—gh. | 1 | 4 | 2.4 | — | 2.3–2.7 |
| El Salto—gh. | 1 | 4 | 2.1 | — | 1.9–2.3 |
| San Luis Potosí—gh. | 1 | 4 | 3.6 | — | 3.4–4.4 |
| **Width** | | | | | |
| Las Vigas | 1 | 8 | 1.2 | — | .9–1.5 |
| El Salto | 1 | 2 | .7 | — | .5–1 |
| Las Vigas—cf. | 6 | 31 | 1.4 | .1 | 1.1–1.9 |
| Acultzingo—cf. | 1 | 4 | 1.4 | — | 1.3–1.7 |
| Malinche—cf. | 2 | 8 | 1.2 | .3 | 1 –1.6 |
| Toluca—cf. | 1 | 4 | 1.3 | — | 1.2–1.5 |
| San Luis Potosí—cf. | 1 | 17 | 1.6 | — | 1.4–1.9 |
| Las Vigas—gh. | 2 | 8 | 1.3 | 0 | 1.1–1.5 |
| Toluca—gh. | 1 | 4 | 1.3 | — | 1.1–1.5 |
| San Luis Potosí—gh. | 1 | 4 | 1.6 | — | 1.5–1.9 |

Petals are lanceolate, acute or obtuse, mucronate-appendaged, white, except red, pink, or green dorsally at apices. On the basis of experiments in both cold frame and greenhouse, the petals of the plant from San Luis Potosí are longer and wider than those of plants from the other populations.

| | n | n-obs. | x̄ (mm.) | s (mm.) | w (mm.) |
|---|---|---|---|---|---|
| **Length** | | | | | |
| Las Vigas | 12 | 39 | 5.2 | .4 | 4.1–5.9 |
| Acultzingo | 4 | 4 | 5.4 | .1 | 5.4–5.5 |
| Malinche | 2 | 3 | 5.4 | .9 | 4.6–5.9 |
| Toluca | 1 | 2 | 5.8 | — | 5.8 |
| El Salto | 1 | 1 | 4.5 | — | 4.5 |
| Las Vigas—cf. | 6 | 31 | 5.6 | .5 | 4.6–6.7 |

| | n | n-obs. | x̄ (mm.) | s (mm.) | u (mm.) |
|---|---|---|---|---|---|
| Acultzingo—cf. | 1 | 4 | 6.1 | — | 5.8-6.7 |
| Malinche—cf. | 2 | 8 | 5.2 | .9 | 4.5-6.1 |
| Toluca—cf. | 1 | 4 | 6.6 | — | 6.4-6.8 |
| El Salto—cf. | 1 | 4 | 4.3 | — | 3.9-4.6 |
| San Luis Potosí—cf. | 1 | 17 | 7.8 | — | 6.8-8.5 |
| Las Vigas—gh. | 4 | 16 | 5.6 | .3 | 5.1-6.4 |
| Malinche—gh. | 1 | 4 | 4.4 | — | 4.2-4.7 |
| Toluca—gh. | 1 | 4 | 5.6 | — | 5.3-5.8 |
| El Salto—gh. | 1 | 4 | 4.3 | — | 4 -4.5 |
| San Luis Potosí—gh. | 1 | 4 | 7.7 | — | 7.2-8.2 |
| Width | | | | | |
| Las Vigas | 1 | 8 | 1.6 | — | 1.4-1.8 |
| El Salto | 1 | 1 | 1.3 | — | 1.3 |
| Las Vigas—cf. | 6 | 31 | 1.9 | .1 | 1.4-2.3 |
| Acultzingo—cf. | 1 | 4 | 2 | — | 1.9-2.4 |
| Malinche—cf. | 2 | 8 | 1.8 | .5 | 1.4-2.4 |
| Toluca—cf. | 1 | 4 | 2 | — | 2 -2.1 |
| San Luis Potosí—cf. | 1 | 17 | 2.6 | — | 2.2-3 |
| Las Vigas—gh. | 2 | 8 | 1.8 | .2 | 1.6-2.1 |
| Toluca—gh. | 1 | 4 | 1.6 | — | 1.6-1.7 |
| San Luis Potosí—gh. | 1 | 4 | 2.2 | — | 2.1-2.4 |

Stamens have red or purple anthers. A stamen alternate with the petals of a flower of the plant from San Luis Potosí was petaloid.

| | n | n-obs. | x̄ (mm.) | s (mm.) | w (mm.) |
|---|---|---|---|---|---|
| Adnation of epipetalous filaments | | | | | |
| Las Vigas | 1 | 1 | 1.1 | — | 1.1 |
| El Salto | 1 | 1 | .5 | — | .5 |
| Las Vigas—gh. | 1 | 4 | .9 | — | .9-1 |
| Anthers—length | | | | | |
| Las Vigas | 10 | 34 | .6 | .05 | .5- .8 |
| Acultzingo | 2 | 2 | .7 | 0 | .7 |
| Toluca | 1 | 2 | .7 | — | .7- .8 |
| Las Vigas—cf. | 1 | 1 | .7 | — | .7 |
| El Salto—cf. | 1 | 3 | .6 | — | .5- .6 |
| San Luis Potosí—cf. | 1 | 7 | .8 | — | .6- .9 |
| Las Vigas—gh. | 3 | 11 | .8 | 0 | .7- .8 |
| Malinche—gh. | 1 | 4 | .7 | — | .7 |
| El Salto—gh. | 1 | 2 | .5 | — | .5 |
| San Luis Potosí—gh. | 1 | 2 | .7 | — | .7- .8 |
| Anthers—diameter | | | | | |
| Las Vigas—cf. | 1 | 1 | .5 | — | .5 |

| | *n* | *n-obs.* | $\bar{x}$ (*mm.*) | *s* (*mm.*) | *w* (*mm.*) |
|---|---|---|---|---|---|
| San Luis Potosí—cf. | 1 | 7 | .5 | — | .5– .6 |
| Las Vigas—gh. | 1 | 4 | .4 | — | .4– .5 |
| San Luis Potosí—gh. | 1 | 2 | .5 | — | .5– .6 |

Nectaries are obovate-subquadrate or subquadrate, truncate and subemarginate, white or pale yellow.

| | *n* | *n-obs.* | $\bar{x}$ (*mm.*) | *s* (*mm.*) | *w* (*mm.*) |
|---|---|---|---|---|---|
| **Length** | | | | | |
| Las Vigas | 12 | 39 | .5 | 0 | .4–.7 |
| Acultzingo | 4 | 4 | .5 | .003 | .5–.6 |
| Malinche | 2 | 3 | .5 | 0 | .5–.6 |
| Toluca | 1 | 2 | .5 | — | .5 |
| El Salto | 1 | 1 | .3 | — | .3 |
| Las Vigas—cf. | 1 | 7 | .4 | — | .4–.6 |
| El Salto—cf. | 1 | 4 | .3 | — | .2–.4 |
| San Luis Potosí—cf. | 1 | 13 | .6 | — | .5–.8 |
| Las Vigas—gh. | 3 | 12 | .5 | .07 | .4–.6 |
| Malinche—gh. | 1 | 4 | .5 | — | .4–.6 |
| El Salto—gh. | 1 | 4 | .3 | — | .3–.4 |
| **Width** | | | | | |
| Las Vigas | 1 | 8 | .4 | — | .3–.5 |
| El Salto | 1 | 1 | .25 | — | .25 |
| Las Vigas—cf. | 1 | 7 | .4 | — | .4–.6 |
| San Luis Potosí—cf. | 1 | 13 | .6 | — | .5–.8 |
| Las Vigas—gh. | 1 | 4 | .5 | — | .5 |

Pistils are erect and white.

| | *n* | *n-obs.* | $\bar{x}$ | *s* | *w* |
|---|---|---|---|---|---|
| **Length** | | | | | |
| El Salto | 1 | 1 | 3.5 mm. | — | 3.5    mm. |
| Las Vigas—gh. | 2 | 5 | 3.6 mm. | .2 mm. | 3.1– 4 mm. |
| **No. of ovules per ovary** | | | | | |
| Las Vigas—gh. | 3 | 12 | 11 | — | 7 –15 |
| Malinche—gh. | 1 | 4 | 13 | — | 12 –14 |

Follicles are divergent, brown, sometimes red when immature.

| | *n* | *n-obs.* | $\bar{x}$ (*mm.*) | *s* (*mm.*) | *w* (*mm.*) |
|---|---|---|---|---|---|
| **Length** | | | | | |
| Las Vigas | 10 | 27 | 3 | .2 | 2.2–3.7 |
| Acultzingo | 1 | 3 | 2.9 | — | 2.4–3.4 |
| Malinche | 4 | 7 | 3.3 | .1 | 2.7–4.1 |

| | $n$ | $n$-obs. | $\bar{x}$ (mm.) | $s$ (mm.) | $w$ (mm.) |
|---|---|---|---|---|---|
| Sierra de las Cruces | 5 | 14 | 3.4 | 0 | 3 –3.9 |
| **Length of beaks** | | | | | |
| Las Vigas | 10 | 27 | .9 | .03 | .6–1.2 |
| Acultzingo | 1 | 3 | .8 | — | .6–1 |
| Malinche | 1 | 2 | .9 | — | .9 |
| Sierra de las Cruces | 5 | 12 | 1 | .05 | .8–1.1 |
| **Width of lips** | | | | | |
| Las Vigas | 10 | 27 | .5 | .02 | .3– .6 |
| Acultzingo | 1 | 3 | .4 | — | .2– .5 |
| Malinche | 4 | 7 | .4 | .04 | .3– .5 |
| Sierra de las Cruces | 5 | 14 | .4 | .02 | .2– .6 |

Seeds are pyriform or ellipsoid, papillose, brown, varying from yellowish brown to dark brown. In my samples only about three seeds were developed per follicle.

| | $n$ | $n$-obs. | $\bar{x}$ (mm.) | $s$ (mm.) | $w$ (mm.) |
|---|---|---|---|---|---|
| **Length** | | | | | |
| Las Vigas | 10 | 28 | .6 | .01 | .5–.7 |
| Acultzingo | 1 | 2 | .7 | — | .7–.8 |
| Malinche | 3 | 5 | .7 | 0 | .7 |
| Sierra de las Cruces | 5 | 14 | .7 | 0 | .6– 8 |
| Toluca | 1 | 3 | .5 | — | .5– 6 |
| **Diameter** | | | | | |
| Las Vigas | 10 | 28 | .3 | 0 | .2–.4 |
| Acultzingo | 1 | 2 | .3 | — | .3–.4 |
| Malinche | 1 | 1 | .4 | — | .4 |
| Sierra de las Cruces | 5 | 14 | .4 | 0 | .3–.4 |
| Toluca | 1 | 3 | .3 | — | .3 |

**Variation.** The populations of *Sedum moranense* which I have studied are remarkably similar morphologically, except that a plant from east of San Luis Potosí has longer, wider sepals and petals than do plants from elsewhere. When I collected that for propagation, I also obtained other plants for pressing and had the impression that they were all alike. Since the plants were not in flower at the time of collection, I have no data on dimensions of sepals and petals of wild specimens. The population east of San Luis Potosí appears to be disjunct from others of the species.

Within five populations of *Sedum moranense* which I have studied in some detail in the wild, I have noted differences in only four characteristics. The explanation for such differences may be environmental. As an illustration, differences in length of leaves among twelve plants on the lava below Las Vigas were not significant, but a thirteenth plant, growing in the shade of a rock, had highly significantly longer leaves than the others. In cultivation, that plant was not different from others. Plants in cultivation have differed in seven characters. More refined conditions of experiment might eliminate some of these differences, but my data suggest the possibility of genetic variation within populations.

Experiments with plant (clone) no. 2 from Las Vigas demonstrate some of the problems involved in the interpretation of variation. The following data for length of leaves indicate that both season of collection of samples and method of sampling are important in determining the average value for this dimension. Some of the differences among results are highly significant. Pairs of means which are not significantly different are underlined.

| | Wild plant, beginning of wet season | Random sample, plant in cold frame | Nonrandom sample, plant in cold frame | Wild plant, late in wet season | Plant in greenhouse |
|---|---|---|---|---|---|
| $\bar{x}$ | 3.4 mm. | 3.5 mm. | 3.9 mm. | 4.7 mm. | 5.2 mm. |
| $n$ | 5 | 15 | 4 | 3 | 4 |

In selecting the nonrandom sample from the cold frame, I tried not to take larger leaves only, yet the result is significantly biased in favor of such leaves.

In contrast, differences in length of petals among samples drawn from the same plant are not significant, indicating both that the petals are less subject to modification by the environment and that they are less variable.

| | From wild plant at beginning of wet season | Random sample from plant in cold frame | Nonrandom sample from plant in cold frame | From plant in greenhouse |
|---|---|---|---|---|
| $\bar{x}$ | 4.8 mm. | 5.3 mm. | 5.4 mm. | 5.5 mm. |
| $n$ | 5 | 7 | 4 | 4 |

## KEY TO SUBSPECIES

A. Sepals averaging 2.4–2.6 mm. long and .7–1.2 mm. wide; petals averaging 4.5–5.8 mm. long and 1.3–1.6 mm. wide . . . . . . . . . . . . . . . . . . . . . . . . . . . . . . . . . . . . . . . . . . . . . . . . . . . . . . . . ssp. *moranense*, p. 269

AA. Sepals averaging 3.9 mm. long and 1.6 mm. wide; petals averaging 7.8 mm. long and 2.6 mm. wide . . . . . . . . . ssp. *grandiflorum*, p. 272

## Sedum moranense ssp. moranense

**Nomenclature.** *Sedum moranense* H. B. K., Nov. Gen et Sp. Plant 6: 37 (1823). Type locality: near Real de Moran, alt. 2,534 m., Hidalgo, Mexico. Type: in the herbarium in Paris. I have for study a photograph of the type, available through the courtesy of the Chicago Natural History Museum. I have also had on loan from the same museum a collection of Sessé, Mociño, Castillo, and Maldonado (Bot. Gard., Madrid), indicating that one of them had collected this species sometime between 1797 and 1804. The name on the label, which might antedate *S. moranense*, was never published.

Synonyms are:

1878. *Sedum arboreum* Masters, Gard. Chron. 2: 717. Type locality: unknown; description based on plants cultivated in English gardens. Type: possibly in the herbarium at Kew. Masters' description of the flowers as one-half inch in diameter suggests the possibility that this might be ssp. *grandiflorum*, but more likely it is ssp. *moranense*.

1903. *Sedum submontanum* Rose, Bull. N.Y. Bot. Gard. 3: 40. Type locality: "on rockwork in public plaza at Monte Escobado, Zacatecas." Probably the plants there originated in the wild somewhere else. Type: J. N. Rose's collection no. 2,042 (US 301,567), Aug. 27, 1897.

1917. *Sedum moranense* H. B. K. var. *arboreum* (Masters) Prager, Jour. Bot. 55: 211.

The sepals of *Sedum moranense* ssp. *moranense* usually are less than 3.5 mm. long and 1.5 mm. wide. In addition, the petals are less than 6.8 mm. long and 2.1 mm. wide. In cultivation, plants flower whether temperatures in winter have been low or high.

**Distribution.** *Sedum moranense* ssp. *moranense* occurs over a wide area in the eastern parts of the Trans-Mexican Volcanic Belt and Central Mexican Plateau, but its range is disjunct. Data for the populations which I have studied in the volcanic belt are as follows:

| Location | n-plants | Area | Alt. range | pH | Drainage |
|---|---|---|---|---|---|
| SE of Las Vigas | ab. 20,000 | >5 km. x 89 m. | ab. 2,100–2,301 m. | 5.6–5.8 | moderate to excessive |
| W of Acultzingo | >10 | >120 m. x 30 m. | 2,140–2,150 m. | — | moderate |
| NW of Malinche | 104 | >2 km. x 2 m. | 2,320–2,400 m. | 6.4 | moderate |
| Sierra de las Cruces | 130 | 55 m. x 5 m. | 3,065 m. | 6.6 | moderate |
| Toluca | ab. 5,000 | ab. 1 sq. km. | 2,600–2,820 m. | 6.6 | moderate to good |

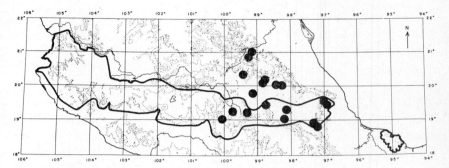

*Fig. 72.* Known distribution of *Sedum moranense* ssp. *moranense.*

Additional populations in the volcanic belt and the discoverers of each are Banderilla, at the ranch Piletas, 1,600–1,800 m., Cantón of Jalapa, Vera Cruz, discoverer unknown (NY); Esperanza, Vera Cruz, C. A. Purpus (US); Puebla, discoverer unknown (NY); Cerro Tepoxuchil, alt. 2,330 m., G. Arsène (US); Barranca de Alseseca, alt. 2,150 m., talus of Champs de Manoeuvres, alt. 2,185 m., and Barranca de Manzanilla, alt. 2,180 m., all in the vicinity of Puebla, G. Arsène (US); 9 km. northeast of Texcoco, Mexico, R. Clausen (CU); and Comunidad, alt. 2,840 m., District of Temascaltepec, Mexico, G. B. Hinton (NY, US). Populations on the Central Mexican Plateau and their discoverers include 21 km. west of Tulancingo, Hidalgo, J. L. Edwards and R. Clausen (CU); below Trinidad Iron Works, Hidalgo, C. G. Pringle (CU, US, Vt); Sierra de Pachuca, C. G. Pringle (CU, Mexu, NY, US, Vt); Peña Barón, Parque Nacional de Miguel, Hidalgo, Edward Balls (US); Pueblo Nuevo, Hidalgo, J. L. Edwards and R. Clausen (CU); Ixmiquilpan, Hidalgo, C. A. Purpus (US); near El Salto, Hidalgo, J. N. Rose and J. H. Painter (US); near km. 253 on the Pan-American Highway 1 km. north of El Salto, Hidalgo, R. Clausen (CU); and Jacala, Hidalgo, V. H. Chase (NY).

*Sedum moranense* was collected on lava near Las Vigas, northeast of the Cofre de Perote, in July, 1888 (NY). The discoverer of the population is unknown. My studies there were on Aug. 3 and 5 and Nov. 1, 1955. The population extends from 3 km. southeast of Las Vigas to 1.8 km. west of La Joya, on either side of Toxlaxcuoya. The plants were on scoria, especially along the banks of the road, exposed in all directions. I saw some seedlings, but probably most reproduction is vegetative. The lava near Las Vigas is old enough to have trees of *Pinus montezumae* established on it. *Baccharis conferta* and *Pteridium aquilinum* (subspecies including var. *feei*) were both common competitors of the *Sedum*. Other common competitors were *Braunia secunda* (identified by Professor Andrews), *Cheilanthes intramarginalis*, *Notholaena aurea*, *Hypoxis mexicana*, *Dichromena colorata*, and *Aegopogon cenchroides*. The only other member of the Crassulaceae there was *S. dendroideum*. That was not in flower in August, when the *S. moranense* was at the height of bloom. On Nov. 1, most plants of *S. moranense* had mature fruits, though a few still had fresh flowers. In the cold frame at Ithaca, flowering time is June and July, and in the greenhouse May to August. Three plants from Las Vigas have survived outdoors, without protection, in the Test Garden at Ithaca, in the winters of 1956–1957 and 1957–1958, and two plants from there survived in my garden on the Slaterville Road, Ithaca, in the winter of 1957–1958.

I studied *Sedum moranense* on the steep slope west of Acultzingo on Aug. 11 and Nov. 11, 1955. The plants were growing on conglomerate and limestone, exposed to the northeast and southeast. They had flowers and a few fruits in August and many fruits in November. The only other species of Crassulaceae growing there was *S. stahlii*. That was not in flower on either of the dates of my visits. In the cold frame at Ithaca, a plant from there flowered in June.

Northwest of Mt. Malinche, A. J. Sharp and E. Hernández-Xolocotzi (Univ. of Tenn.) collected *Sedum moranense* on rocks beside the Zahuapan River near San Bernabé Amaxac de Guerrero on Aug. 20, 1944. I found it in two places near there in 1955—on a bank of conglomerate about .3 km. southwest of the waterfalls at Atlihuitzia and on low bluffs of conglomerate along the east bank of the river about .3–.5 km. north of the bridge in Santa Elena. Exposure was to the west-northwest. The plants were just past flowering and had a few ripe follicles on Aug. 23. By Oct. 18, they were generally in fruit. Competing species included *Pellaea sagittata*, *Salvia polystachya*, *Mimosa biuncifera*, *Baccharis glutinosa*, and *Muhlenbergia rigida*. A tree of *Juniperus deppeana* shaded some of the plants. No other Crassulaceae were in intimate association with the *Sedum moranense*, but not far away were *Sedum quevae* and *Villadia scopulina*, both in flower in October, and *V. misera*, in flower in August. In the cold frame and greenhouse at Ithaca, plants of *Sedum moranense* from northwest of Malinche have flowered in June.

Pringle (Mexu, NY, US, Vt) collected *Sedum moranense* in the Sierra de las Cruces in 1893. Rose (Britton and Rose, 1903) cited as *S. submontanum* the collection from there, erroneously labeled as from Jalisco. On Oct. 20, 1955, I studied plants in the Sierra de las Cruces, on the bank of a side road south of the Mexico-Toluca Road, by the fish hatchery at El Zarco. The site, southeast of Salazar, was in a forest of *Abies religiosa*. Exposure was to the north-northeast, and drainage was moderate. The plants were in partial shade. Frosts are frequent, and snow occasionally falls at that locality. A frost had occurred on the morning of my visit. Balls of ice still were present near the *Sedum* which was then in fruit. No other Crassulaceae were in the vicinity. *Baccharis conferta* and *Stipa mucronata* were competing species. In cultivation for three years in Ithaca, five plants of *Sedum moranense* from the Sierra de las Cruces have not flowered in either the greenhouse or the cold frame.

Rose and Painter (US) found *Sedum moranense* near Toluca in 1903. I studied it there on Sept. 8, 1955, when plants were in flower, and on Nov. 23, 1955, when they were in fruit. Although the plants were intermixed with *S. napiferum* and that was in flower at the same time, I found no hybrids. *Tagetes tenuifolia* was a common competing species. At Ithaca, plants of *S. moranense* from Toluca have flowered in the cold frame and the greenhouse in June.

## *Sedum moranense* ssp. **grandiflorum**

Subspecies nova *Sedi moranensis* cum floribus majoribus; sepala 3.9 (3.4–4.4) mm. longa et 1.6 (1.4–1.9) mm. lata; petala 7.8 (6.8–8.5) mm. longa et 2.6 (2.1–3.0) mm. lata. Typus in Herbario Wiegand, Universitatis Cornellianae, ab montibus 35 km. ad orientem San Luis Potosí, collectio Roberti Clausenii, num. 7,451, 1949, Martio 14, cultus in loco ad plantas colendas vitreis munito ad Ithaca, N.Y., 1956, Junio 27, est.

Except for the larger flowers, *Sedum moranense* ssp. *grandiflorum* has the same appearance as ssp. *moranense*. The sepals and petals are both longer and wider, however. Some dried specimens in

*Fig. 73.* Flowers of plants of *Sedum moranense* ssp. *moranense* (left) and ssp. *grandiflorum* (right) cultivated in the cold frame at Ithaca, N.Y., ssp. *moranense* from between Puebla and Tehuacán and ssp. *grandiflorum* the type, June 26, 1956 (x 4.5).

herbaria, collected in the state of San Luis Potosí, have petals as long as 7 mm. Perhaps all populations of *S. moranense* from there are ssp. *grandiflorum*. If that is correct, J. G. Schaffner discovered the subspecies near San Luis Potosí in 1877 (NY) and E. Palmer collected it in mountains near there in 1902 (NY, US) and again at Alvarez in 1904 (NY, US). A definite cold period in winter seems more necessary for the initiation of flowering in ssp. *grandiflorum* than in ssp. *moranense*.

**Relationships.** The species most closely related to *Sedum moranense* is *S. liebmannianum* of the Sierra Madre del Sur. The bases of the withered leaves of the latter are enlarged, white, and persistent. This condition is distinctive and makes identification easy. Other differences need to be substantiated by further study of *S. liebmannianum*.

*Sedum parvum* of the Northern Mexican Plateau and the Sierra Madre Oriental and *S. cupressoides* of the Sierra Madre del Sur are both related to *S. moranense*, but are easily distinguished by their yellow petals. In addition, *S. cupressoides* has smaller, closely imbricate leaves.

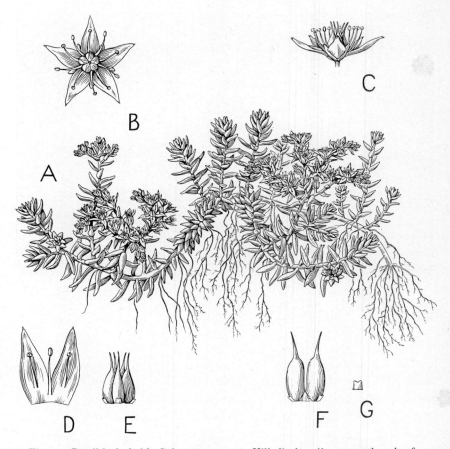

*Fig. 74.* Possible hybrid, *Sedum moranense* x *Villadia batesii*, reported to be from Nevado de Toluca, cultivated in the greenhouse, Ithaca, N.Y. A. Habit sketch (x .4). B. Flower from above (x 1.6). C. Flower from side (x 1.6). D. Petals and stamens (x 2.4). E. Pistils (x 2.4). F. Single pistil (x 3.2). G. Nectary (x 4).

Of species in the Trans-Mexican Volcanic Belt, perhaps *Sedum stahlii* is closest to *S. moranense.* It differs in having hairy, opposite leaves and yellow petals, but, like *S. moranense,* has divergent follicles with broad, marginal lips and papillose seeds, features which may be important in indicating relationships.

Still another possible relationship of *Sedum moranense* is with *Villadia batesii.* A plant, sent to me by Paul Hutchison of the University of California and reported to have been collected on the northern slope of the Nevado de Toluca, at alt. 4,270 m., by Eric

Walther, might be a hybrid between the two species. If it is not, then it is an undescribed species of *Sedum*. The idea that it might be a hybrid is based on circumstantial evidence—abortive pollen and ovules and also an intermediate morphology. This last is partially illustrated in the following table, in which all data are for plants cultivated in the greenhouse at Ithaca, N.Y.

| | | | | | Plant from | | | | | |
|---|---|---|---|---|---|---|---|---|---|---|
| | *Sedum moranense* | | | | *Nevado de Toluca* | | *Villadia batesii* | | | |
| | $n$ | n-obs. | $\bar{x}$ | $s$ | n-obs. | $\bar{x}$ | $n$ | n-obs. | $\bar{x}$ | $s$ |
| Leaves | | | (mm.) | (mm.) | | (mm.) | | | (mm.) | (mm.) |
| Length | 8 | 32 | 4.3 | 0 | 8 | 10.8 | 2 | 6 | 9 | 3.7 |
| Width | 8 | 32 | 2 | .1 | 8 | 4 | 2 | 6 | 2.2 | .5 |
| Thickness | 1 | 4 | 1.3 | — | 8 | 2.6 | 1 | 3 | 1.8 | — |
| | | | | | | | | | | |
| Inflorescences | | | | | | | | | | |
| No. of flowers | 2 | 5 | 11 | — | 5 | 31 | 1 | 3 | 17 | — |
| | | | | | | | | | | |
| Petals | | | (mm.) | (mm.) | | (mm.) | | | (mm.) | (mm.) |
| Length | 8 | 32 | 5.6 | .2 | 6 | 6.8 | 2 | 6 | 7.3 | .2 |
| Length of cohe- | | | | | | | | | | |
| sion | 8 | 32 | 0 | 0 | 6 | .4 | 2 | 6 | 2.8 | .5 |
| Width | 4 | 16 | 1.9 | .2 | 6 | 2.7 | 1 | 3 | 2.8 | — |

The plant from the Nevado de Toluca has larger leaves and more flowers per inflorescence than either *Sedum moranense* or *Villadia batesii*, and it also produces flowers over a longer period of time. Since I did not see anything like it on my visits to the Nevado de Toluca, I lack data from the field to substantiate the idea that it might be a hybrid. Obviously its proper status requires more attention.

## 26. *SEDUM JALISCANUM* (figs. 75-77)

Distinctive features of *Sedum jaliscanum* are biennial growth, corms, petiolate leaves which are spatulate, oblanceolate, or elliptic-oblong, and white petals. Other biennial species of the Trans-Mexican Volcanic Belt are *S. cormiferum* with greenish petals, flowers on slender pedicels, and conspicuous nectaries; *S. napiferum*

*Fig. 75. Sedum jaliscanum* on lava in Cerro Azul, Michoacán, Sept. 22, 1955.

with lanceolate or ovate leaves and petals usually marked with transverse bands of red streaks; and *S. minimum,* of dwarf habit, less than 3 cm. tall, with clavate or oblanceolate leaves and with petals which are slightly connate and white, each marked with bands of dark red below the middle.

**Description.** Materials: 119 plants—10 from El Tezcal, 9 km. southwest of Tepoztlán, Morelos; 43 from the Sierra de Tepoztlán, Morelos; 17 from near Taxco, Guerrero; 7 from east of Triguillo in the Sierra de Ozumatlán, Michoacán; 15 from the Cerro Azul 4 km. southeast of Jesús del Monte, Michoacán; and 27 from the slope of Las Piñas southeast of Ciudad Guzmán, Jalisco. Measurements marked cult. are of plants cultivated in the greenhouse at Ithaca, N.Y.

Plants of *Sedum jaliscanum* are herbs, geophytes, each producing in the first rainy season rosettes of 2–5 petiolate leaves, with ovate, orbicular, or reniform blades, and small corms; leaves wither in the subsequent dry season, but floriferous branches develop from

the corms in the second rainy season; floriferous branches are
usually red and tuberculate.

| | $n$ | $n$-obs. | $\bar{x}$ | $s$ | $w$ |
|---|---|---|---|---|---|
| Corms—diameter—in first rainy season | | | | | |
| Sierra de Tepoztlán—Sept. | 6 | 6 | .9 mm. | .5 mm. | .2– 1.5 mm. |
| Corms—diameter—at end of first rainy season | | | | | |
| Sierra de Tepoztlán—Nov. | 11 | 11 | 3.5 mm. | 1.1 mm. | 2 – 5 mm. |
| Ciudad Guzmán—Oct. | 5 | 5 | 2.8 mm. | .8 mm. | 2 – 4 mm. |
| Height of floriferous branches | | | | | |
| El Tezcal | 1 | 1 | 9 cm. | — | 9 cm. |
| Sierra de Tepoztlán | 6 | 6 | 13.3 cm. | 6.3 cm. | 9 –25 cm. |
| Taxco | 3 | 3 | 10.3 cm. | 8.5 cm. | 1.5–18.5 cm. |
| Sierra de Ozumatlán | 4 | 4 | 15 cm. | 4.2 cm. | 9 –18 cm. |
| Cerro Azul | 4 | 4 | 8.3 cm. | 4.5 cm. | 2.8–12 cm. |
| Ciudad Guzmán | 9 | 9 | 5.1 cm. | 1.4 cm. | 3.7–11 cm. |

Leaves of seedlings are 2–5 per plant, petiolate, with ovate,
orbicular, or reniform blades; those of floriferous branches elliptic-
oblanceolate, spatulate, or elliptic-oblong, with spurs .1–1.1 mm.
long, often petiolate, obtuse, sometimes papillose, concave ventrally and convex dorsally. The difference in width of leaves
between wild plants from the three eastern populations and those
from the three western populations is highly significant, but the
leaves of a single plant from the Sierra de Tepoztlán, cultivated
at Ithaca, N.Y., were broader than the average for plants in the
western populations. The differences in thickness of leaves are
likewise highly significant among populations, plants in the Sierra
de Ozumatlán and Cerro Azul having the thickest leaves.

| | $n$ | $n$-obs. | $\bar{x}$ (mm.) | $s$ (mm.) | $w$ (mm.) |
|---|---|---|---|---|---|
| Length of leaves of seedlings | | | | | |
| Sierra de Tepoztlán | 6 | 6 | 26.2 | 7.5 | 19 –38 |
| Taxco | 3 | 3 | 22.3 | 1.1 | 21 –23 |
| Ciudad Guzmán | 5 | 5 | 18.2 | 7.4 | 9 –28 |
| Length of leaves of floriferous branches | | | | | |
| El Tezcal | 7 | 35 | 14.1 | 3.6 | 8 –30 |
| Sierra de Tepoztlán | 22 | 56 | 11.6 | 5 | 5.6–30 |
| Taxco | 14 | 50 | 11.5 | 1.9 | 5 –18 |
| Sierra de Ozumatlán | 4 | 20 | 16.5 | 4 | 10 –25 |
| Cerro Azul | 9 | 29 | 13.8 | 1.8 | 8.5–22 |

|  | n | n-obs. | $\bar{x}$ (mm.) | s (mm.) | w (mm.) |
|---|---|---|---|---|---|
| Ciudad Guzmán | 13 | 28 | 10.3 | 0 | 6 −18 |
| Sierra de Tepoztlán—cult. | 1 | 3 | 19.3 | — | 18 −20 |
| Length of petioles—leaves of floriferous branches | | | | | |
| Sierra de Ozumatlán | 4 | 20 | 2 | .4 | 0 − 4 |
| Cerro Azul | 9 | 29 | 2 | 0 | 0 − 9.8 |
| Ciudad Guzmán | 13 | 27 | 1.6 | 0 | 0 − 9 |
| Width of leaves of seedlings | | | | | |
| Sierra de Tepoztlán | 6 | 6 | 4.2 | 1.2 | 3 − 6 |
| Taxco | 3 | 3 | 7 | 1 | 6 − 8 |
| Ciudad Guzmán | 5 | 5 | 6.2 | 2.2 | 3 − 9 |
| Width of leaves of floriferous branches | | | | | |
| El Tezcal | 7 | 35 | 2.4 | .4 | 1 − 5 |
| Sierra de Tepoztlán | 22 | 59 | 2.3 | .8 | 1.3− 6 |
| Taxco | 14 | 50 | 2.5 | .4 | 1.5− 4 |
| Sierra de Ozumatlán | 4 | 20 | 3.4 | .8 | 2.4− 5 |
| Cerro Azul | 9 | 29 | 3.4 | .9 | 2.6− 5.5 |
| Ciudad Guzmán | 13 | 28 | 3.8 | 0 | 2.6− 6.2 |
| Sierra de Tepoztlán—cult. | 1 | 3 | 3.7 | — | 3 − 4 |
| Thickness of leaves of seedlings | | | | | |
| Sierra de Tepoztlán | 6 | 6 | .4 | .1 | .4− .5 |
| Ciudad Guzmán | 5 | 5 | .8 | .2 | .6− 1 |
| Thickness of leaves of floriferous branches | | | | | |
| Sierra de Tepoztlán | 17 | 36 | .8 | .1 | .5− 1.1 |
| Sierra de Ozumatlán | 4 | 20 | 1.1 | .1 | .8− 1.5 |
| Cerro Azul | 9 | 28 | 1.1 | .2 | .6− 1.6 |
| Ciudad Guzmán | 12 | 27 | .9 | 0 | .6− 1.2 |
| Sierra de Tepoztlán—cult. | 1 | 3 | .7 | — | .6− .7 |

Inflorescences are cymes of 1–7 cincinni. Sometimes the apex of the floriferous branch is damaged or destroyed. On such a stem, flowers develop on axillary shoots, and the inflorescence appears racemose.

|  | n | n-obs. | $\bar{x}$ | w |
|---|---|---|---|---|
| No. of flowers per cyme | | | | |
| El Tezcal | 7 | 30 | 14 | 5–27 |
| Sierra de Tepoztlán | 5 | 8 | 20 | 10–41 |
| Taxco | 14 | 33 | 15 | 2–37 |

Flowers are sometimes 4- or 6-merous; those first to expand are near centers of cymes, largest, and on pedicels up to 3 mm. long; those expanding later are both smaller and sessile. The measurements of the torus are of flowers preserved in 70 per cent alcohol.

*Fig. 76.* Flower of a plant of *Sedum jaliscanum* from Cerro Azul, Michoacán, cultivated in the greenhouse, Ithaca, N.Y., June 18, 1956 (x 10).

|                   | $n$ | $n$-obs. | $\bar{x}$ (mm.) | $w$ (mm.) |
|-------------------|-----|----------|-----------------|-----------|
| Flowers—diameter  |     |          |                 |           |
| Taxco             | 1   | 2        | 6.5             | 5 –8      |
| Torus—length      |     |          |                 |           |
| Cerro Azul        | 1   | 3        | 1.1             | .9–1.3    |

Sepals are of unequal size in each flower, linear-lanceolate, elliptic-oblong, or oblanceolate, with spurs .4–1.1 mm. long, obtuse, green, sometimes speckled with red. All measurements are of the longest sepal in each flower studied. Sepals of plants at El Tezcal, the Sierra de Tepoztlán, and Taxco are significantly longer than those of plants in the three western populations. In addition, differences among populations in width of sepals are highly significant, but the variation is not on a regional basis.

|  | $n$ | $n$-obs. | $\bar{x}$ (mm.) | $s$ (mm.) | $w$ (mm.) |
|---|---|---|---|---|---|
| **Length** | | | | | |
| El Tezcal | 7 | 30 | 5.8 | 1 | 3.6– 7.9 |
| Sierra de Tepoztlán | 22 | 47 | 6.7 | 2.3 | 3 –13.1 |
| Taxco | 14 | 49 | 5 | .6 | 2.9– 6.8 |
| Sierra de Ozumatlán | 4 | 20 | 3.2 | .4 | 2.4– 4.1 |
| Cerro Azul | 14 | 70 | 3.2 | .5 | 1.8– 5 |
| Ciudad Guzmán | 14 | 30 | 3 | .3 | 1.9– 5.6 |
| Sierra de Tepoztlán—cult. | 1 | 3 | 4.2 | — | 3.7– 5.2 |
| Cerro Azul—cult. | 1 | 1 | 2.5 | — | 2.5 |
| **Width** | | | | | |
| El Tezcal | 7 | 30 | 1 | .1 | .6– 1.3 |
| Sierra de Tepoztlán | 22 | 46 | 1.5 | .4 | .9– 2.5 |
| Taxco | 14 | 49 | 1.1 | .1 | .8– 1.7 |
| Sierra de Ozumatlán | 4 | 20 | .9 | 0 | .8– 1 |
| Cerro Azul | 14 | 70 | 1.1 | .1 | .7– 1.4 |
| Ciudad Guzmán | 14 | 30 | 1.3 | 0 | .7– 2 |
| Sierra de Tepoztlán—cult. | 1 | 3 | .8 | — | .6– 1.2 |

Petals are lanceolate or elliptic-lanceolate, acute or obtuse, mucronate-appendaged, white, sometimes pinkish basally or on midribs dorsally. Differences among populations in both length and width of petals are highly significant, but the pattern of variation is not on a regional basis. The difference in length between the sample from the Sierra de Ozumatlán and that from the Cerro Azul—these are geographically adjacent—is highly significant. The sample from near Ciudad Guzmán has significantly shorter petals than any of the other samples.

|  | $n$ | $n$-obs. | $\bar{x}$ (mm.) | $s$ (mm.) | $w$ (mm.) |
|---|---|---|---|---|---|
| **Length** | | | | | |
| El Tezcal | 7 | 30 | 4.8 | .2 | 4.2–6 |
| Sierra de Tepoztlán | 22 | 47 | 5 | .5 | 3.6–6.4 |
| Taxco | 14 | 49 | 4.5 | .3 | 3.7–5.1 |
| Sierra de Ozumatlán | 4 | 20 | 5 | .1 | 4.3–5.7 |
| Cerro Azul | 14 | 70 | 4.3 | .3 | 3.3–5 |
| Ciudad Guzmán | 13 | 27 | 3.8 | .2 | 3 –4.6 |
| Sierra de Tepoztlán—cult. | 1 | 3 | 4.3 | — | 3.9–4.8 |
| Cerro Azul—cult. | 1 | 1 | 4.2 | — | 4.2 |
| **Length of connate portion** | | | | | |
| El Tezcal | 7 | 30 | .4 | .03 | .3– .6 |

|  | $n$ | $n$-obs. | $\bar{x}$ (mm.) | $s$ (mm.) | $w$ (mm.) |
|---|---|---|---|---|---|
| Sierra de Tepoztlán | 5 | 14 | .5 | .1 | 0 − .9 |
| Taxco | 7 | 23 | 4 | .1 | .2− .8 |
| Cerro Azul | 1 | 1 | .5 | — | .5 |
| Sierra de Tepoztlán—cult. | 1 | 1 | .3 | — | .3 |
| Cerro Azul—cult. | 1 | 1 | .3 | — | .3 |
| Width |  |  |  |  |  |
| El Tezcal | 7 | 30 | 1.6 | .1 | 1.4−1.8 |
| Sierra de Tepoztlán | 22 | 46 | 1.8 | .2 | 1.3−2.3 |
| Taxco | 14 | 49 | 1.6 | .2 | 1.3−2 |
| Sierra de Ozumatlán | 4 | 20 | 1.4 | .1 | 1.2−1.7 |
| Cerro Azul | 14 | 70 | 1.3 | .1 | 1 −1.6 |
| Ciudad Guzmán | 13 | 27 | 1.5 | .1 | 1.1−1.7 |
| Sierra de Tepoztlán—cult. | 1 | 3 | 1.3 | — | 1.3−1.4 |
| Cerro Azul—cult. | 1 | 1 | 1.4 | — | 1.4 |

Stamens have dark red anthers. One epipetalous stamen of a flower of a plant near Ciudad Guzmán was petaloid, with a malformed red anther and four well-developed ovules on the ventral surface. The adnation to the petals of the epipetalous stamens of five plants in the Sierra de Tepoztlán is highly significantly greater than in samples from El Tezcal or Taxco. Furthermore, differences among populations in length of anthers are highly significant.

|  | $n$ | $n$-obs. | $\bar{x}$ (mm.) | $s$ (mm.) | $w$ (mm.) |
|---|---|---|---|---|---|
| Adnation of epipetalous filaments |  |  |  |  |  |
| El Tezcal | 7 | 30 | .7 | .1 | .5−1 |
| Sierra de Tepoztlán | 5 | 14 | 1.1 | .1 | .8−1.4 |
| Taxco | 7 | 23 | .9 | .1 | .6−1.1 |
| Cerro Azul—cult. | 1 | 1 | 1.2 | — | 1.2 |
| Anthers—length |  |  |  |  |  |
| El Tezcal | 6 | 17 | .61 | 0 | .6− .7 |
| Sierra de Tepoztlán | 5 | 14 | .61 | 0 | .6− .7 |
| Taxco | 11 | 28 | .61 | .04 | .5− .7 |
| Sierra de Ozumatlán | 4 | 18 | .56 | .03 | .5− .6 |
| Cerro Azul | 8 | 20 | .49 | .05 | .4− .6 |
| Ciudad Guzmán | 6 | 6 | .68 | .08 | .6− .8 |

Nectaries are oblong or spatulate-oblong, rounded or emarginate at apices, dark red, sometimes yellow basally. Differences among populations in both length and width are highly significant.

|  | $n$ | $n$-obs. | $\bar{x}$ (mm.) | $s$ (mm.) | $w$ (mm.) |
|---|---|---|---|---|---|
| Length |  |  |  |  |  |
| El Tezcal | 7 | 30 | .6 | .07 | .5– .8 |
| Sierra de Tepoztlán | 22 | 47 | .8 | .08 | .6–1.1 |
| Taxco | 14 | 49 | .6 | .05 | .5– .8 |
| Sierra de Ozumatlán | 4 | 20 | .7 | .08 | .6– .9 |
| Cerro Azul | 14 | 70 | .6 | .03 | .4– .8 |
| Ciudad Guzmán | 13 | 28 | .6 | .01 | .4– .8 |
| Sierra de Tepoztlán—cult. | 1 | 3 | .5 | — | .5– .6 |
| Cerro Azul—cult. | 1 | 1 | .9 | — | .9 |
| Width |  |  |  |  |  |
| El Tezcal | 7 | 30 | .2 | .03 | .1– .3 |
| Sierra de Tepoztlán | 5 | 14 | .3 | .03 | .3– .4 |
| Taxco | 14 | 49 | .3 | .04 | .2– .4 |

Pistils are erect, white or green, sometimes pink above the middle.

|  | $n$ | $n$-obs. | $\bar{x}$ | $s$ | $w$ |
|---|---|---|---|---|---|
| Length |  |  |  |  |  |
| Sierra de Tepoztlán | 1 | 1 | 3 mm. | — | 3 mm. |
| Cerro Azul | 2 | 2 | 4.3 mm. | .9 mm. | 3.7– 5 mm. |
| Ciudad Guzmán | 3 | 3 | 2.9 mm. | .5 mm. | 2.4– 3.3 mm. |
| Cerro Azul—cult. | 1 | 1 | 3 mm. | — | 3 mm. |
| No. of ovules per ovary |  |  |  |  |  |
| Cerro Azul | 1 | 3 | 11 | — | 10 –12 |
| Sierra de Tepoztlán—cult. | 1 | 3 | 13 | — | 12 –16 |
| Cerro Azul—cult. | 1 | 1 | 6 | — | 6 |

Follicles are erect or subdivergent. The differences among populations in length is significant and in length of beaks highly significant.

|  | $n$ | $n$-obs. | $\bar{x}$ (mm.) | $s$ (mm.) | $w$ (mm.) |
|---|---|---|---|---|---|
| Length |  |  |  |  |  |
| Sierra de Tepoztlán | 10 | 19 | 2.6 | 0 | 1.7–3.4 |
| Sierra de Ozumatlán | 4 | 8 | 3.1 | 0 | 2.3–4.2 |
| Cerro Azul | 10 | 20 | 2.7 | 0 | 2.3–3.3 |
| Ciudad Guzmán | 8 | 16 | 2.7 | .4 | 2 –3.4 |
| Length of beaks |  |  |  |  |  |
| Sierra de Tepoztlán | 8 | 14 | .5 | .1 | .2– .8 |
| Sierra de Ozumatlán | 4 | 8 | .6 | 0 | .4– .7 |
| Cerro Azul | 10 | 19 | .5 | 0 | .3– .7 |
| Ciudad Guzmán | 8 | 16 | .4 | 0 | .2– .5 |
| Width of lips |  |  |  |  |  |
| Sierra de Tepoztlán | 10 | 19 | .11 | 0 | .1– .2 |

|  | n | n-obs. | $\bar{x}$ (mm.) | s (mm.) | w (mm.) |
|---|---|---|---|---|---|
| Sierra de Ozumatlán | 4 | 8 | .1 | 0 | .1 |
| Cerro Azul | 10 | 20 | .1 | 0 | .1 |
| Ciudad Guzmán | 8 | 16 | .1 | 0 | .1 |

Seeds are pyriform, finely verrucose, brown. Differences among populations in both length and diameter of seeds are highly significant.

|  | n | n-obs. | $\bar{x}$ (mm.) | s (mm.) | w (mm.) |
|---|---|---|---|---|---|
| **Length** |  |  |  |  |  |
| Sierra de Tepoztlán | 10 | 19 | .57 | .05 | .5–.7 |
| Sierra de Ozumatlán | 4 | 8 | .69 | .05 | .6–.9 |
| Cerro Azul | 10 | 18 | .73 | .06 | .6–.8 |
| Ciudad Guzmán | 9 | 17 | .58 | .04 | .4–.7 |
| **Diameter** |  |  |  |  |  |
| Sierra de Tepoztlán | 10 | 19 | .28 | 0 | .2–.3 |
| Sierra de Ozumatlán | 4 | 8 | .3 | .02 | .2–.4 |
| Cerro Azul | 10 | 18 | .29 | 0 | .2–.3 |
| Ciudad Guzmán | 9 | 17 | .25 | .01 | .2–.3 |

**Variation.** Except for data from two plants which flowered in the greenhouse at Ithaca, N.Y., my information about variation of *Sedum jaliscanum* is derived from study of wild plants. On the basis of samples from six localities, differences among populations are significant in fourteen out of eighteen characters studied. Without experiment, I am unable to distinguish between those differences which have a genetic basis and those which are the result of environmental modification.

Some trends in variation of populations are indicated in the following tables, in which listings are according to my estimates of the average expressions of plants. Figures indicate the number of plants in each size class. Highly significant differences exist among samples in each of the characters listed; all measurements are in millimeters.

| Population | n | .1–1 | 1.1–2 | 2.1–3 | 3.1–4 | 4.1–5 |
|---|---|---|---|---|---|---|
| El Tezcal | 7 |  | 3 | 4 |  |  |
| Sierra de Tepoztlán | 22 |  | 8 | 11 | 2 | 1 |
| Taxco | 14 |  | 5 | 8 | 1 |  |
| Sierra de Ozumatlán | 4 |  |  | 2 | 1 | 1 |
| Cerro Azul | 9 | 1 |  | 1 | 5 | 2 |
| Ciudad Guzmán | 13 |  |  | 2 | 7 | 4 |

*Leaves—width*

*Leaves—thickness*

| Population | n | .5 | .6 | .7 | .8 | .9 | 1 | 1.1 | 1.2 | 1.3 | 1.4 | 1.5 | 1.6 |
|---|---|---|---|---|---|---|---|---|---|---|---|---|---|
| Sierra de Tepoztlán | 17 | 1 | 2 | 6 | 4 | 3 | 1 | | | | | | |
| Sierra de Ozumatlán | 4 | | | | | 1 | | 2 | 1 | | | | |
| Cerro Azul | 9 | | | 1 | 1 | 1 | 1 | 1 | 2 | 1 | | | 1 |
| Ciudad Guzmán | 12 | | | 1 | 2 | 5 | 3 | 1 | | | | | |

*Sepals—length*

| | n | 1.1–3 | 3.1–5 | 5.1–7 | 7.1–9 | 9.1–11 | 11.1–13 |
|---|---|---|---|---|---|---|---|
| El Tezcal | 7 | | 1 | 5 | 1 | | |
| Sierra de Tepoztlán | 22 | | 8 | 6 | 6 | | 2 |
| Taxco | 14 | | 8 | 6 | | | |
| Sierra de Ozumatlán | 4 | 1 | 3 | | | | |
| Cerro Azul | 14 | 4 | 10 | | | | |
| Ciudad Guzmán | 14 | 9 | 4 | 1 | | | |

*Sepals—width*

| | n | .8–.9 | 1–1.1 | 1.2–1.3 | 1.4–1.5 | 1.6–1.7 | 1.8–1.9 | 2–2.1 | 2.2–2.3 | 2.4–2.5 |
|---|---|---|---|---|---|---|---|---|---|---|
| El Tezcal | 7 | 2 | 5 | | | | | | | |
| Sierra de Tepoztlán | 22 | | 4 | 7 | 4 | 2 | 2 | | 2 | 1 |
| Taxco | 14 | 1 | 5 | 7 | 1 | | | | | |
| Sierra de Ozumatlán | 4 | 4 | | | | | | | | |
| Cerro Azul | 14 | 4 | 5 | 5 | | | | | | |
| Ciudad Guzmán | 14 | 1 | 3 | 7 | 2 | 1 | | | | |

*Petals—length*

| | n | 2.6–3 | 3.1–3.5 | 3.6–4 | 4.1–4.5 | 4.6–5 | 5.1–5.5 | 5.6–6 | 6.1–6.5 |
|---|---|---|---|---|---|---|---|---|---|
| El Tezcal | 7 | | | | 2 | 4 | 1 | | |
| Sierra de Tepoztlán | 22 | | | 1 | 3 | 8 | 9 | | 1 |
| Taxco | 14 | | | 1 | 7 | 6 | | | |
| Sierra de Ozumatlán | 4 | | | | | 2 | 2 | | |
| Cerro Azul | 14 | | | | 2 | 8 | 4 | | |
| Ciudad Guzmán | 13 | | 1 | 2 | 7 | 3 | | | |

*Anthers—length*

| | n | .4 | .5 | .6 | .7 | .8 |
|---|---|---|---|---|---|---|
| El Tezcal | 6 | | | 6 | | |
| Sierra de Tepoztlán | 5 | | | 5 | | |
| Taxco | 11 | | | 6 | 5 | |
| Sierra de Ozumatlán | 4 | | 1 | 3 | | |
| Cerro Azul | 8 | 3 | 4 | 1 | | |
| Ciudad Guzmán | 6 | | | 2 | 3 | 1 |

| Population | n | .4 | .5 | .6 | .7 | .8 | .9 | 1 |
|---|---|---|---|---|---|---|---|---|
| | | | | *Nectaries—length* | | | | |
| El Tezcal | 7 | | 1 | 4 | 2 | | | |
| Sierra de Tepoztlán | 22 | | | 1 | 8 | 8 | 3 | 2 |
| Taxco | 14 | | 1 | 9 | 4 | | | |
| Sierra de Ozumatlán | 4 | | | 2 | 1 | 1 | | |
| Cerro Azul | 14 | | 3 | 11 | | | | |
| Ciudad Guzmán | 13 | 1 | | 7 | 4 | 1 | | |

| | n | .5 | .6 | .7 | .8 |
|---|---|---|---|---|---|
| | | | *Seeds—length* | | |
| Sierra de Tepoztlán | 10 | 5 | 4 | 1 | |
| Sierra de Ozumatlán | 4 | | 2 | 1 | 1 |
| Cerro Azul | 10 | | 2 | 4 | 4 |
| Ciudad Guzmán | 9 | 4 | 4 | 1 | |

Certain patterns of variation are evident: the sample from the Sierra de Tepoztlán has the longest petals and nectaries; the samples from the Cerro Azul and Ciudad Guzmán have the broadest leaves; the sample from the Cerro Azul has the shortest anthers and longest seeds; and that from Ciudad Guzmán has the shortest sepals and petals. The plants of my sample from the Sierra de Tepoztlán are topotypes of *Sedum naviculare*, those from the Cerro Azul of *S. syncarpum*. Until we know which, if any, of the differences have a genetic basis, taxonomic designation of these populations is tenuous. Even if some of the differences do prove to have a genic basis, unless they are in some way correlated, no basis may exist for designation of subspecies.

**Nomenclature.** *Sedum jaliscanum* S. Watson, Proc. Am. Acad. 25: 148 (1890). Type locality: shaded mossy rocks near Guadalajara. Type: C. G. Pringle's collection no. 2,451 (GH), September, 1889. Watson cited both of Pringle's collections, nos. 2,192 and 2,451. Fröderström's (1930–1935) selection of no. 2,451 as the type seems satisfactory. A collection of Sessé, Mociño, Castillo, and Maldonado (Bot. Gard., Madrid), available through the courtesy of the Chicago Natural History Museum, indicates that one of these collectors found the species sometime between 1787 and 1804. The unpublished name on the label very likely antedates *S. jaliscanum*.

Synonyms are:

1903. *Sedum naviculare* Rose, Bull. N.Y. Bot. Gard. 3: 42. Type locality: rocky knobs of Sierra de Tepoztlán, Morelos, alt. 2,250 m. Type: C. G. Pringle's collection no. 8,384 (US 381,868). Britton and Rose (1905) separated *S. naviculare* from *S. jaliscanum* on the basis of the fact that flowers were close together on the branches of the cymes in *S. naviculare*, but distant, on long, leafy branches, in *S. jaliscanum.* Since the closeness of flowers in cymes is determined by both age and environment, this is a poor basis for separation.

1936. *Sedum syncarpum* Fröderström, Act. Hort. Goth. 10 (App.): 133. Type locality: vicinity of Morelia, Cerro Azul, Michoacán, alt. 2,200 m. Type: G. Arsène's collection no. 5,772 (GH). Fröderström separated this from *S. jaliscanum* on the basis of form of leaves, shape of nectaries, and greater union of carpels. Plants which I studied in the region of the type locality did not differ in form of leaves. The petioles were longer than those of plants near Ciudad Guzmán, Jalisco. None of the nectaries were as long as stated by Fröderström. The longest of seventy measured was .8 mm. Two plants in the Sierra de Tepoztlán had the longest which I have seen, the maximum length being 1.1 mm. The pistils and follicles of plants in the Cerro Azul were erect. Their bases were attached to short tori. Above these their ventral margins were connivent, but not connate, for more than half their lengths. The condition in the plants of the Cerro Azul was not unique.

**Distribution.** *Sedum jaliscanum* is widely distributed in the central and western portions of the Trans-Mexican Volcanic Belt, and it also occurs in the western part of the Central Mexican Plateau and in the northern part of the Sierra Madre del Sur. Data for the six populations which I have studied in the field are as follows:

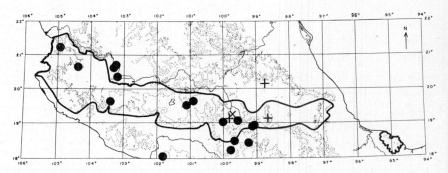

*Fig. 77.* Known distribution of *Sedum jaliscanum* (•), *S. minimum* (+), and *S. napiferum* (x).

| Location | n-plants | Area | Alt. range | pH | Drainage |
|----------|----------|------|-----------|-----|----------|
| El Tezcal | 248 | ab. 10 m. x 10 m. | 1,755 m. | 5 6–6.4 | excessive |
| Sierra de Tepoztlán | 934 | ab. 7 km. x 100 m. | 1,800–2,320 m. | 5 4–6 | moderate to excessive |
| Taxco | ab. 407 | ab. 1 km. x .5 km. | 1,806–1,906 m. | — | moderate |
| Sierra de Ozumatlán | ab. 600 | ab. 5 m. x 5 m. | 2,270–2,273 m. | 6.6 | moderate |
| Cerro Azul | 635 | ab. 15 m. x 10 m. | 2,220–2,240 m. | 5.2–5.8 | poor to moderate |
| Ciudad Guzmán | 430 | >30 m. x 20 m. | 1,570–1,602 m. | 6.6–7.4 | moderate to excessive |

Populations additional to those which I studied and the discoverers of each are as follows: Cerro Frío, Morelos, P. Maury (NY); Tenancingo, Mexico, Villada (Mexu); Bejucos (US), Cajones (NY), Mesón Viejo, 2,880 m. (GH, US), Rincón del Carmen, 1,340 m. (US), and Sierrita (CU, GH, NY, US) all in the District of Temascaltepec, Mexico, George Hinton; Mt. San Miguel near Morelia, Gerfroy Arsène (US); near Mascota, Sierra de la Campana, Jalisco, Rogers McVaugh (CU); and mountains 14 km. north of Compostela, Nayarit, 1,000–1,200 m., Rogers McVaugh (Univ. of Mich.). Localities on the Central Mexican Plateau are the Barranca de Guadalajara, Cyrus Pringle (GH), and the hill at Chapala, Jalisco, Rose and Painter (Mexu). Localities in the Sierra Madre del Sur, all in Guerrero, are the canyon 25 km. west of Iguala, on the road to Teloapán L. F. Randolph; Pilas and Arroyo, both in the District of Mina, George Hinton (GH); Vallecitos, District of Montes de Oca, Hinton (CU, GH); and Piedra Ancha, 3,100 m., Galeana, Hinton (CU, GH).

Otto Nagel (GH) collected *Sedum jaliscanum* at El Tezcal, near Tepoztlán, on Aug. 29, 1938. I visited the population there on Aug. 30 and Nov. 17, 1955. Plants were in flower on Aug. 30 and in fruit on Nov. 17. They were growing in crevices in lava, exposed to the southeast and east. The only other species of Crassulaceae present was *S. quevae*. That flowered when *S. jaliscanum* was in fruit: I did not find hybrids. Plants competing with *S. jaliscanum* included *Prionosciadium nelsonii*, *Jaegeria hirta*, and *Dahlia coccinea*.

Pringle found *Sedum jaliscanum* in the Sierra de Tepoztlán in 1900. I studied it there on Sept. 6, 13, and 15 and on Nov. 17, 1955. The plants were in flower in September and in fruit in November. They grew in a variety of conditions: on a wall along a street on the north side of Tepoztlán, on cliffs of conglomerate in ravines, on lava west of the knobs of conglomerate, on lava north of El Parque, and on boulders along the railroad. My sample for study included fifteen plants from cliffs of conglomerate in the deep ravine just north of Tepoztlán, five from lava west of the knobs, and twelve from lava north of El Parque. Exposure was primarily to the south and south-southwest. Although *S. cremnophila*, *S. frutescens*, *S. longipes*, and *S. oxypetalum* all occur in the Sierra de Tepoztlán, only the last was anywhere close to *S. jaliscanum* and in flower at the same time. I found no hybrids. Reproduction appeared to be entirely by seeds. Seedlings were common. Competing species included *Reboulia hemisphaerica*, *Notholaena candida*, *Polypodium polypodioides* (subspecies including var. *aciculare*), and *Pilea hyalina*.

Near Taxco, Moore and Wood collected *Sedum jaliscanum* in 1948. It occurs there in moss on conglomerate on both sides of the Chacoalco River. Plants were abundantly in flower on Aug. 25 and Sept. 1, 1955. The only other species of Crassulaceae nearby was *S. frutescens*, which flowers in the dry season.

My sample of *Sedum jaliscanum* from the Sierra de Ozumatlán grew on a huge boulder of conglomerate on the north side of the Morelia-Toluca highway, southeast of Triguillo, Michoacán. The plants were in flower on Sept. 25 and Oct. 4 and in fruit on Dec. 1, 1955. Seedlings were common at the time of my earlier visits, but by December their leaves were withered. Exposure was to the south. No other Crassulaceae were in the vicinity.

In the Cerro Azul, Gerfroy Arsène collected *Sedum jaliscanum* in 1910 and subsequently. The population which I studied there on Sept. 23 and Dec. 2, 1955, was on a slope facing northwest. The plants were growing on large boulders of conglomerate below and at the west end of cliffs south of the river at Campo Vello, which is 4 km. southeast of Jesús del Monte. They were in flower in September and in fruit in December. Seedlings were abundant. Some still had green leaves in December. No other Crassulaceae were present. Common competing species were *Braunia secunda*, *Echeandia macrocarpa*, and *Aegopogon tenellus*.

On Oct. 22, 1940, H. E. Moore, Jr., collected *Sedum jaliscanum* southeast of Ciudad Guzmán, Jalisco. I visited the population there on Oct. 2, 1955, when plants were in flower, and on Dec. 9, when they were in fruit. They were on the rocky slope of Las Piñas, growing on conglomerate, exposed for the most part to the southwest. I saw no other Crassulaceae in the vicinity.

**Relationships.** Among the biennial, corm-bearing stonecrops of the Trans-Mexican Volcanic Belt, *Sedum jaliscanum* has in common with *S. cormiferum* oblanceolate or spatulate, petiolate leaves and dark red nectaries. Its petals are white, however, not greenish; its flowers are sessile or on pedicels less than 3 mm. long; and its nectaries are small. A further comparison is available in the following table, in which data are for wild plants.

|  | S. jaliscanum | | | | S. cormiferum | | | |
|---|---|---|---|---|---|---|---|---|
|  | $n$ | $n$-obs. | $\bar{x}$ (mm.) | $s$ (mm.) | $n$ | $n$-obs. | $\bar{x}$ (mm.) | $s$ (mm.) |
| Leaves of floriferous branches | | | | | | | | |
| Length* | 69 | 218 | 12.5 | 3.4 | 7 | 9 | 28.2 | 12.7 |
| Petals | | | | | | | | |
| Length* | 74 | 243 | 4.5 | .3 | 21 | 29 | 3.1 | .1 |
| Length of connate portion* | 19 | 67 | .4 | .1 | 21 | 29 | 0 | 0 |
| Nectaries | | | | | | | | |
| Length** | 74 | 244 | .6 | .1 | 21 | 29 | 1.6 | 0 |
| Width** | 26 | 93 | .3 | .04 | 21 | 29 | .8 | .1 |
| Seeds | | | | | | | | |
| Length** | 33 | 62 | .63 | .04 | 24 | 60 | .46 | 0 |

Outside of the Trans-Mexican Volcanic Belt, *Sedum batesii* of the Sierra Madre del Sur and possibly of Central America is most closely related to *S. jaliscanum*, but it is distinguished by linear nectaries, about 2 mm. long, and linear-spatulate leaves. *Sedum calcaratum* of the Central Mexican Plateau may also be related. Its diagnostic characteristics are red petals and long, narrow nectaries.

The other two corm-bearing species of the Trans-Mexican Volcanic Belt are *Sedum minimum* and *S. napiferum*. Both usually have red markings on the petals. *Sedum minimum* is dwarf, less than 3 cm. tall, with clavate or oblanceolate leaves. *Sedum napiferum* has lanceolate or ovate leaves.

## 27. *SEDUM NAPIFERUM* (fig. 78)

Plants of *Sedum napiferum* are biennial with elongate corms. Seedlings have the leaves either nearly globular or clavate. These wither at the end of the first rainy season. Leaves of floriferous branches are lanceolate or ovate. The petals are white, generally with three or four transverse bands of dark red streaks. In the Trans-Mexican Volcanic Belt, only *S. minimum* is likely to be confused with *S. napiferum*. That is dwarf, less than 3 cm. high, with clavate or oblanceolate leaves and with the petals slightly connate basally.

**Description.** Materials: 32 plants, all from the Cerro Teresona on the northern side of Toluca, Mexico.

Plants of *Sedum napiferum* are biennials, geophytes, each producing in the first rainy season an elongate, white corm with a nearly globular first leaf and a clavate upper leaf; leaves of the first rainy season wither in the subsequent dry season; 1–5 floriferous branches develop in the second rainy season, these often again branched; corms shrink during the period of flowering and fruiting, after which the plants die. Reproduction appears to be entirely by seeds.

|  | $n$ | $n$-obs. | $\bar{x}$ | $s$ | $w$ |
|---|---|---|---|---|---|
| Corms—diameter |  |  |  |  |  |
| At end of first rainy season | 7 | 7 | 2.4 mm. | .8 mm. | 1.1–3.6 mm. |
| When plants are in flower | 1 | 1 | 6 mm. | — | 6 mm. |
| When plants are in fruit | 7 | 7 | 2 mm. | .8 mm. | 1 –3 mm. |
| Height |  |  |  |  |  |
| At time of flowering | 3 | 8 | 3.3 cm. | .7 cm. | 2.5–4.4 cm. |
| At time of fruiting | 10 | 10 | 3.1 cm. | .9 cm. | 2 –4.5 cm. |

Leaves of seedlings are unlike, the first nearly globular, about 2 mm. long, the upper clavate, about 9.5 mm. long, both pale green speckled with pink. Leaves of floriferous branches are lanceolate or ovate, very short-spurred, obtuse, plane ventrally, convex dorsally, pale green speckled with red.

|  | $n$ | $n$-obs. | $\bar{x}$ *(mm.)* | $s$ *(mm.)* | $w$ *(mm.)* |
|---|---|---|---|---|---|
| Length | 8 | 18 | 5.7 | .4 | 4.3–7.9 |
| Width | 8 | 18 | 2.7 | .4 | 2 –3.6 |
| Thickness | 4 | 9 | 2 | 0 | 1.6–2.7 |

*Fig. 78. Sedum napiferum* on Cerro Teresona, Toluca, Sept. 8, 1955.

Inflorescences are elongate, cincinnal cymes.

|  | n | n-obs. | $\bar{x}$ | w |
|---|---|---|---|---|
| No. of flowers per cyme | 13 | 31 | 10 | 3–30 |

Flowers are on short pedicels which are sometimes papillose. The information about the torus is derived from flowers preserved in alcohol.

|  | n | n-obs. | $\bar{x}$ (mm.) | s (mm.) | w (mm.) |
|---|---|---|---|---|---|
| Pedicels—length | 7 | 23 | 2.8 | .2 | 2 – 4 |
| Flowers—diameter | 1 | 2 | 10.5 | — | 10 –11 |
| Torus—length | 1 | 3 | 1.2 | — | .9– 1.4 |

Sepals are ovate, short-spurred, obtuse, green speckled with red.

|  | n | n-obs. | $\bar{x}$ (mm.) | s (mm.) | w (mm.) |
|---|---|---|---|---|---|
| Length | 18 | 54 | 3.6 | .7 | 2.4–5 |
| Length of spurs | 7 | 23 | .8 | .1 | .5–1.2 |
| Width | 18 | 54 | 1.9 | .3 | 1.2–2.7 |

Petals are lanceolate, completely separate from each other at

bases, bluntly appendaged at apices, white, usually with three or
four, rarely five, transverse bands of dark red streaks.

|  | n | n-obs. | x̄ (mm.) | s (mm.) | w (mm.) |
|---|---|---|---|---|---|
| Length | 18 | 54 | 5.3 | .6 | 4.4–6.7 |
| Width | 18 | 54 | 1.9 | .2 | 1.5–2.5 |

Stamens have pink or dark red filaments and dark red anthers;
filaments are curved outward after anthesis. A few plants with
white petals, without bands of red, had white filaments and orange
anthers. An anther of one plant was divided, appearing as two.

|  | n | n-obs. | x̄ (mm.) | s (mm.) | w (mm.) |
|---|---|---|---|---|---|
| Adnation of epipetalous filaments | 16 | 45 | .4 | .04 | .2–.6 |
| Anthers—length | 18 | 37 | .7 | .07 | .5–.8 |

Nectaries are spatulate-oblong or oblong, truncate, subemarginate, usually dark red and either greenish or yellowish basally.
Plants with the petals white, without red bands, had pale yellow
nectaries.

|  | n | n-obs. | x̄ (mm.) | s (mm.) | w (mm.) |
|---|---|---|---|---|---|
| Length | 18 | 54 | .8 | .03 | .7–1.1 |
| Width | 18 | 54 | .26 | .03 | .2–.4 |

Pistils are erect, constricted basally and slightly bent inward at
apices, usually dark red, almost white basally, but on plants with
the petals not heavily marked with red, pale green streaked with
red. As the pistils mature, they become divergent and markedly
two-lipped.

|  | n | n-obs. | x̄ | w |
|---|---|---|---|---|
| Length | 1 | 1 | 2.4 mm. | 2.4 mm. |
| No. of ovules per ovary | 1 | 3 | 14 | 13 –14 |

Follicles are divergent.

|  | n | n-obs. | x̄ (mm.) | s (mm.) | w (mm.) |
|---|---|---|---|---|---|
| Length | 10 | 30 | 2.7 | .07 | 2.2–3.3 |
| Length of beaks | 10 | 30 | .4 | 0 | .2–.5 |
| Width of lips | 10 | 30 | .2 | 0 | .1–.3 |

Seeds are pyriform, glabrous, finely reticulate, yellow-brown.

|  | $n$ | $n$-obs. | $\bar{x}$ (mm.) | $s$ (mm.) | $w$ (mm.) |
|---|---|---|---|---|---|
| Length | 10 | 30 | .7 | 0 | .6–.8 |
| Diameter | 10 | 30 | .3 | 0 | .2–.3 |

**Variation.** Opportunity for study of intraspecific variation of *Sedum napiferum* is possible only in the one known population on the slopes of the Cerro Teresona on the north side of Toluca. Eighteen plants studied in flowering condition differed in eight dimensions. These include length and width of both sepals and petals, length of anthers, width of nectaries, width of leaves, and height. Differences in dimensions of follicles and seeds are slight. Since corms brought to Ithaca did not grow, no data are available for plants cultivated in a neutral environment. How many, if any, of the differences observed in the field are environmental modifications still is a question.

Conspicuous in the field were five albino plants in which red pigmentation was slight. The petals were nearly pure white, with just a faint trace of red streaking below the middle. The sepals were yellow-green, filaments white, anthers orange, nectaries pale yellow, and ovaries pale green streaked with red. Presumably this condition had arisen through mutation. In all respects except pigmentation, the albinos matched other plants in the population.

**Nomenclature.** *Sedum napiferum* Peyritsch, Linnaea 30: 50–51 (1859). Type locality: near the city of Toluca, 2,440 m. Type: Carl Heller's collection no. 457, Aug. 27, 1846, cited as in the herbarium in Vienna. I have not seen the type, but have depended upon the original description and topotypes for correct interpretation of the species.

**Distribution.** *Sedum napiferum* is known only from the Trans-Mexican Volcanic Belt, near the city of Toluca. Data for the population which I have studied are as follows:

| Location | $n$-plants | Area (km.) | Alt. range (m.) | pH | Drainage |
|---|---|---|---|---|---|
| Cerro Teresona | >462 | .3 x .2 | 2,820–2,890 | 5.4–6.8 | moderate to excessive |

Carl Heller collected *Sedum napiferum* near Toluca in 1846. Pringle collected it there in 1900, and Rose and Painter in 1903. My first visit to the site was on March 28, 1949. At that time I could find no evidence of the species, although I visited the same place where plants in flower were conspicuous on Sept. 5, 1955.

After the time of flowering, the stems and leaves wither. On Nov. 23, 1955, most follicles had already split open, but seeds remained enclosed, and a few flowers still were in anthesis. The plants were on conglomerate, exposed to the west and southwest. The only other species of Crassulaceae growing with them was *S. moranense*. That was in flower at the same time, but I found no evidence of interspecific hybridization. Competing species included *Braunia secunda* and *Grimmia laevigata*, both identified by Professor Andrews, *Achyropappus anthemoides*, and *Microchloa kunthii*. The only insect which I observed on flowers of *S. napiferum* was a species of Diptera.

**Relationships.** *Sedum napiferum* is closely related to *S. minimum*. Dried specimens appear so similar that for a long time, on the basis of studies in the herbarium, I combined the two species. *Sedum minimum* is of lower stature, less than 3 cm. high, with clavate or oblanceolate leaves and with petals which are connate basally and marked with red only below the middle. For a further discussion and comparison, see the section on relationships under *S. minimum*.

Other species related to *Sedum napiferum* are *S. flaccidum* and *S. vinicolor*, both of the Sierra Madre Occidental; *S. vinicolor* is also found on the Northern Mexican Plateau. As in *S. napiferum*, the petals of *S. flaccidum* are banded with purple. The petals are connate basally, however, and the plants are taller, attaining a height of 10 cm. Likewise, plants of *S. vinicolor* are taller, attaining a height of 11 cm., with the petals connate basally and either white or greenish white, though becoming purple in drying. These species are close to *S. napiferum*. Further study may reveal that all comprise a single species which must be called *S. napiferum*, since that is the earliest name.

The transverse bands of red streaks usually on the petals of *Sedum napiferum* easily distinguish it from *S. jaliscanum*. Moreover, its seeds are finely reticulate, not verrucose. Other differences include the following:

|  | S. napiferum | | | | S. jaliscanum | | | |
|  | n | n-obs. | x̄ (mm.) | s (mm.) | n | n-obs. | x̄ (mm.) | s (mm.) |
|---|---|---|---|---|---|---|---|---|
| Leaves |  |  |  |  |  |  |  |  |
| Length of petioles* | 8 | 18 | 0 | 0 | 26 | 76 | 1.9 | .5 |
| Petals |  |  |  |  |  |  |  |  |
| Length of connate portion** | 18 | 54 | 0 | 0 | 20 | 68 | .4 | .1 |
| Follicles |  |  |  |  |  |  |  |  |
| Width of lips** | 10 | 30 | .2 | 0 | 32 | 63 | .1 | 0 |

## 28. *SEDUM MINIMUM* (fig. 79)

*Sedum minimum* is an appropriate name for this little stonecrop. The plants are the smallest of any species of the Trans-Mexican Volcanic Belt. In the alpine zone of Mt. Iztaccihuatl and of the Nevado de Toluca, the branches of the inflorescences are prostrate, with the clusters of flowers appearing on the surface of the ground. The petals are white, each streaked with dark red below the middle, and connate basally. The leaves are either clavate or oblanceolate. *Sedum napiferum*, the only species likely to be confused with it, is taller, averaging 3.3 cm. high, with the petals separate basally and usually prominently marked with three or four transverse bands of red streaks. Its leaves are lanceolate or ovate.

**Description.** Materials: 107 plants—58 from Mt. Iztaccihuatl and 49 from the Nevado de Toluca.

Plants of *Sedum minimum* are biennials, geophytes, with corms and fibrous, white roots; main stems are mostly hypogean, leafless, and white; branches are prostrate, divergent, glabrous, to 27 mm. long.

| | $n$ | $n$-obs. | $\bar{x}$ | $s$ | $v$ |
|---|---|---|---|---|---|
| Corms—diameter—at end of first rainy season | | | | | |
| Iztaccihuatl | 22 | 22 | 2.3 mm. | 1 mm. | .7–4.8 mm. |
| Nevado de Toluca | 25 | 25 | 2.7 mm. | 1 mm. | .9–5.5 mm. |
| Corms—diameter—when plants are in fruit | | | | | |
| Iztaccihuatl | 3 | 3 | 1.7 mm. | .9 mm. | 1.2–2.7 mm. |
| Nevado de Toluca | 11 | 11 | 1.3 mm. | .7 mm. | .5–5 mm. |
| Height at time of flowering | | | | | |
| Iztaccihuatl | 1 | 1 | 1.2 cm. | — | 1.2 cm. |
| Nevado de Toluca | 10 | 10 | 1 cm. | .1 cm. | .7–1.2 cm. |
| Height at time of fruiting | | | | | |
| Iztaccihuatl | 3 | 7 | 1.7 cm. | 0 cm. | .6–2.5 cm. |
| Nevado de Toluca | 13 | 13 | 1 cm. | .3 cm. | .5–1.8 cm. |

Leaves of seedlings are clavate, those of floriferous branches clavate, oblanceolate, oblanceolate-elliptical, or elliptic-oblong, subterete, plane adaxially, rounded abaxially, short-spurred.

*Fig. 79. Sedum minimum* on Nevado de Toluca, Sept. 11, 1955.

| | n | n-obs. | x̄ (mm.) | s (mm.) | w (mm.) |
|---|---|---|---|---|---|
| Length of leaves of seedlings | | | | | |
| Iztaccihuatl | 26 | 26 | 8.2 | 3 | 3.6–14.7 |
| Length of leaves of plants with flowers | | | | | |
| Iztaccihuatl | 1 | 5 | 9.2 | — | 9 –10 |
| Nevado de Toluca | 15 | 21 | 6.8 | 2.2 | 3.9–15.4 |
| Width of leaves of seedlings | | | | | |
| Iztaccihuatl | 26 | 26 | 2.4 | .8 | 1.1– 4 |
| Width of leaves of plants with flowers | | | | | |
| Iztaccihuatl | 1 | 5 | 2.3 | — | 2.2– 2.5 |
| Nevado de Toluca | 15 | 21 | 2.3 | .5 | 1.7– 4 |
| Thickness of leaves of seedlings | | | | | |
| Iztaccihuatl | 26 | 26 | 2.1 | .8 | .4– 3.3 |
| Thickness of leaves of plants with flowers | | | | | |
| Iztaccihuatl | 1 | 5 | 1.8 | — | 1.6– 2.2 |

Five leaves, measured in fresh condition on July 31, 1955, and again in dried condition on Aug. 9, 1958, had shrunk significantly in width and highly significantly in both length and thickness.

|  | $\bar{x}$ (mm.) | $s$ (mm.) | $w$ (mm.) |
|---|---|---|---|
| Length—fresh | 9.2 | .4 | 9 –10 |
| —dried | 7.1 | 1.3 | 5.6– 9 |
| Width—fresh | 2.3 | .1 | 2.2– 2.5 |
| —dried | 1.7 | .5 | .8– 2 |
| Thickness—fresh | 1.8 | .2 | 1.6– 2.2 |
| —dried | .2 | .2 | .1– .6 |

Inflorescences are few-flowered cincinni; floriferous branches are often secondarily branched, and the whole plant above ground appears as a complex inflorescence.

|  | $n$ | $n$-obs. | $\bar{x}$ | $w$ |
|---|---|---|---|---|
| No. of flowers per cyme |  |  |  |  |
| Iztaccihuatl | 3 | 14 | 5 | 2– 9 |
| Nevado de Toluca | 10 | 17 | 6 | 3–17 |

Flowers are on white pedicels. Measurements of the diameter of flowers and length of tori are of specimens preserved in alcohol.

|  | $n$ | $n$-obs. | $\bar{x}$ (mm.) | $s$ (mm.) | $w$ (mm.) |
|---|---|---|---|---|---|
| Pedicels—length |  |  |  |  |  |
| Iztaccihuatl | 3 | 14 | 2 | .6 | 1 –4.4 |
| Nevado de Toluca | 10 | 18 | 1.7 | 0 | .6–3.3 |
| Flowers—diameter |  |  |  |  |  |
| Iztaccihuatl | 1 | 3 | 6.2 | — | 5.2–6.8 |
| Torus—length |  |  |  |  |  |
| Iztaccihuatl | 1 | 3 | 1.5 | — | 1.2–1.8 |

Sepals are of different sizes in the same flower, oblanceolate-oblong, short-spurred. Measurements are of the largest sepal per flower. The sample from Iztaccihuatl has the sepals highly significantly longer and broader than those of the one from the Nevado de Toluca.

|  | $n$ | $n$-obs. | $\bar{x}$ (mm.) | $s$ (mm.) | $w$ (mm.) |
|---|---|---|---|---|---|
| Length |  |  |  |  |  |
| Iztaccihuatl | 3 | 14 | 7 | .9 | 5.1–8.9 |
| Nevado de Toluca | 20 | 39 | 3.8 | .6 | 2.4–6.3 |
| Width |  |  |  |  |  |
| Iztaccihuatl | 3 | 14 | 2 | .3 | 1.6–2.6 |
| Nevado de Toluca | 20 | 39 | 1.2 | .1 | .7–1.8 |

Petals are suberect, lanceolate-oblong or elliptic-oblong, obtuse, hooded, white or creamy white, streaked with red below middle, rarely 4, 6, or even 7 per flower. The sample from Iztaccihuatl has the petals highly significantly more connate and wider than those of the one from the Nevado de Toluca.

| | n | n-obs. | $\bar{x}$ (mm.) | s (mm.) | w (mm.) |
|---|---|---|---|---|---|
| Length | | | | | |
| Iztaccihuatl | 32 | 89 | 4.9 | .5 | 3.9–6.2 |
| Nevado de Toluca | 20 | 39 | 4.5 | 1.1 | 3.4–5.9 |
| Length of connate portion | | | | | |
| Iztaccihuatl | 32 | 83 | .4 | 0 | .2– .7 |
| Nevado de Toluca | 20 | 39 | .2 | .06 | 0 – .3 |
| Width | | | | | |
| Iztaccihuatl | 1 | 10 | 2 | — | 1.7–2.2 |
| Nevado de Toluca | 19 | 29 | 1.6 | .06 | 1.4–2.2 |

Ten petals, measured in fresh condition on Aug. 1, 1955, and again in dried condition on Aug. 9, 1958, had shrunk highly significantly in both length and width.

| | $\bar{x}$ (mm.) | s (mm.) | w (mm.) |
|---|---|---|---|
| Length—fresh | 5.5 | .4 | 5 –6.1 |
| —dried | 4.6 | .6 | 3.5–5.3 |
| Width—fresh | 2 | .2 | 1.7–2.2 |
| —dried | 1.2 | .4 | .6–1.5 |

Stamens have dark red anthers, rarely creamy white, sometimes 8 or 12. Two plants at 4,200 m. on Mt. Iztaccihuatl had flowers in which one stamen was petaloid, in one case with a two-celled anther and the other with an abaxial anther.

| | n | n-obs. | $\bar{x}$ (mm.) | s (mm.) | w (mm.) |
|---|---|---|---|---|---|
| Adnation of epipetalous filaments | | | | | |
| Iztaccihuatl | 1 | 1 | .5 | — | .5 |
| Nevado de Toluca | 10 | 20 | .3 | 0 | .2–.5 |
| Anthers—length | | | | | |
| Iztaccihuatl | 5 | 11 | .7 | .1 | .5–.8 |
| Nevado de Toluca | 8 | 14 | .6 | .04 | .5–.7 |

Five anthers, measured in fresh condition on Aug. 1, 1955, and again in dried condition on Aug. 9, 1958, had shrunk highly significantly in length.

|                | $\bar{x}$ (mm.) | $s$ (mm.) | $w$ (mm.) |
|----------------|------|------|--------|
| Length—fresh   | .68  | .05  | .6–.7  |
| —dried         | .38  | .05  | .3–.4  |

Nectaries are oblong, truncate, emarginate, dark red, yellowish basally. The nectaries of the sample from Iztaccihuatl are significantly longer and highly significantly wider than those of the sample from the Nevado de Toluca.

|                    | $n$ | $n$-obs. | $\bar{x}$ (mm.) | $s$ (mm.) | $w$ (mm.) |
|--------------------|-----|----------|------|------|--------|
| Length             |     |          |      |      |        |
| Iztaccihuatl       | 32  | 89       | 1.1  | .2   | .8–1.4 |
| Nevado de Toluca   | 20  | 39       | 1    | .05  | .7–1.2 |
| Width              |     |          |      |      |        |
| Iztaccihuatl       | 32  | 88       | .3   | .03  | .2–.5  |
| Nevado de Toluca   | 20  | 39       | .2   | 0    | .2–.4  |

Six nectaries, measured in fresh condition on Aug. 1, 1955, and again in dried condition on Aug. 9, 1958, had shrunk in both length and width, significantly in the latter.

|                | $\bar{x}$ (mm.) | $s$ (mm.) | $w$ (mm.) |
|----------------|------|------|----------|
| Length—fresh   | 1.2  | .06  | 1.1–1.3  |
| —dried         | 1    | .25  | .5–1.2   |
| Width—fresh    | .3   | 0    | .3       |
| —dried         | .2   | .05  | .2–.3    |

Pistils are erect, connate basally; ovaries are dark red, green basally; styles are sometimes greenish white. One flower with 7 petals had 13 pistils.

|                        | $n$ | $n$-obs. | $\bar{x}$ |        | $w$ |       |
|------------------------|-----|----------|--------|------|--------|-------|
| Length                 |     |          |        |      |        |       |
| Iztaccihuatl           | 1   | 1        | 3.3 mm.|      | 3.3    | mm.   |
| No. of ovules per ovary |    |          |        |      |        |       |
| Iztaccihuatl           | 1   | 3        | 13     |      | 10 –16 |       |

Follicles are widely divergent, pale brown, connate basally for .3–1.2 mm. The follicles of the sample from Iztaccihuatl, compared with those of the sample from the Nevado de Toluca, are highly significantly larger in the three dimensions measured.

| | $n$ | $n$-obs. | $\bar{x}$ (mm.) | $s$ (mm.) | $w$ (mm.) |
|---|---|---|---|---|---|
| Length | | | | | |
| Iztaccihuatl | 15 | 40 | 2.5 | .4 | 1.1–3.7 |
| Nevado de Toluca | 13 | 28 | 2.2 | .3 | 1.3–2.8 |
| Length of beaks | | | | | |
| Iztaccihuatl | 14 | 36 | .4 | 0 | .2– .6 |
| Nevado de Toluca | 13 | 26 | .3 | 0 | .2– .4 |
| Width of lips | | | | | |
| Iztaccihuatl | 15 | 40 | .13 | .02 | .1– .2 |
| Nevado de Toluca | 13 | 28 | .1 | 0 | .1 |

Seeds are oblong or pyriform, often curved, finely reticulate, fuscous or dark brown.

| | $n$ | $n$-obs. | $\bar{x}$ (mm.) | $s$ (mm.) | $w$ (mm.) |
|---|---|---|---|---|---|
| Length | | | | | |
| Iztaccihuatl | 15 | 37 | .8 | .1 | .5–1 |
| Nevado de Toluca | 12 | 25 | .7 | .02 | .6–1 |
| Diameter | | | | | |
| Iztaccihuatl | 14 | 32 | .3 | .03 | .2– .4 |
| Nevado de Toluca | 12 | 25 | .3 | 0 | .2– .4 |

**Variation.** On both Mt. Iztaccihuatl and the Nevado de Toluca, *Sedum minimum* occurs in the alpine and subalpine zones. As shown in chapter III, temperatures are similar at corresponding elevations on the two mountains. The distribution of rainfall in the year is about the same. Since both mountains are at approximately the same latitude, differences in photoperiod are negligible. The ranges of pH, as well as the gravel and ash in which the plants grow, are similar. Yet the two populations of *S. minimum* are not the same. Plants of my sample from Iztaccihuatl have highly significantly longer, wider sepals, more connate, wider petals, longer, wider nectaries, and longer follicles with longer beaks and broader lips. The primary sample from Iztaccihuatl originated as follows: A—9 plants from a slope facing southeast, at 4,000 m.; B—5 plants from a slope facing east at 4,050 m.; C—3 plants from the depression between two small peaks at 4,230 m.; D—5 plants from the crest of a ridge, facing south, about 1 km. north of C, alt. 4,150 m.; E—5 plants from a slope facing south 1 km. west of D, alt. 4,150 m.; F—3 plants from a slope facing southeast about 500 m. east of D, at 4,200 m.; and G—2 plants from rocks facing south about 400 m. southwest of E. The primary sample from the Nevado de Toluca consisted of 6 subsamples: A—10 plants from a slope facing west at 3,940 m.; B—10 plants from a slope facing northeast at 4,040 m.; C—1 plant from a slope facing southwest at 3,935 m.; D—1 plant from a slope facing east at 4,060 m.; E—1 plant from a slope facing north at 4,080 m.; and F—1 plant from a slope facing northeast at 4,100 m. The distance between A and F, the two most widely separated subsamples, was 2 km. The study of plants in the wild suggests that the populations on the two mountains are different. Since corms did not grow satisfactorily in either the cold frame or the greenhouse, I was unable to confirm this conclusion with data for plants cultivated in a similar environment. Superficially, plants of the two populations look alike. They must be closely related, even if slightly different. My opinion is that they are subspecies and that the population on the Nevado de Toluca is closest otherwise to *S. napiferum*.

Rose (Britton and Rose, 1903) had the idea that plants on the Nevado de Toluca have only five anther-bearing stamens. In twenty plants which I checked there with respect to this character, sixteen had ten anther-bearing stamens, two had nine, one had seven, and one had five. In several cases, the number of stamens with anthers fluctuated in different flowers of the same plant. The normal condition seems to be for all ten stamens to have anthers, but insects sometimes eat the anthers and upper ends of the filaments.

Within populations, wild plants of my samples differ in at least nine characters. The two populations appear to be about equally variable. Present information does not permit a decision whether the variation has a genetic basis or is the result of environmental modification.

### KEY TO SUBSPECIES

A. Sepals usually shorter than or about as long as petals; average cohesion of bases of petals .2 mm. . . . . . . . . . . . . . . . . . . . . .ssp. *minimum*, p. 301

AA. Sepals usually longer than petals; average cohesion of bases of petals .4 mm. . . . . . . . . . . . . . . . . . . . . . . . . .ssp. *delicatum*, p. 302

## Sedum minimum ssp. minimum

**Nomenclature.** *Sedum minimum* Rose, Bull. N.Y. Bot. Gard. 3: 40 (1903). Type locality: bare earth, summit of Nevado de

Toluca. Type: C. G. Pringle's collection no. 4,240 (US 48,385), Sept. 6, 1893. Rose cited as a synonym *Sedum Pringlei minus.*
   A synonym is:

1893. *Sedum Pringlei* Watson var. ? *minus* Robinson et Seaton, Proc. Am. Acad. 28: 105. Type locality: bare earth, summit of Nevado de Toluca. Type: C. G. Pringle's collection no. 4,240 (GH), Sept. 6, 1892.

   The petals of ssp. *minimum* generally are connate basally for less than .3 mm., sometimes not at all. The sepals usually are shorter than the petals, only rarely surpassing them, and average less than 6 mm. long per plant. Since this subspecies is effectively isolated geographically, problems of identification of wild plants do not exist.
   The only known population of *Sedum minimum* ssp. *minimum* is in the alpine zone of the Nevado de Toluca. My data for that population are as follows:

| Location | n-plants | Area | Alt. range | pH | Drainage |
|----------|----------|------|------------|-----|----------|
| Nevado de Toluca | >985 | 2 km. x 125 m. | 3,935–4,100 m. | 5.2–5.8 | moderate to good |

   Pringle discovered *Sedum minimum* on the Nevado de Toluca in September, 1892. His designation of the habitat as the summit of the mountain probably should be interpreted broadly. At least I did not find plants at any elevation above 4,100 m. My visits to the population were on Sept. 11, 1955, when plants still were in flower, and on Nov. 27, when they were in fruit. The plants were growing in black volcanic ash and pumice. Although *Villadia batesii* reached an elevation of 4,200 m., I did not find it in association with the *Sedum.* Competing species included *Draba jorullensis, Lupinus* (? *aschenbornii*), *Festuca tolucensis,* and *Calamagrostis tolucensis,* the last two the most important species in the area of occurrence of the *Sedum.*

### *Sedum minimum* ssp. *delicatum*

   **Nomenclature.** *Sedum minimum* ssp. **delicatum** (Rose), comb. nov., fundatum super *Sedum delicatum* Rose, Contr. U.S. Nat. Herb. 13: 297 (1911). Type locality: on rocks near and above timber line on Iztaccihuatl. Type: a collection of C. A. Purpus (US 474,951), October, 1905.
   The most practical characters for separating ssp. *delicatum* from

ssp. *minimum* are greater cohesion of bases of petals, the average cohesion per plant being at least .3 mm., and longer sepals which usually surpass the petals.

My data for the only known population of *Sedum minimum* ssp. *delicatum*, in the alpine and subalpine zone of Mt. Iztaccihuatl, are as follows:

| Location | n-plants | Area | Alt. range | pH | Drainage |
|---|---|---|---|---|---|
| Iztaccihuatl | 4,259 | 2 km. x 1 km. | 3,700–4,230 m. | 5.6–6.4 | poor to moderate |

Carl Purpus found ssp. *delicatum* on Mt. Iztaccihuatl in October, 1905. E. K. Balls collected it there in 1938, and Moore, Wood, and Atchison in 1948. My first visit to the habitat was on March 10, 1949, at which time plants were not in evidence since all aerial parts were gone and corms had not yet begun to sprout. In 1955, I visited the population on July 31, Aug. 13 and 28, Sept. 4, and Oct. 8. Plants were abundantly in flower on all except the last of these dates. On Oct. 8, fruits were mature and in many cases dehisced, but with seeds often still in position in the open follicles. The corms were growing in ash and pumice. No other Crassulaceae were closely associated, though *Echeveria secunda* and *Villadia batesii* sometimes were nearby. Competing species included *Reboulia hemisphaerica* and *Pohlia integridens*, both identified by Professor Andrews, *Cystopteris fragilis*, *Ranunculus donianus*, *Oreobroma megarhizum*, *Plantago tolucensis*, *Eryngium proteaeflorum*, *Senecio gerberaefolius*, *Luzula racemosa*, *Agrostis tolucensis*, *Calamagrostis tolucensis*, and *Muhlenbergia ramulosa*.

On Oct. 17, 1946, H. E. Moore, Jr., found plants resembling *Sedum minimum* abundant on a gravelly hillock in an open meadow in a fir forest, altitude about 3,000 m., above Pueblo Nuevo and below "Parque Nacional El Chico," on the road from Real del Monte to El Chico. The petals of these are connate basally for as much as .5 mm. This precludes the possibility that they might be *S. napiferum*, despite the fact that they are much taller than *S. minimum*, the average height of five flowering specimens being 3.6 cm. The plants above Pueblo Nuevo agree with ssp. *minimum* in having the sepals a little shorter than the petals, but are in agreement with ssp. *delicatum* in the greater cohesion of the petals. At present I know this population only from dried, flowering specimens. I have not seen fruits or seeds. Whether or not these plants belong to one or the other subspecies of *S. minimum* or perhaps to a third subspecies cannot be satisfactorily decided on the basis of present evidence. The possibility even exists that they belong to an undescribed species, but this seems less likely.

**Relationships.** The species most closely related to *Sedum minimum* is *S. napiferum*. Because ssp. *minimum* is nearest to *S. napiferum*, both geographically and morphologically, it is the population of *S. minimum* which should be considered in any comparison. The data in the following table are all for wild plants, since attempts at culture for comparison under experimental conditions were unsuccessful.

| | *S. minimum* ssp. *minimum* | | | | *S. napiferum* | | | |
| --- | --- | --- | --- | --- | --- | --- | --- | --- |
| | n | n-obs. | x̄ | s | n | n-obs. | x̄ | s |
| | | | (cm.) | (cm.) | | | (cm.) | (cm.) |
| Height at time of flowering** | 10 | 10 | 1 | .1 | 3 | 8 | 3.3 | .7 |
| Height at time of fruiting** | 13 | 13 | 1 | .3 | 10 | 10 | 3.1 | .9 |
| Pedicels | | | (mm.) | (mm.) | | | (mm.) | (mm.) |
| Length** | 10 | 18 | 1.7 | 0 | 7 | 23 | 2.8 | .2 |
| Sepals | | | | | | | | |
| Width** | 20 | 39 | 1.2 | .1 | 18 | 54 | 1.9 | .3 |
| Petals | | | | | | | | |
| Length** | 20 | 39 | 4.5 | 1.1 | 18 | 54 | 5.3 | .6 |
| Length of connate portion** | 20 | 39 | .2 | .06 | 18 | 54 | 0 | 0 |
| Nectaries | | | | | | | | |
| Length** | 20 | 39 | 1 | .05 | 18 | 54 | .8 | .03 |
| Follicles | | | | | | | | |
| Width of lips** | 13 | 28 | .1 | 0 | 10 | 30 | .2 | 0 |

In addition to the above differences, another obvious distinction is in the pigmentation of the petals. In *Sedum napiferum*, three or four transverse bands of red streaks usually are conspicuous, whereas the red markings are restricted to the area below the middle of the petals in *S. minimum*.

*Sedum minimum* probably also is related to species such as *S. flaccidum* and *S. vinicolor*, discussed under *S. napiferum*, but is further removed from them. Possibly these are all descendants of a wider-ranging ancestral type which, when the climate became warmer and drier, was geographically segmented. Some of the disjunct populations have become adjusted to the frigid conditions of the alpine zone, others to the more arid conditions of the central plateau. The word disjunct for these populations is correct. At Toluca, I searched in vain on the lower slopes of the Nevado for any evidence of this kind of *Sedum*. The areas where plants of this type do not occur are larger than the ones where they do occur.

Fröderström (1930–1935), in his classification of *Sedum*, emphasized the presence or absence of a gibbosity on the ventral sides of carpels. In follicles, these gibbosities appear as prominent lips. On this basis, Fröderström included *S. minimum* and *S. delicatum* in the *Americana Orthocarpia* and *S. napiferum*, *S. naviculare*, *S. jaliscanum*, and *S. syncarpum* in the *Americana Kyphocarpia*. The development of gibbosities impresses me as something which occurs in varying degrees among related species. Its use as a primary basis of classification of species in the Trans-Mexican Volcanic Belt would result in an artificial classification.

# CHAPTER V

# The Species of *Sedum* Cultivated in the Trans-Mexican Volcanic Belt

STONECROPS are common in cultivation in Mexico, especially in cans and pots around houses, in patios, and on piazzas. People most frequently cultivate the native species, but also several exotic ones.

In my travels in the Trans-Mexican Volcanic Belt, I devoted little attention to the cultivated species of *Sedum*. Study of them appeared to offer little opportunity to improve the knowledge of the native species. On my trips I never found an exotic species naturalized. As far as I am aware, no spontaneous hybridization occurs between cultivated and native species. From the standpoint of evolution, the cultivated stonecrops have had no effect on the native ones. Since an effect is possible, however, some attention to the horticultural species is desirable. Making no great effort in this direction and omitting nurseries and fanciers' collections, I did note the species growing in patios and on piazzas of houses, hotels, and governmental buildings. All together I listed fourteen species in cultivation, six of them native in the volcanic belt and the remainder of other origin: one each from the Sierra Madre Oriental, Sierra Madre del Sur, Europe, and Asia and four the nativity of which is uncertain. The two species most commonly cultivated were *S. mexicanum* and *S. morganianum*, then *S. longipes* ssp. *rosulare*, and less commonly than that, but frequently, *S. pachyphyllum* and *S. diffusum*.

The selection of species in five horticultural collections is indicated in the following table. The collection at Ohuapa, a village in Vera Cruz about 6 km. northwest of Totutla, was in a garden by a house; that at Fortín de las Flores, Vera Cruz, in gardens in the central plaza; that at Perote, Vera Cruz, on the piazza of the prison; that at Ciudad Serdán, Puebla, in the patio of the Hotel Fausto; and that at Amecameca, Mexico, on the piazza of the Hotel San Augustín.

| Species | Ohuapa | Fortín | Perote | Ciudad Serdán | Amecameca |
|---|---|---|---|---|---|
| 1. *S. dendroideum* (ssp.?) | + | | | + | |
| 2. *S. luteoviride* | | | | + | |
| 3. *S. pachyphyllum* | + | + | + | + | + |
| 4. *S. nussbaumerianum* | | + | | | |
| 5. *S. morganianum* | + | + | + | + | + |
| 6. *S. griseum* | | | + | + | |
| 7. *S. stahlii* | | + | + | + | |
| 8. *S. longipes* ssp. *rosulare* | + | + | + | + | + |
| 9. *S. ebracteatum* ssp. *ebracteatum* | | | + | | |
| 10. *S. mexicanum* | + | + | + | | + |
| 11. *S. lineare* | | + | | | + |
| 12. *S. diffusum* | + | + | + | + | |
| 13. *S. moranense* | + | + | | + | |
| 14. *S. dasyphyllum* | | + | + | + | |
| Totals | 7 | 10 | 9 | 10 | 5 |

Since I did not collect for propagation and study in a neutral environment samples of the cultivated *Sedum dendroideum*, identification of subspecies is uncertain.

### ANNOTATED LIST OF *Sedum* IN CULTIVATION IN THE TRANS-MEXICAN VOLCANIC BELT, EXCLUDING NATIVE SPECIES

1. *Sedum luteoviride* R. T. Clausen, Cact. Succ. Jour. 18: 74–77 (1946). Diagnostic characteristics (based on plants of horticultural origin, cultivated at Ithaca, N.Y.): subshrubs with oblong-elliptical or subspatulate leaves, 4–16 mm. long, 3–6 mm. wide; flowers with sepals 1.8–2.7 mm. long and yellow petals 4–6 mm. long. Distribution: unknown, possibly the Sierra Madre del Sur. Type locality: unknown, the type being a cultivated plant of unknown nativity. Plants cultivated at Ciudad Serdán and Toluca were not in flower in September and October, 1955.

2. *Sedum pachyphyllum* Rose, Contr. U.S. Nat. Herb. 13: 299

(1911). Diagnostic characteristics (based on plants of horticultural origin, cultivated at Ithaca, N.Y.): subshrubs with glaucous, terete, clavately oblong-oblanceolate leaves, 1–4 cm. long, 6–10 mm. in diameter; flowers with clavately oblanceolate sepals 3–7 mm. long and yellow petals 6–7 mm. long. Distribution: Sierra Madre del Sur, near San Luis, Oaxaca. Type locality: San Luis, Oaxaca. Plants were not in flower at any of the places where I saw them from August to November, 1955.

3. *Sedum morganianum* Walther, Cact. Succ. Jour. 10: 35 (1938). Diagnostic characteristics (based on cultivated plants in the Trans-Mexican Volcanic Belt and California): perennial subshrubs with long, pendulous stems, attaining lengths of 9 dm. or more; leaves glaucous, falcate, oblong-lanceolate or elliptical and acute, subterete, 15–30 mm. long, 5–8 mm. thick; flowers with erect, orchid-purple petals 10–12 mm. long. Distribution: unknown. Type locality: unknown, the type being a cultivated plant of unknown origin in the wild. Plants were not in flower at any of the places where seen from August to November, 1955.

This species, known popularly in Mexico as *Cola de Borrego* or *Cola de Burro*, is particularly common in cultivation in Vera Cruz in the region from Jalapa to Coscomatepec and Orizaba. Search in the wild for it in this area was unsuccessful. Likewise I did not find it on the slopes of the Cofre de Perote.

4. *Sedum mexicanum* Britton, Bull. N.Y. Bot. Gard. 1: 257 (1899). (See fig. 80.) Diagnostic characteristics (based on plants cultivated in the Trans-Mexican Volcanic Belt): perennial herbs with decumbent stems and linear, subterete leaves, usually in whorls of four; flowers with yellow petals. Distribution: not known certainly, but a note accompanying a collection of Calderón, no. 552 (US), indicates that it is native at Chalchuapa, El Salvador. Type locality: trap dike near the city of Mexico. Plants were in flower in Jalapa, Vera Cruz, in August.

Descriptive data follow for a plant cultivated in the greenhouse at Ithaca, N.Y.; the number of observations of each character is indicated in parentheses, and the observed ranges are indicated after averages. Floriferous branches (3) av. 17 cm., 8.5–30 cm. long; leaves (25) in whorls of four or five, spurred, linear-lanceolate, acute, av. 12.8 mm., 9–17 mm. long, av. 2.4 mm., 1.9–3.0 mm. wide, and av. 1.6 mm., 1.1–2 mm. thick, smaller and alternate upward on the younger portions of the floriferous branches; cymes

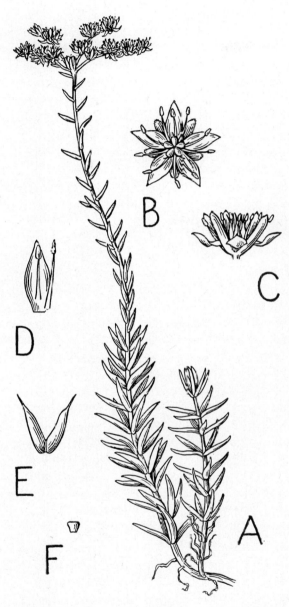

*Fig. 80.* Floriferous branch, flower, and floral parts
of a plant of *Sedum mexicanum* cultivated in the greenhouse, Ithaca, N.Y. A. Habit sketch (x .8). B.
Flower from above (x 3.2). C. Flower from side
(x 3.2). D. Petal and two stamens (x 4.8). E. Pistils
(x 4.8). F. Nectary (x 8).

(4) of av. 3, 2–4 cincinni; flowers (16) sessile, av. 8.5 mm., 7–10 mm. in diameter; tori (19) av. .4 mm., 0–.8 mm. long; sepals (19) unequal in each flower, spurred, lanceolate, acute, av. 4 mm., 3.3–4.7 mm. long, av. 1.3 mm., .9–1.6 mm. wide; petals (19) elliptical, acute and yellow, av. 4.4 mm., 3.3–4.8 mm. long, av. 1.5 mm., 1.3–1.8 mm. wide; epipetalous stamen (1) attached 1.6 mm. above base of petal; anthers (3) yellow, av. .83 mm., .8–.9 mm. long, av. .43 mm., .4–.5 mm. in diameter; pollen well developed, .02–.025 mm. in diameter; nectaries (19) obovately subquadrate, rounded, pale yellow, av. .37 mm., .3–.4 mm. long, av. .37 mm., .3–.4 mm. wide; pistils (1) erect, yellow, with 12 ovules; seeds (5) elliptical, dark brown, finely papillose, av. .66 mm., .6–.7 mm. long, .3 mm. in diameter.

5. *Sedum lineare* Thunberg, Flora Iapon., p. 187 (1784). Diagnostic characteristics (based on plants of horticultural origin, cultivated at Ithaca, N.Y.): perennial herbs with decumbent stems and linear or linear-lanceolate leaves in whorls of three; flowers with yellow petals. Distribution: eastern Asia and adjacent islands. Type locality: Japan. Plants were not in flower at Fortín or Amecameca in August and September, 1955.

6. *Sedum diffusum* Watson, Proc. Am. Acad. 25: 148 (1890). Diagnostic characteristics (based on plants in the Sierra Madre Oriental and cultivated at Ithaca, N.Y.): perennial herbs with subterete, oblong-linear leaves, 3–12 mm. long, 1–3 mm. wide, 1–2 mm. thick; flowers with white, elliptic-lanceolate, acute petals, 4–4.8 mm. long, slightly connate basally; follicles widely divergent; seeds pyriform, dark brown, .6–.7 mm. long. Distribution: Sierra Madre Oriental of Mexico in the states of Nuevo León and San Luis Potosí and also either native or naturalized in Hidalgo. Type locality: Saddle Mountain near Monterrey, Nuevo León. Plants were in flower in Ciudad Serdán in October.

7. *Sedum dasyphyllum* L., Sp. Pl. 1: 431 (1753). Diagnostic characteristics (based on plants of horticultural origin, cultivated at Ithaca, N.Y.): perennial herbs with decumbent, glandular-pubescent stems; leaves opposite or alternate, obovate, suborbicular, or elliptic-oblong, blunt, glaucous, pale bluish green or gray; flowers with pinkish white petals, sometimes heavily streaked with pink dorsally. Distribution: southern Europe and northern Africa. Type locality: southern Europe. Plants which I saw in 1955 were not in flower in August, October, and November.

CHAPTER VI

# Keys to Species

FOUR sets of keys are available here, the first for the identification of the native species in flowering condition, the second for the identification of the native species in vegetative or fruiting condition, the third for the identification of cultivated species in flowering condition, and the fourth for the identification of cultivated species in vegetative or fruiting condition. The first key includes the twenty-eight species of *Sedum* native in the Trans-Mexican Volcanic Belt and also the six other genera which occur in the region. This feature makes possible the identification, at least to genus, of any plants of Crassulaceae which may be found in the volcanic belt. Of the other genera, only *Echeveria* and *Villadia* are widespread in the region. The species of *Echeveria* may be as numerous as those of *Sedum*.

The keys are intended for the identification of living plants. Because of loss of color and change in dimensions through shrinkage, dried specimens are not satisfactory for identification with these keys, though someone familiar with the species often may recognize them. To use the keys, general knowledge of the floral parts is necessary, and a hand lens and a ruler with metric scale are also needed. All measurements in the keys are extremes of variation which I have observed under different conditions of growth, both in the field and in cultivation. Most specimens should fall within these ranges.

## KEY TO NATIVE SPECIES:
### PLANTS IN FLOWERING CONDITION

A. Stamens twice as many as petals, those opposite petals adnate to their bases.........................................................B

  B. Bases of petals separate or connate for less than 1 mm.........C

    C. Leaves usually borne spirally on stems, not opposite.......D

      D. Petals yellow, not streaked or speckled with pink or red...E

        E. Leaves spatulate, oblanceolate, or obovate, 7–54 mm. wide; subshrubs with the floriferous branches clearly axillary.......................................F

          F. Leaves 1–5 mm. thick; nectaries pale yellow or translucent, .3–.9 mm. long..................G

            G. Sepals 1.5–9.6 mm. long; anthers .9–1.6 mm. long; ovules 18–71 per ovary ...3. *S. dendroideum*

            GG. Sepals .8–2.1 mm. long; anthers .6–.9 mm. long; ovules 15–28 per ovary......4. *S. aoikon*

          FF. Leaves 7–17 mm. thick; nectaries pale orange, .7–1.1 mm. long...............5. *S. cremnophila*

        EE. Leaves lanceolate, linear-lanceolate, elliptical, oblanceolate, or obovate, 1.2–8 mm. wide; herbs with the main branches of the current season bearing terminal inflorescences........................F

          F. Leaves of floriferous branches lanceolate or linear-lanceolate, 7.5–21 mm. long; nectaries .5–1.1 mm. wide........................23. *S. grandipetalum*

          FF. Leaves of floriferous branches obovate, oblanceolate, or elliptical, 2.8–12 mm. long; nectaries .3–.5 mm. wide........................24. *S. greggii*

      DD. Petals white or pale green, sometimes streaked or speckled with red, rarely pale yellow speckled with pink.......E

        E. Nectaries red or purple, sometimes speckled with yellow.......................................F

          F. Petals pale green, streaked or speckled with pink, red, or purple.............................G

            G. Petals 6.8–8.9 mm. long; leaves 6–22 mm. wide........................1. *S. botterii*

            GG. Petals 1.4–6.5 mm. long; leaves .9–12 mm. wide................................H

              H. Nectaries 1.2–2.1 mm. wide; stems repent; leaves sessile, 4.5–15.4 mm. long.........
.........................16. *S. longipes*

HH. Nectaries .6–1.3 mm. wide; floriferous branches erect or ascending; leaves, at least the lower ones, petiolate, 4.7–34 mm. long . . . . . . . . . . . . . . . . . . . . . . . . . . . . . . . . . . . . . . I

    I. Leaves .9–5 mm. wide; cymes of 1–14 flowers; perennials with rhizomes . . . . . . . . . . . . . . . . . . . . . 18. *S. clavifolium*

    II. Leaves 5–12 mm. wide; cymes of 4–27 flowers; biennials with corms . . . . . . . . . . . . . . . . . . . . . . 19. *S. cormiferum*

FF. Petals white, sometimes with red markings . . . . . . . . . . . . . . . . . . G

  G. Leaves linear; nectaries purple; subshrubs . . . . . . 12. *S. bourgaei*

  GG. Leaves not linear, either spatulate, elliptic-oblanceolate, clavate-oblanceolate, elliptic-oblong, lanceolate, or ovate; nectaries red; biennial herbs with corms . . . . . . . . . . . . . . . H

    H. Leaves spatulate, elliptic-oblanceolate, or elliptic-oblong, often petiolate, .5–1.6 mm. thick; petals white . . . . . . . . . .
    . . . . . . . . . . . . . . . . . . . . . . . . . . . . . . . . 26. *S. jaliscanum*

    HH. Leaves clavate-oblanceolate, elliptic-oblong, lanceolate, or ovate, sessile, 1.6–2.7 mm. thick; petals white, usually conspicuously marked with red . . . . . . . . . . . . . . . . . . . . . I

      I. Petals usually with three or four transverse bands of red streaks; bases of petals separate; leaves lanceolate or ovate . . . . . . . . . . . . . . . . . . . . . . . . . . . 27. *S. napiferum*

      II. Petals white streaked with red below middle; bases of petals usually slightly connate; leaves clavate-oblanceolate or elliptic-oblong . . . . . . . . . . . . . . . 28. *S. minimum*

EE. Nectaries white or pale yellow . . . . . . . . . . . . . . . . . . . . . . . . . . . . . . . F

F. Petals pinkish or greenish white or pale yellow streaked or speckled with pink, often deep pink below middle and dorsally; leaves retuse or emarginate . . . . . . . . . . . . . . . . . . . . . . . . 9. *S. oxypetalum*

FF. Petals white; leaves not retuse, rarely emarginate . . . . . . . . . . . . G

  G. Leaves neither linear nor lanceolate-linear, more than 3 mm. wide . . . . . . . . . . . . . . . . . . . . . . . . . . . . . . . . . . . . . . . . . . . . H

    H. Leaves glabrous . . . . . . . . . . . . . . . . . . . . . . . . . . . . . . . . . I

      I. Leaves oblanceolate, spatulate, obovate, clavate, elliptical, elliptic-linear, or elliptic-oblong, 9–63 mm. long, 3–29 mm. wide . . . . . . . . . . . . . . . . . . . . . . . . . . . . . . . J

      J. Leaves flat, usually twice as broad as thick, .6–2.4 mm. thick . . . . . . . . . . . . . . . . . . . . . . . . . . . . . . . . . K

        K. Petals separate basally . . . . . . . . . . . . . . . . . . . . . L

        L. Leaves oblanceolate or elliptic-spatulate; nectaries pale yellow; submarginal placentas near bases of ovaries; bark of older parts of stems not peeling . . . . . . . . . . . . . . . . . . . 2. *S. tortuosum*

LL. Leaves elliptic-linear or elliptic-oblong; nectaries white; submarginal placentas extending most of lengths of ovaries; bark of older portions of stems peeling in papery layers......10. *S. frutescens*

KK. Petals connate basally for .3–1 mm..... ......................11. *S. quevae*

JJ. Leaves plano-convex or clavate, 3–13 mm. thick.............................K

K. Sepals ovate or oblong, .6–2.8 mm. long; leaves not glaucous.................L

L. Anthers yellow; pedicels 1–7 mm. long; sepals either separate basally or connate for as much as .5 mm......6. *S. lucidum*

LL. Anthers salmon-pink; pedicels 8–18 mm. long; sepals connate for .6–1.2 mm..........8. *S. nussbaumerianum*

KK. Sepals clavate, 5–8 mm. long; leaves glaucous....7. *S.* of the Tiscalatengo Gorge

II. Leaves ovate or lanceolate, 2–6.7 mm. long, 1.2–2.8 mm. wide............25. *S. moranense*

HH. Leaves puberulent or hirtellous...............I

I. Leaves cuneate basally, truncate or rounded apically; nectaries .2–.7 mm. long; pistils without basal concavities..............20. *S. versadense*

II. Leaves not cuneate basally, instead cordate or truncate, obtuse or subacute apically; nectaries .6–1.3 mm. long; pistils with basal concavities on dorsal sides........................J

J. Leaves of floriferous branches 4–13 mm. wide ......................21. *S. hemsleyanum*

JJ. Leaves of floriferous branches 8–28 mm. wide.................22. *S. ebracteatum*

GG. Leaves linear or lanceolate-linear, 1.7–3.2 mm. wide ...................................13. *S. griseum*

CC. Leaves usually opposite...................................D

D. Leaves flat, obcordate, obovate, or suborbicular, glabrous, 16–27 mm. long, 6–25 mm. wide; sepals 8.7–15.1 mm. long; petals 9.4–12.4 mm. long........................14. *S. obcordatum*

DD. Leaves terete, elliptic-oblong, elliptical, or globular, puberulent, 7–14 mm. long, 4–8 mm. wide; sepals 2.4–5.2 mm. long; petals 5.8–8.6 mm. long.........................15. *S. stahlii*

BB. Bases of petals connate for more than 1 mm. or else petals erect,
thick, and fleshy, and floral stems axillary . . . . . . . . . . . . . . . .C

    C. Sepals separate at bases or nearly so, neither much enlarged
nor forming an inflated tube; leaves simple; floriferous branches
either terminal or clearly axillary. . . . . . . . . . . . . . . . . . . .D

        D. Petals spreading from near middle, sometimes banded or
spotted with red or purple. . . . . . . . . . . . . . . . . . . . . . . . . .E

           E. Petals not banded with red or purple; floriferous
branches terminal. . . . . . . . . . . . . . . . . . . . . . . . . .*Villadia*

           EE. Petals either banded or spotted with red or purple;
floriferous branches axillary. . . . . . . . . . . .*Graptopetalum*

        DD. Petals usually erect, thick, and fleshy, not banded or
spotted. . . . . . . . . . . . . . . . . . . . . . . . . . . . . . . . . . . . . . .E

           E. Petals without appendages beside bases of epipetalous
stamens. . . . . . . . . . . . . . . . . . . . . . . . . . . . .*Echeveria*

           EE. Petals with appendages beside bases of epipetalous
stamens. . . . . . . . . . . . . . . . . . . . . . . . . . . . .*Pachyphytum*

    CC. Sepals connate for more than half their lengths, in each
flower forming an inflated tube; leaves often compound;
main stems terminating in inflorescences. . . .*Kalanchoe pinnata*

AA. Stamens of same number as petals and alternating with them. . . .B

    B. Leaves alternate or opposite; nectaries large, about a third of the
length of the petals. . . . . . . . . . . . . . . . . . . . . .17. *S. pentastamineum*

    BB. Leaves all opposite; nectaries small, shorter than a third of the
length of the petals. . .*Crassula* (including *Tillaea* and *Tillaeastrum*)


           KEY TO NATIVE SPECIES:
    PLANTS IN VEGETATIVE OR FRUITING CONDITION

A. Leaves generally one per node, arranged spirally on stems. . . . . . . .B

    B. Leaves glabrous. . . . . . . . . . . . . . . . . . . . . . . . . . . . . . . . . . . .C

        C. Leaves broadest above middle. . . . . . . . . . . . . . . . . . . . . . .D

           D. Leaves averaging more than 5 mm. wide. . . . . . . . . . . . .E

             E. Leaves averaging less than 4.5 mm. thick. . . . . . . . . .F

               F. Plants perennial; subshrubs; seeds averaging more
than .5 mm. long. . . . . . . . . . . . . . . . . . . . . . . . .G

                 G. Leaves averaging more than 14 mm. long . . . .H

                   H. Stems angulate. . . . . . . . . . . . . . . .1. *S. botterii*

                   HH. Stems not angulate. . . . . . . . . . . . . . . . . . .I

                     I. Twigs smooth, not papillose. . . . . . . . . . .J

                       J. Leaves averaging 2 mm. or more in
thickness. . . . . . . . . . . .3. *S. dendroideum*

JJ. Leaves averaging 1.8 mm. in thickness........
.................................4. *S. aoikon*

II. Twigs papillose.............................J
J. Bark of older portions of trunks and branches not peeling in papery layers; seeds 1.9–2.8 mm. long; plants usually epiphytic..........2. *S. tortuosum*
JJ. Bark of older portions of trunks and branches peeling in papery layers; seeds .6–1.1 mm. long; plants not epiphytic......................K
K. Leaves retuse or emarginate; follicles divergent; plants not bearing tubers..........
.........................9. *S. oxypetalum*
KK. Leaves usually rounded, sometimes emarginate; follicles erect; plants bearing tubers..
.........................11. *S. quevae*
GG. Leaves averaging less than 14 mm. long....16. *S. longipes*
FF. Plants biennial; herbs with corms; seeds averaging less than .5 mm. long...........................19. *S. cormiferum*
EE. Leaves averaging more than 4.5 mm. thick...............F
F. Leaves averaging less than 10 mm. thick................G
G. Leaves not glaucous...............................H
H. Leaves lustrous green, rounded, obtuse, or acute apically.............................6. *S. lucidum*
HH. Leaves yellow-green, yellow, or orange, not lustrous, acute......................8. *S. nussbaumerianum*
GG. Leaves glaucous.....7. *Sedum* of the Tiscalatengo Gorge
FF. Leaves averaging more than 10 mm. thick....5. *S. cremnophila*
DD. Leaves averaging less than 5 mm. wide......................E
E. Lower leaves of fructiferous branches sessile.................F
F. Stems gray and finely papillose, commonly with filiform, brown aerial roots; follicles erect....................16. *S. longipes*
FF. Stems green and smooth, without aerial roots; follicles divergent.............................................G
G. Perennial herbs always with dense, basal rosettes of leaves on axillary shoots........................24. *S. greggii*
GG. Biennial herbs lacking basal rosettes of leaves at fruiting time................................28. *S. minimum*
EE. Lower leaves of fructiferous branches petiolate.............F
F. Plants perennial with rhizomes; follicles erect; seeds with irregular longitudinal ridges................18. *S. clavifolium*
FF. Plants biennial with corms; follicles erect or subdivergent; seeds verrucose........................26. *S. jaliscanum*

CC. Leaves broadest at or below middle.......................D
  D. Leaves linear, lanceolate-linear, or elliptic-linear...........E
    E. Leaves averaging less than 3 mm. wide, less than twice as broad as thick.............................................F
      F. Leaves averaging 1.5–2.1 mm. wide, .6–1.2 mm. thick ...............................................12. *S. bourgaei*
      FF. Leaves averaging 2.3–2.7 mm. wide, 1.4–2 mm. thick.............................................13. *S. griseum*
    EE. Leaves averaging more than 3 mm. wide, more than twice as broad as thick..................10. *S. frutescens*
  DD. Leaves ovate, lanceolate, elliptic-oblong, or orbicular.....E
    E. Leaves sessile, not petiolate............................F
      F. Leaves ovate or lanceolate............................G
        G. Low shrubs, less than 1 dm. high; marginal lips of follicles averaging .4–.5 mm. wide; seeds papillose ...............................................25. *S. moranense*
        GG. Herbs; marginal lips of follicles averaging less than 2 mm. wide; seeds finely reticulate or longitudinally wrinkled................................H
          H. Leaves 7.5–21 mm. long, 3.5–8 mm. wide, glaucous; plants perennial.......23. *S. grandipetalum*
          HH. Leaves 4.3–7.9 mm. long, 2–3.6 mm. wide, not glaucous; plants biennial......27. *S. napiferum*
      FF. Leaves elliptic-oblong or elliptical................G
        G. Follicles erect; stems gray and finely papillose, commonly with brown, aerial roots.......16. *S. longipes*
        GG. Follicles divergent; stems without aerial roots...H
          H. Shrubs with bark peeling in papery layers; leaves 14–58 mm. long.........10. *S. frutescens*
          HH. Herbs with smooth stems; leaves 2.8–15.4 mm. long.............................................I
            I. Perennial herbs always with dense basal rosettes of leaves on axillary shoots......... ..............................24. *S. greggii*
            II. Biennial herbs lacking basal rosettes of leaves at fruiting time.......28. *S. minimum*
    EE. Leaves petiolate, elliptical, suborbicular, or orbicular, sometimes opposite................17. *S. pentastamineum*
BB. Leaves puberulent or hirtellous.........................C
  C. Leaves linear or lanceolate-linear, 1.7–3.2 mm. wide; subshrubs ...............................................13. *S. griseum*

   CC. Leaves obovate, spatulate, oblanceolate-oblong, oblong, or
        ovate; herbs. . . . . . . . . . . . . . . . . . . . . . . . . . . . . . . . . . . . . . . .D
        D. Leaves cuneate basally, truncate or rounded apically;
             seeds .4 mm. long. . . . . . . . . . . . . . . . . . . . .20. *S. versadense*
        DD. Leaves not cuneate basally, instead cordate or truncate,
             obtuse or subacute apically; seeds .6–.7 mm. long. . . . .E
             E. Leaves of fructiferous branches 4–13 mm. wide. . . . . . .
             . . . . . . . . . . . . . . . . . . . . . . . . . . . . .21. *S. hemsleyanum*
             EE. Leaves of fructiferous branches 8–28 mm. wide. . . . . .
             . . . . . . . . . . . . . . . . . . . . . . . . . . . . .22. *S. ebracteatum*
AA. Leaves generally two per node, decussately opposite on stems. . . .B
   B. Leaves flat, obcordate, obovate, or suborbicular, glabrous, 16–27
        mm. long, 6–25 mm. wide; seeds verrucose, winged terminally,
        1.1–1.7 mm. long. . . . . . . . . . . . . . . . . . . . . .14. *S. obcordatum*
   BB. Leaves terete, elliptic-oblong, elliptical, or globular, puberulent,
        7–14 mm. long, 4–8 mm. wide; seeds finely papillose, not winged,
        .6 mm. long. . . . . . . . . . . . . . . . . . . . . . . . . . . . .15. *S. stahlii*


### KEY TO CULTIVATED SPECIES:
### PLANTS IN FLOWERING CONDITION

A. Leaves one per node, spirally arranged on stems. . . . . . . . . . . . . . .B
   B. Petals yellow. . . . . . . . . . . . . . . . . . . . . . . . . . . . . . . . . . . . . .C
        C. Leaves flat, broader than thick, not glaucous. . . . . . . . . . . .D
             D. Leaves 7–37 mm. wide. . . . . . . . . . . . . . (3. *S. dendroideum*)[1]
             DD. Leaves 3–6 mm. wide. . . . . . . . . . . . . . . . .1. *S. luteoviride*
        CC. Leaves terete, clavately oblong-oblanceolate, glaucous. . . . .
             . . . . . . . . . . . . . . . . . . . . . . . . . . . . . .2. *S. pachyphyllum*
   BB. Petals white, purple, or pale green streaked or speckled with
        red. . . . . . . . . . . . . . . . . . . . . . . . . . . . . . . . . . . . . . . . . . . . .C
   C. Petals white. . . . . . . . . . . . . . . . . . . . . . . . . . . . . . . . . . . . . .D
        D. Leaves linear, lanceolate-linear, or oblong-linear. . . . . . .E
             E. Petals 5.1–8.7 mm. long; subshrubs with erect or pro-
                  cumbent stems. . . . . . . . . . . . . . . . . . . . . (13. *S. griseum*)
             EE. Petals 4–4.8 mm. long; herbs with decumbent or
                  prostrate stems. . . . . . . . . . . . . . . . . . . . .6. *S. diffusum*
        DD. Leaves oblanceolate-elliptical, oblong, obovate, ovate,
             lanceolate, or suborbicular. . . . . . . . . . . . . . . . . . . . . . .E
             E. Stems and leaves both glabrous; subshrubs. . . . . . . . . .F

_____

[1] Native species which are sometimes cultivated are indicated in parentheses.

F. Leaves oblanceolate-elliptical, 22–39 mm. long,
10–16 mm. wide, 5.4–8.2 mm. thick. . . . . . . . . . . . .
. . . . . . . . . . . . . . . . . . . . . .(8. *S. nussbaumerianum*)

FF. Leaves ovate or lanceolate, 2–6.7 mm. long, 1.2–2.8
mm. wide, .5–1.7 mm. thick. . . . .(25. *S. moranense*)

EE. Either stems or leaves or both pubescent; herbs. . . . .F

F. Pubescence eglandular; leaves not glaucous. . . . . . .
. . . . . . . . . . . . . . . . . . . . . . .(22. *S. ebracteatum*)

FF. Pubescence glandular; leaves glaucous. . . . . . . . . .
. . . . . . . . . . . . . . . . . . . . . . .7. *S. dasyphyllum*

CC. Petals purple or pale green streaked or speckled with red. . .D

D. Petals purple, erect, 10–12 mm. long; leaves falcate, glaucous, 15–30 mm. long. . . . . . . . . . . . . . . .3. *S. morganianum*

DD. Petals pale green streaked or speckled with red, widely
spreading, 3.7–4.5 mm. long; leaves elliptical or lanceolate, not glaucous, 5.5–15 mm. long. . . . . . . . . . . . . . . .
. . . . . . . . . . . . . . . . . . . . . .(16. *S. longipes ssp. rosulare*)

AA. Leaves two to five per node, decussately opposite or in whorls. . . .B

B. Petals yellow. . . . . . . . . . . . . . . . . . . . . . . . . . . . . . . . .C

C. Leaves decussately opposite, elliptic-oblong, elliptical or
globular, puberulent; subshrubs. . . . . . . . . . . . .(15 *S. stahlii*)

CC. Leaves mostly in whorls, linear-lanceolate or linear, glabrous;
herbs. . . . . . . . . . . . . . . . . . . . . . . . . . . . . . . . . . . . . . .D

D. Leaves mostly in whorls of four or five. . . . . .4. *S. mexicanum*

DD. Leaves in whorls of three. . . . . . . . . . . . . . . .5. *S. lineare*

BB. Petals pinkish white. . . . . . . . . . . . . . . . . .7. *S. dasyphyllum*


### KEY TO CULTIVATED SPECIES:
### PLANTS IN VEGETATIVE OR FRUITING CONDITION

A. Leaves one per node, spirally arranged on stems. . . . . . . . . . . . . . . .B

B. Leaves and stems both glabrous. . . . . . . . . . . . . . . . . . . . . . . . . . .C

C. Leaves broadest above middle. . . . . . . . . . . . . . . . . . . . . . . .D

D. Leaves flat, less than 5 mm. thick. . . . . . . . . . . . . . . . .E

E. Stems and young leaves smooth, not papillose. . . . . . .F

F. Leaves 7–37 mm. wide. . . . . . . . . .(3. *S. dendroideum*)

FF. Leaves 3–6 mm. wide. . . . . . . . . . . . .1. *S. luteoviride*

EE. Stems and young leaves papillose. . . . . . . . . . . . . . . .
. . . . . . . . . . . . . . . . . . . . . . .(16. *S. longipes* ssp *rosulare*)

DD. Leaves subterete or terete, 5.4–10 mm. thick. . . . . . . . . .E

E. Leaves oblanceolate-elliptical, acute, 10–16 mm. wide,
not glaucous. . . . . . . . . . . . . . . .(8. *S. nussbaumerianum*)

EE. Leaves clavately oblong-oblanceolate, blunt, 6–10 mm. wide, glaucous.............2. *S. pachyphyllum*

CC. Leaves broadest at or below middle..................D

    D. Leaves linear, lanceolate-linear, or oblong-linear........E

       E. Follicles erect; subshrubs with erect or procumbent stems...........................(13. *S. griseum*)

       EE. Follicles widely divergent; herbs with decumbent or prostrate stems.......................6. *S. diffusum*

    DD. Leaves oblong-lanceolate, elliptical, ovate, or lanceolate...........................................E

       E. Leaves oblong-lanceolate, falcate, glaucous, 5–8 mm. thick.........................3. *S. morganianum*

       EE. Leaves elliptical, ovate, or lanceolate, neither falcate nor glaucous, .5–4.1 mm. thick.................F

          F. Leaves elliptical, 5.5–15 mm. long; stems papillose ......................(16. *S. longipes* ssp. *rosulare*)

          FF. Leaves ovate or lanceolate, 2–6.7 mm. long; stems smooth......................(25. *S. moranense*)

BB. Either leaves or stems or sometimes both hairy.............C

    C. Pubescence eglandular; leaves not glaucous.............. ....................................(22. *S. ebracteatum*)

    CC. Pubescence glandular; leaves glaucous......7. *S. dasyphyllum*

AA. Leaves two to five per node, decussately opposite or in whorls....B

    B. Leaves decussately opposite, elliptic-oblong, elliptical, globular, suborbicular, or obovate; stems puberulent.................C

       C. Hairs eglandular; leaves not glaucous; subshrubs.......... ........................................(15. *S. stahlii*)

       CC. Hairs glandular; leaves glaucous; herbs.....7. *S. dasyphyllum*

    BB. Leaves in whorls, linear-lanceolate or linear; stems glabrous...C

       C. Leaves mostly in whorls of four or five........4. *S. mexicanum*

       CC. Leaves in whorls of three.....................5. *S. lineare*

# CHAPTER VII

# Relationships of Species

THE relationships of any group of organisms are of many kinds: geographical, ecological, morphological, physiological, genetic, and phylogenetic, as well as others. Sharp distinctions between one kind of relationships and another often are lacking. The more aspects from which a group may be considered, the better may be the understanding of its status, both with respect to other groups and within itself.

## GEOGRAPHICAL RELATIONSHIPS

One of the purposes of the study of *Sedum* of the Trans-Mexican Volcanic Belt was to determine how many species are widespread throughout the entire volcanic region. To learn this, I subdivided the belt into eight sections, as indicated in chapter III (fig. 2), and then spent time in all but one of these (Tuxtla Mountains), listing every species which I could find in each section and then noting how many species there were which occurred in all seven sections, how many in six, and so on down to how many in just one. The results are summarized in the following table:

| No. of sections | No. of species |
|:---:|:---:|
| 7 | 0 |
| 6 | 0 |
| 5 | 2 |
| 4 | 3 |
| 3 | 5 |
| 2 | 2 |
| 1 | 16 |
| Total | 28 |

Despite similar environmental conditions across most of the volcanic belt, no one species is found in six or more sections. Most are local endemics. Although similar conditions for growth occur elsewhere, disseminules either have not reached other favorable localities or have not become established there. Migration must be slow and usually for short distances. Historical changes in the environment may be more important than the present arrangement of physical conditions in determining the modern distribution of species. Factors which have prevented the spread of species probably are many. Some species are sensitive to frost. Presumably they would not cross a highland where frosts are frequent. Others probably would perish in competition in humid, tropical forests. Likewise, others would perish in a desert. Most inhabit cliffs and rocky slopes where the kinds of plants which occur are few. Were competition not a limiting factor, the species of *Sedum* might occur in many other situations. Certainly the plants grow well in cultivation in a mixture of silt loam, sand, and leaf mold. For most, this is a very different edaphic condition from that which they inhabited in nature.

Since the divides between drainage systems often are highlands with more severe climates than lowlands and slopes, these sometimes may limit the spread of organisms. In the Trans-Mexican Volcanic Belt, the main divide is between the drainage into the Gulf of Mexico and that into the Pacific Ocean. The following table shows the arrangement of species on the basis of drainage systems.

| *Slope* | *No. of species* |
|---|---|
| Gulf | 7 |
| Pacific | 13 |
| Both Gulf and Pacific | 8 |
| Total | 28 |

Of the eight species occurring in both Gulf and Pacific drainages, seven are frost-resistant. These could have migrated across highlands. They include the two species each of which is found in five sections of the volcanic belt, one of those which is found in four sections, two of those found in three, and one found in two. Many of the other twenty species may be limited in their spread by an inability to cross highlands with unfavorable climate.

Another indication of geographical relationships is the altitudinal distribution. This is shown in the following table:

| Altitudinal level | No. of species |
|---|---|
| 0–1,000 m. | 0 |
| 1,001–2,000 m. | 9 |
| 2,001–3,000 m. | 17 |
| 3,001–4,000 m. | 5 |
| 4,001–5,000 m. | 2 |

Still another relationship is shown by the number of species in each section of the volcanic belt and also the number of endemics per section.

| Section | Total no. of species | No. of endemics |
|---|---|---|
| Tuxtla Mountains | 0 | 0 |
| Orizaba | 9 | 3 |
| Malinche | 5 | 0 |
| Sierra Nevada | 5 | 1 |
| Ajusco | 10 | 1 |
| Toluca | 14 | 4 |
| Michoacán | 9 | 0 |
| Colima | 3 | 1 |

The Tuxtla Mountains, though high enough to have conditions favorable for some species of *Sedum*, perhaps are too recent to have been invaded by them. Since other botanists had not found *Sedum* there, I did not include these mountains in my itinerary. In contrast, the Toluca section, extending from the valley of the Tenancingo River to that of the Tuxpan River, has both the most species and the most endemics. The richest part of this section for *Sedum* is that draining southward into the basin of the Balsas River.

To learn about the rapidity with which stonecrops colonize sites, I noted the numbers of species on rocks of different ages. In view of the emphasis sometimes placed on disturbed habitats in connection with interspecific hybridization, as by Anderson (1948), I was interested to notice whether hybrids were more common on young lava flows. These provide as disturbed situations as one can expect to find. The results are shown in the following table:

| *Kinds of rocks* | *No. of species* | *No. of interspecific and intergeneric hybrids* |
|---|---|---|
| Lava <15 years old | 0 | 0 |
| Lava <3,000 years old | 6 | 0 |
| Volcanic rocks of all ages | 19 | 1 |
| Conglomerates of all ages | 12 | 1 |
| Cretaceous limestones | 4 | 0 |

When one compares the species of *Sedum* in the Trans-Mexican Volcanic Belt with those of other physiographic regions, only thirteen of the twenty-eight are found to occur elsewhere, some of them in two or more regions. These are summarized as follows:

| *No. of species* | *Other regions* |
|---|---|
| 7 | Central Mexican Plateau |
| 8 | Sierra Madre del Sur |
| 1 | Sierra Madre Oriental |
| 1 | Sierra Madre Occidental |
| 2 | Mountains of Chiapas and Central America |

Fifteen species appear to be endemic in the volcanic belt, ten of them restricted to single sections of the belt. Probably the high volcanoes have been an effective barrier to the northward spread of many of the species and to the southward spread of others. Similarly, the arid and semiarid regions to the north, on the Northern Mexican Plateau and Coastal Plain, as well as in the northern part of the Sierra Madre Oriental, have been a deterrent to migration in either direction. Martin and Harrell (1957) have discussed this topic. The data from *Sedum* are in agreement with their findings. I found no evidence on any of the high volcanoes of species of *Sedum* which might have come southward during the ice ages of the Pleistocene. No species is common both to temperate North America and to the volcanic belt. The species in the two regions must have been separate for a long time, probably at least since before the Pleistocene.

### ECOLOGICAL RELATIONSHIPS

The species of *Sedum* of the Trans-Mexican Volcanic Belt illustrate four life forms. Therophytes and hydrophytes are lacking.

| *Life form* | *No. of species* |
|---|---|
| Phanerophytes | 10 |
| Chamaephytes | 13 |
| Hemicryptophytes | 1 |
| Geophytes | 4 |

Despite a wide tolerance with respect to pH in cultivation, at which time competition is lacking, most species occur in nature within rather narrow limits of pH. This is shown in the following table, in which plus signs indicate the ranges of pH for each species.

| | 5.1–6 | 6.1–7 | 7.1–8 |
|---|---|---|---|
| 1. S. botterii | + | | |
| 2. S. tortuosum | + | + | + |
| 3. S. dendroideum | | + | + |
| 4. S. aoikon | | | |
| 5. S. cremnophila | + | + | |
| 6. S. lucidum | | | + |
| 7. S. of Tiscalatengo Gorge | + | | |
| 8. S. nussbaumerianum | | | |
| 9. S. oxypetalum | + | + | |
| 10. S. frutescens | + | + | |
| 11. S. quevae | + | + | |
| 12. S. bourgaei | | + | |
| 13. S. griseum | | + | + |
| 14. S. obcordatum | | + | + |
| 15. S. stahlii | | | + |
| 16. S. longipes | + | + | |
| 17. S. pentastamineum | | | + |
| 18. S. clavifolium | + | | |
| 19. S. cormiferum | + | + | |
| 20. S. versadense | | + | |
| 21. S. hemsleyanum | + | + | |
| 22. S. ebracteatum | + | | |
| 23. S. grandipetalum | | + | |
| 24. S. greggii | | + | |
| 25. S. moranense | + | + | |
| 26. S. jaliscanum | + | + | + |
| 27. S. napiferum | + | + | |
| 28. S. minimum | + | + | |

Ability to compete more successfully at one level of pH than at another could be a factor in determining the spread of populations, and differential adjustment of a group of populations with respect to pH could favor subspecific segregation.

Differences in time of flowering may be important in preventing hybridization. In the following chart, plus marks indicate the months when I observed species in flower in 1955 and 1956. All together, nineteen species were in flower in the period of field work from July 27, 1955, to Jan. 1, 1956.

| | July | Aug. | Sept. | Oct. | Nov. | Dec. | Jan. |
|---|---|---|---|---|---|---|---|
| 1. *S. botterii* | | | | | | | |
| 2. *S. tortuosum* | | | | | | + | + |
| 3. *S. dendroideum* | | | | + | | + | |
| 4. *S. aoikon* | | | | | | | |
| 5. *S. cremnophila* | | | | | | + | |
| 6. *S. lucidum* | | | | | | | |
| 7. *S. of Tiscalatengo Gorge* | | | | | | | |
| 8. *S. nussbaumerianum* | | | | | | | |
| 9. *S. oxypetalum* | | + | + | | | | |
| 10. *S. frutescens* | | | | | | | |
| 11. *S. quevae* | | | | + | + | | |
| 12. *S. bourgaei* | | | | + | + | + | |
| 13. *S. griseum* | | | | | | + | |
| 14. *S. obcordatum* | | | | + | | | |
| 15. *S. stahlii* | | | | | | | |
| 16. *S. longipes* | | | | | + | + | |
| 17. *S. pentastamineum* | | | | | | | + |
| 18. *S. clavifolium* | | | + | | | | |
| 19. *S. cormiferum* | + | + | | | | | |
| 20. *S. versadense* | | | | | | | |
| 21. *S. hemsleyanum* | | | | | + | + | |
| 22. *S. ebracteatum* | | | | + | | | |
| 23. *S. grandipetalum* | | | | | | + | |
| 24. *S. greggii* | | | | | | | |
| 25. *S. moranense* | | + | + | | + | | |
| 26. *S. jaliscanum* | | + | + | + | | | |
| 27. *S. napiferum* | | | + | | + | | |
| 28. *S. minimum* | + | + | + | | | | |
| Total no. of species | 2 | 5 | 6 | 6 | 6 | 8 | 2 |

Populations of *Sedum* are mostly small, both in geographical extent and in number of individuals. They range in size from the single plant of *S. versadense* which was all that I found after several days of searching in the gorge of the Tenancingo River to an approximate 20,000 plants of *S. moranense* on the extensive area of lava below Las Vigas on the northeastern slope of the Cofre de Perote. On the basis of counts or estimates of the size of seventy-five populations of *Sedum* in the Trans-Mexican Volcanic Belt, the average number of plants per population is 611. This figure is low, but is considerably higher than the one mentioned by Walther (1935) for *Echeveria*. He stated that few colonies of *Echeveria* consist of more than a hundred plants and also that the colonies are very localized and isolated.

The places where two species occur together in the same habitat are few. The details are shown in the following table. These data indicate how small is the potential for interspecific hybridization.

| | |
|---|---|
| No. of species | 28 |
| No. of interspecific gaps | 378 |
| No. of interspecific gaps with species on either side in the same square kilometer | 31 |
| No. of interspecific gaps with species on either side in same square meter | 15 |
| No. of interspecific gaps bridged by natural hybrids | 0 |
| No. of interspecific gaps, involving species of other genera, bridged by natural hybrids | 2 (+?1) |

Following is a list of fifteen species which occur close enough to one another so that hybridization is a reasonable possibility. The flowering time of each is indicated, as well as the species which occur with each one and the flowering time of those.

1. *S. tortuosum*—December: *S. grandipetalum*—December.
2. *S. dendroideum*
    a. ssp. *dendroideum*—dry season: *S. lucidum*—dry season; *S. stahlii,*— dry season; *S. hemsleyanum*—November, December
    b. ssp. *praealtum*—dry season: *S. hemsleyanum*—November, December.
    c. ssp. ?—dry season: *S. moranense* ssp. *moranense*—August to November.
3. *S. cremnophila*—December: *S. longipes* ssp. *longipes*—November, December.
4. *S. lucidum*—dry season: *S. dendroideum* ssp. *dendroideum* and *S. stahlii*— both dry season; *S. hemsleyanum*—November, December.
5. *S. oxypetalum*—August, September: *S. frutescens*—dry season; *S. bourgaei* —October to December; *S. jaliscanum*—August to October.
6. *S. frutescens*—dry season: *S. oxypetalum*—August, September.
7. *S. quevae*—October, November: *S. jaliscanum*—August to October.
8. *S. bourgaei*—October to December: *S. oxypetalum*—August, September.

9. *S. stahlii*—dry season: *S. dendroideum* ssp. *dendroideum* and *S. lucidum*—both dry season; *S. hemsleyanum*—November, December; *S. moranense* ssp. *moranense*—August to November.

10. *S. longipes*
    a. ssp. *longipes*—November, December: *S. cremnophila*—December.

11. *S. hemsleyanum*—November, December: *S. dendroideum* ssp. *dendroideum* and ssp. *praealtum*, *S. lucidum*, and *S. stahlii*—all dry season.

12. *S. grandipetalum*—December: *S. tortuosum*—December.

13. *S. moranense*
    a. ssp. *moranense*—August to November: *S. dendroideum* ssp. ?—dry season; *S. stahlii*—dry season; *S. napiferum*—September to November.

14. *S. jaliscanum*—August to October: *S. quevae*—October, November; *S. oxypetalum*—August, September.

15. *S. napiferum*—September to November: *S. moranense*—August to November.

With two exceptions (*Sedum bourgaei* and *S. oxypetalum; S. frutescens* and *S. oxypetalum*), species which occur in intimate association, as shown above, either flower at the same time or else their flowering times overlap. Yet I found no hybrids between any pair of species occurring together. This suggests that genetic isolation is effective. Under present conditions hybridization appears to be of negligible evolutionary importance in this group of species. Its importance in the past is uncertain.

Insects pollinate the flowers of *Sedum*. Those which I saw visiting blossoms in Mexico belonged to the orders Thysanoptera, Hemiptera, Coleoptera, and Diptera. Insects visiting flowers appeared to be indiscriminate in their visitations. No special contrivances were evident in connection with pollination. The lack of interspecific hybrids apparently is not the result of differential behavior of pollinators.

Except as competition, other vegetation appears to have little effect on the distribution of *Sedum* in the Trans-Mexican Volcanic Belt. Most species occur on cliffs and rocky slopes independent of the surrounding vegetational associations, though the predominantly epiphytic species, *S. botterii* and *S. tortuosum*, occur primarily in forests of *Quercus*. Lists of plants competing with the other species have little pattern. The influence of other kinds of plants on the sites in which *Sedum* occurs apparently is slight, though *Sedum* may not be able to compete if other species are too common or luxuriant in growth.

## MORPHOLOGICAL RELATIONSHIPS

Quimby (1939), in an unpublished thesis, reported briefly on the floral anatomy of cultivated plants of three species of *Sedum* of the Trans-Mexican Volcanic Belt. These were *S. dendroideum* ssp. *praealtum*, *S. bourgaei*, and *S. ebracteatum* ssp. *ebracteatum*. According to him, the three species are all moderately specialized and similar in their floral anatomy. His data are of no help in appraising their phylogenetic status.

With respect to gross morphology, certain conditions appear to be specializations. A list of some of these morphological specializations follows:

1. Corms or tubers
2. Cohesion of sepals
3. Cohesion of petals
4. Stamens in one whorl
5. Cohesion of carpels
6. Submarginal placentas near bases of carpels
7. Follicles with corky lips
8. Seeds winged

The belief that these conditions are specializations is largely a matter of practical, common sense. No array of fossils is available to demonstrate that evolution has progressed toward these conditions. The list might be longer, but the additional items would be more controversial. The foregoing list is based on the idea that separate parts preceded joined parts and that modifications of structures or conditions must be derived. I have deliberately excluded phyllotaxy and habit of growth from the list because of some uncertainty about each. Possibly the sequence has been from spiral arrangement of leaves to opposite and whorled. Likewise the biennial condition perhaps is derived, and the shrubby habit may have preceded the herbaceous. An appraisal of the twenty-eight species of *Sedum* of the Trans-Mexican Volcanic Belt on the basis of the above eight specializations yields the following results; the number of specializations is indicated at the left, followed by the number of species with that many specializations and the names of these species.

No specializations—11: *S. botterii, S. dendroideum, S. cremnophila,*
        *S.* of the Tiscalatengo Gorge, *S. frutescens,*
        *S. longipes, S. clavifolium, S. versadense,*
        *S. hemsleyanum, S. grandipetalum,* and *S. greggii.*
1 specialization   —11: *S. aoikon, S. lucidum, S. nussbaumerianum,*
        *S. oxypetalum, S. bourgaei, S. griseum, S. stahlii,*
        *S. pentastamineum, S. cormiferum, S. ebracteatum,*
        and *S. moranense.*
2 specializations   —4: *S. quevae, S. obcordatum, S. jaliscanum,* and
        *S. napiferum.*
3 specializations   —2: *S. tortuosum* and *S. minimum.*

No species has all eight of the listed specializations. Most have none or only one. Viewed in this way, the similarities in number of specializations are more impressive than the differences.

## PHYSIOLOGICAL RELATIONSHIPS

Almost no published information is available concerning the physiology of species of *Sedum* of the Trans-Mexican Volcanic Belt. Thomas and Ranson (1954) studied metabolism in *S. dendroideum*, but reports on other species are lacking. As a result, a detailed discussion of physiological relationships is impossible on the basis of available information.

Adaptations to freezing and aridity are specializations. Some species have progressed much further in these adjustments than others. From the standpoint of tolerance of low temperatures, for example, *Sedum minimum* appears to be more specialized than *S. tortuosum.*

## GENETIC RELATIONSHIPS

An obvious indication of genetic relationship is that shown by plants which interbreed. Conversely, those which do not or cannot interbreed may be more distant, but the factors causing incompatibility are numerous. Sometimes individuals which are intersterile are really very close genetically in every characteristic except compatibility. Because of the great amount of geographical isolation, both among species of *Sedum* of the Trans-Mexican Volcanic Belt and among populations within species, little direct evidence of potential for interbreeding is available from study in the field. In the thirteen cases where pairs of species occur together and flower at the same time, no hybridization takes place, suggesting incompatibility between the members of each pair.

Information about chromosomes, especially when interpreted in connection with the results of genetic experiments, sometimes is useful in indicating relationships. Until now, scant data have been published concerning the chromosomes of the twenty-eight species of *Sedum* of the Trans-Mexican Volcanic Belt. Dr. C. H. Uhl has counted chromosomes of one or more plants of at least twenty-three of the species. In most cases, the plants studied are my collections. The twenty-three species have at least twenty different numbers of chromosomes, *S. rapiferum* the lowest and *S. etracteatum* the highest. Sometimes the numbers are the same for closely related species; at other times they are the same for species which appear distantly related. Conversely, different numbers occur in at least two species and also in species which otherwise appear closely related. A detailed report on the chromosomes should be interesting, though the cytological evidence by itself may not affect the classification. Presumably gene mutations, reciprocal translocations, and both autoploidy and alloploidy have occurred. Of all, my opinion is that gene mutations have been most important in producing the obvious differences among the species in morphology and physiology, whereas the changes involving chromosomes and genomes have led to the sort of genetic isolation which exists wherever two species occur together and flower at the same time.

To indicate the frequency of possible genetic differences within species, I have listed below all species grown in experiments at Ithaca and have noted in addition the number of populations of each in which my data suggest that genetic variation may exist. In the tabulation, populations are considered only when two or more plants have been cultivated under similar conditions at Ithaca.

| Species | Populations cultivated | Populations with possible genetic variation |
|---------|------------------------|---------------------------------------------|
| 1. *S. botterii* | 1 | 1 |
| 2. *S. tortuosum* | 2 | 2 |
| 3. *S. dendroideum* | 3 | 2 |
| 4. *S. cremnophila* | 1 | 1 |
| 5. *S. lucidum* | 3 | 3 |
| 6. *S.* of Tiscalatengo Gorge | 1 | 1 |

| Species | Populations cultivated | Populations with possible genetic variation |
|---|---|---|
| 7. *S. oxypetalum* | 3 | 2 |
| 8. *S. frutescens* | 2 | 2 |
| 9. *S. quevae* | 2 | 1 |
| 10. *S. bourgaei* | 2 | 1 |
| 11. *S. griseum* | 2 | 2 |
| 12. *S. obcordatum* | 2 | 2 |
| 13. *S. stahlii* | 1 | 1 |
| 14. *S. longipes* | 1 | 1 |
| 15. *S. pentastamineum* | 1 | 1 |
| 16. *S. clavifolium* | 1 | 1 |
| 17. *S. cormiferum* | 1 | 1 |
| 18. *S. hemsleyanum* | 3 | 3 |
| 19. *S. ebracteatum* | 1 | 1 |
| 20. *S. grandipetalum* | 1 | 1 |
| 21. *S. greggii* | 1 | 0 |
| 22. *S. moranense* | 4 | 2 |
| Totals | 39 | 32 |

Only one of the twenty-two species studied in the greenhouse and the cold frame at Ithaca did not show evidence of possible genetic variation. Likewise, only seven of the thirty-nine populations which were studied under similar conditions lacked such evidence. The failure of plants within samples to flower simultaneously, possibly itself a real difference, forced me to study plants at different times. This is not a good condition for samples which are to be compared statistically. Further, although I have used the words similar, neutral, and even uniform at different times, the experimental conditions were not ideally uniform. For these reasons, the results with respect to genetic variation within populations of species must be regarded as more suggestive than absolute.

## PHYLOGENETIC RELATIONSHIPS

The twenty-eight species of *Sedum* of the Trans-Mexican Volcanic Belt comprise a group the members of which are more closely related to each other and to species of other parts of the Mexican and Central American highlands than to those of any other part of the world. This group possibly has been disjunct from groups of species in temperate North America since the beginning of the Pleistocene, perhaps earlier. Because no fossils are available and the species have differentiated in radial fashion, both geographically and ecologically, a linear sequence for them is both unrealistic and impossible. Instead, the species are best arranged like the spokes of wheels, with smaller spokes radiating from points on the larger spokes. *Sedum botterii*, one of the least specialized species of the group, impresses me as near the starting point. Presumably the primitive stonecrops were flat-leaved plants which inhabited humid forests. Their floral parts were all separate, and specializations were none or few. *Sedum botterii* fits these specifications. Further, species such as *S. epidendrum* seem to be its counterpart in tropical Africa. Possibly these are descendants of an ancestral group of *Sedum* which flourished in tropical forests around the world in earlier geological time. Although this is a guess, I have no better suggestion to make at present.

The groups of species which I conceive as of natural relationship in the Trans-Mexican Volcanic Belt are nine. They are as follows:

1. *S. botterii* and *S. tortuosum*.
2. *S. dendroideum*, *S. aoikon*, *S. cremnophila*, *S. lucidum*, *S.* of the Tiscalatengo Gorge, and *S. nussbaumerianum*.
3. *S. oxypetalum*, *S. frutescens*, *S. quevae*, *S. bourgaei*, and *S. griseum*.
4. *S. obcordatum* and *S. stahlii*.
5. *S. longipes*, *S. pentastamineum*, *S. clavifolium*, and *S. cormiferum*.
6. *S. versadense*, *S. hemsleyanum*, and *S. ebracteatum*.
7. *S. grandipetalum* and *S. greggii*.
8. *S. moranense*.
9. *S. jaliscanum*, *S. napiferum*, and *S. minimum*.

*Villadia* is close to *Sedum*. Possibly it is derived from group 3. *Villadia scopulina* apparently hybridizes with *S. quevae* of group 3, though *V. batesii* hybridizes with *S. dendroideum* of group 2. Moreover, *V. batesii* may hybridize with *S. moranense* of group 8. If these ideas, based entirely on circumstantial evidence, are correct, they indicate that *Villadia* is still genetically close to *Sedum*.

*Graptopetalum* also appears to be close to *Sedum* and a possible derivative from it, most likely from group 2, but the petals usually are banded with red or purple as in *S. napiferum* of group 9. Apparent hybrids between species of *Graptopetalum* and species of *Sedum* of group 2 have been produced in cultivation.

*Echeveria* and its generic derivative, *Pachyphytum*, possibly are also derived from group 2 of *Sedum*. Walther (1953) described intergeneric hybrids, made artificially, between *Echeveria* and *Sedum*. I found no hybrids between these two genera in the wild.

## SUMMARY

1. The species of *Sedum* of the Trans-Mexican Volcanic Belt are mostly of limited geographical distribution. Fifteen of them are endemic.

2. Migration of populations apparently is slow and usually for short distances. The species are slow to invade new sites. Only six inhabit lava less than 3,000 years old, and none have invaded the recent lava of Paricutín.

3. The species are predominantly chamaephytes and phanerophytes.

4. Populations are small, averaging 611 plants.

5. Of 378 interspecific gaps, none are bridged by hybrids. Species on either side of interspecific gaps occur in the same square kilometer in only 31 cases and within the same square meter in only 15.

6. Interspecific hybridization is a negligible evolutionary factor under present conditions of dispersal of the species.

7. Although the twenty-eight species of *Sedum* of the Trans-Mexican Volcanic Belt are easy to distinguish morphologically, they are remarkably similar in many characteristics and comparatively unspecialized. Different species have acquired different specializations, and no species possesses a large number of specializations.

8. *Sedum botterii* is the least specialized and *S. minimum* the most specialized species in the volcanic belt.

9. Genetic differences probably exist within most of the species. These are most reasonably explained as the result of the mutations of genes.

10. The twenty-eight species of *Sedum* of the volcanic belt comprise nine groups of seemingly natural relationship. *Villadia*, *Graptopetalum*, and *Echeveria* probably are all derived from *Sedum* and are closely related.

# CHAPTER VIII

# Comparison and Evaluation of Methods of Taxonomic Study

BERGER (1930) and Fröderström (1930–1935) both prepared comprehensive accounts of the genus *Sedum*. Their treatments, world-wide in scope, include the species of the Trans-Mexican Volcanic Belt. Berger depended considerably on Praeger (1921) and Hamet for his opinions about classification. Either he or Praeger had experience with cultivated plants of many species. Fröderström, though with brief experience in Mexico in 1932 and with access to plants in the garden of E. L. Magnus, worked largely with dried specimens and the literature. A comparison of my own classification of the species of the Trans-Mexican Volcanic Belt with those of the other two men is revealing, especially since the methods of study were different. This comparison follows:

| Species in this book | Species according to Berger | Species according to Fröderström |
|---|---|---|
| 1. *S. botterii* | *S. botteri* | *S. botterii* |
| 2. *S. tortuosum* | *S. tortuosum* | *S. tortuosum* |
| | *S. nelsonii* | *S. nelsoni* |
| | | *S. lignicaule* |
| 3. *S. dendroideum* | *S. dendroideum* | *S. dendroideum* |
| | *S. praealtum* | *S. praealtum* |
| | | *S. monticola* |
| (*S. dendroideum* x *Villadia batesii*) | *S. amecamecanum* | *S. amecamecanum* |
| 4. *S. aoikon* | *S. aoikon* | *S. aoikon* |
| | *S. purpusii* | *S. purpusi* |

| *Species in this book* | *Species according to Berger* | *Species according to Fröderström* |
| --- | --- | --- |
| 5. *S. cremnophila* | *S. nutans* | *S. nutans* |
| 6. *S. lucidum* | not listed | not listed |
| 7. *S.* of Tiscalatengo Gorge | not listed | not listed |
| 8. *S. nussbaumerianum* | *S. nussbaumerianum* | *S. adolphi* |
| 9. *S. oxypetalum* | *S. oxypetalum* | *S. oxypetalum* |
| 10. *S. frutescens* | *S. frutescens* | *S. frutescens* |
| 11. *S. quevae* | *S. quevae* | *S. quevae* |
| | | *S. falconis* |
| 12. *S. bourgaei* | *S. bourgaei* | *S. bourgaei* |
| 13. *S. griseum* | *S. griseum* | *S. griseum* |
| 14. *S. obcordatum* | not listed | not listed |
| 15. *S. stahlii* | *S. stahlii* | *S. stahlii* |
| 16. *S. longipes* | *S. longipes* | *S. longipes* |
| 17. *S. pentastamineum* | not listed | not listed |
| 18. *S. clavifolium* | *S. clavifolium* | *S. clavifolium* |
| 19. *S. cormiferum* | not listed | not listed |
| 20. *S. versadense* | *S. versadense* | *S. versadense* |
| 21. *S. hemsleyanum* | *S. hemsleyanum* | *S. hemsleyanum* |
| | *S. pachucense* | *S. pachucense* |
| | *S. painteri* | *S. painteri* |
| 22. *S. ebracteatum* | *S. ebracteatum* | *S. ebracteatum* |
| | *S. incertum* | *S. incertum* |
| | *S. chapalense* | *S. chapalense* |
| | *S. rubricaule* | |
| 23. *S. grandipetalum* | not listed | *S. grandipetalum* |
| 24. *S. greggii* | *S. greggii* | *S. greggii* |
| | *S. diversifolium* | *S. diversifolium* |
| 25. *S. moranense* | *S. moranense* | *S. moranense* |
| 26. *S. jaliscanum* | *S. jaliscanum* | *S. jaliscanum* |
| | | *S. naviculare* |
| | | *S. syncarpum* |
| 27. *S. napiferum* | *S. napiferum* | *S. napiferum* |
| 28. *S. minimum* | *S. minimum* | *S. minimum* |
| | *S. delicatum* | *S. delicatum* |
| Totals     28 | 33 | 38 |

One result of the study of wild populations and the experimental culture of plants from these is reduction of the number of species which are recognized. A more conservative taxonomy is the outcome. Another result is the accumulation of more comprehensive descriptive data. An illustration is afforded by the following comparison of Fröderström's data for dried specimens and my own data for living plants of *Sedum napiferum*. Both samples were from the vicinity of Toluca, the type locality. Several of the contrasted characteristics are important in distinguishing between *S. napiferum* and *S. minimum*.

| | Data from Fröderström | | | | Data from living plants | | | |
|---|---|---|---|---|---|---|---|---|
| | n | n-obs. | w (mm.) | n | n-obs. | w (mm.) | z̄ (mm.) | s (mm.) |
| Leaves | | | | | | | | |
|   Length | ? | ? | 3–6 | 8 | 18 | 4.3–7.9 | 5.7 | .4 |
| Pedicels | | | | | | | | |
|   Length | ? | ? | 3–6 | 7 | 23 | 2 –4 | 2.3 | .2 |
| Sepals | | | | | | | | |
|   Length | ? | ? | 3–3.5 | 18 | 54 | 2.4–5 | 3.3 | .7 |
| Petals | | | | | | | | |
|   Length | ? | ? | ab. 5 | 18 | 54 | 4.4–6.7 | 5.3 | .6 |
|   Length of cohesion | ? | ? | .5 | 18 | 54 | 0 | 0 | 0 |
| Stamens | | | | | | | | |
|   Length of adnation of | | | | | | | | |
|     epipetalous filaments | ? | ? | .5 | 16 | 45 | .2– .6 | .4 | .04 |
| Nectaries | | | | | | | | |
|   Length | ? | ? | .6 | 18 | 54 | .7–1.1 | .8 | .03 |
|   Width | ? | ? | .4 | 18 | 54 | .2– .4 | .26 | .03 |
| Seeds | | | | | | | | |
|   Length | ? | ? | .7 | 10 | 30 | .6– .8 | .7 | 0 |
|   Diameter | ? | ? | .3 | 10 | 30 | .2– .3 | .3 | 0 |

Dried specimens can be the source of erroneous impressions concerning the dimensions and shapes of structures, as well as the habit of plants. This is particularly true of *Sedum* and other genera of Crassulaceae of which the stems, leaves, and sepals are usually succulent. In the course of the present study, I made sixteen experiments concerned with the effect of drying on the dimensions of leaves and of floral parts. These experiments have involved eleven species. Leaves decreased significantly in length in 42 per cent of the tests, in width in 58 per cent, and in thickness in 100 per cent. In a single experiment with sepals, a significant reduction occurred in both length and width. In two tests with petals, loss in width was significant in both tests and in length in one. Finally, in a single experiment, anthers shrank significantly in length and nectaries in width, but not in length. These results confirm the opinion that dried specimens of *Sedum* in herbaria are not reliable for descriptive data, regardless of how valuable they may be for indicating the distribution of species.

Before 1955, I knew only from herbarium specimens and the literature two groups of species of *Sedum* of the volcanic belt, with the exception of *S. longipes.* The groups concerned are nos. 5 and 9 (as listed in previous chapter).

| Species | Opinion before 1955 | Opinion after 1955 |
|---|---|---|
| *S. longipes* | each of the 2 subspecies a separate species | a polytypic species comprising 2 subspecies |
| *S. pentastamineum* | either a variation or subspecies of *S. longipes* | a valid species related to *S. longipes* |
| *S. clavifolium* | a valid species | a valid species |
| *S. cormiferum* | either a variation of *S. longipes* or a separate species closest to that | a valid species closest to *S. clavifolium* |
| *S. jaliscanum* | 2 separate, but related species: *S. jaliscanum* and *S. naviculare,* the latter doubtfully including *S. syncarpum* | a single variable species |
| *S. napiferum* | a valid species close to *S. delicatum, S. minimum,* and *S. vinicolor* | a valid species closest to *S. minimum* |
| *S. minimum* | 2 separate, but related species: *S. minimum* and *S. delicatum* | a single, polytypic species comprising 2 subspecies |
| No. of species recognized | 9 | 7 |

In only two of the seven cases cited above did field work fail to change the taxonomic opinion, and in each of those the additional descriptive data greatly enlarged the body of information concerning them.

In the same way, the culture of plants under similar conditions has demonstrated that many variations observed in the field are environmental modifications which do not deserve taxonomic recognition. Three simple examples of this are illustrated graphically in figures 81–83. In figure 81, solid vertical lines indicate observed ranges of characteristics, and broken lines estimated ranges based on the mean plus or minus three standard deviations. In all cases, the plants studied in the wild and in cultivation are the same clones. Examples of this sort are common and are discussed under the heading of variation in the accounts of the species.

They indicate the unreliability of data derived from plants in the field in drawing inferences about precise patterns of variation. Experiments are necessary in which environmental differences either are eliminated or are greatly minimized. Although data from the field have often been useful in this study in suggesting

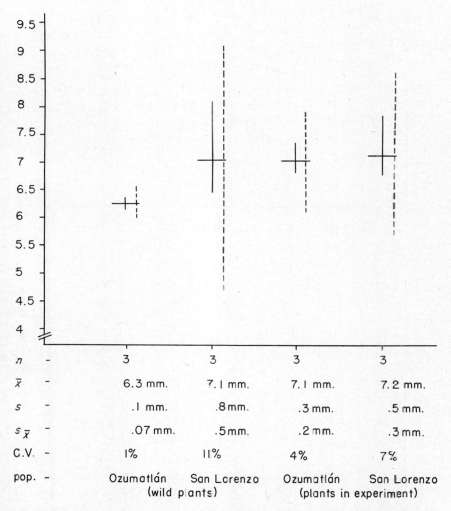

*Fig. 81.* Variation in length of petals of *Sedum griseum.* Scale at left is in millimeters. Solid vertical lines indicate observed ranges of variation, and broken vertical lines the means plus or minus three standard deviations. Horizontal crossbars indicate the means of samples.

trends in variation, conclusions have wherever possible been based on plants grown under experimental conditions.

Because environmental modification is so common, special demonstrations under each species should be unnecessary. The reduction in number of significant differences among populations when plants are cultivated under similar conditions and the usually

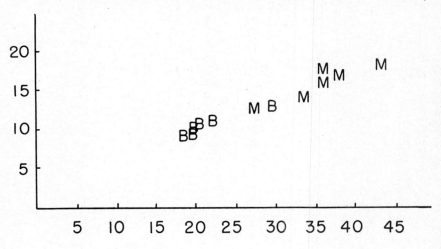

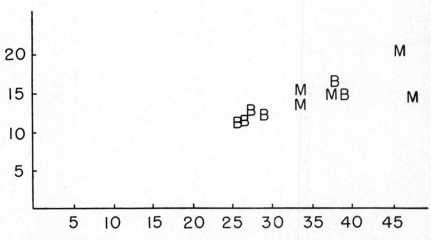

*Fig. 82.* Graphs showing average expressions in millimeters of length (horizontal axes) and width (vertical axes) of leaves of plants of *Sedum lucidum.* B = Cerro Borrego; M = Maltrata. Above are data for wild plants; below, data for the same clones in cultivation. Each letter stands for one plant.

smaller standard deviations of samples in cultivation indicate the situation. This has been mentioned frequently in the text.

In the description of species, primary purposes have been to show observed ranges of variation of each character and also to indicate whether significant differences exist among samples. All

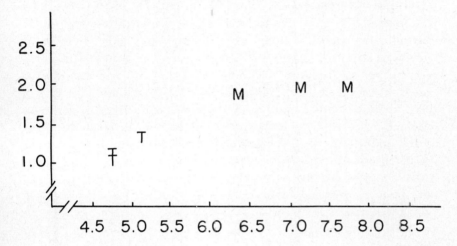

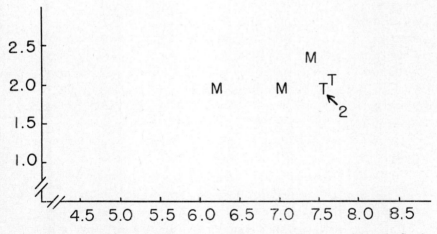

*Fig. 82.* Graphs showing average expressions in millimeters of length (horizontal axes) and width (vertical axes) of petals of plants of *Sedum quevae.* M = northwest of Mt. Malinche, Tlaxcala; T = El Tezcal, Morelos. Above are data for wild plants; below, data for the same clones in cultivation. Each letter stands for one plant.

data for plants in the field include the effect of the environment, and that effect may be profound. Such data are of little value for discriminatory purposes when fine distinctions are necessary, but for large differences they may be adequate. I have used variance ratios for comparing samples, whether from the field or from completely randomized experiments. The usefulness of the results for wild plants has been chiefly to suggest possible differences which need further study, using experimental methods. Sometimes cultural experiments were impossible. Some species would not grow in any of the four situations which I used for cultivation of *Sedum* at Ithaca. Other plants survived, but did not flower. For these reasons, some conclusions about classification had to be reached from study of wild plants alone. Such conclusions are clearly indicated. Possibly they can be tested in the future by the use of superior methods of study.

An important aspect of any taxonomic study is sampling. Unless sampling is adequate, analyses of data and conclusions derived from them may both be faulty. Further, sampling cannot be satisfactory unless the objectives of the investigation are clearly defined. For the present study, the title indicates the purpose, namely, to gain information about *Sedum* in the Trans-Mexican Volcanic Belt. To achieve such a purpose, logical steps of procedure might be the following:

Step 1. To explore the area in order to list all populations.

Problem 1. Since populations sometimes are small, scanning the complete area is necessary if all populations are to be listed. Since the volcanic belt comprises about 97,000 sq. km., one person spending every day per year in the field would need 265 years to accomplish this task.

Step 2. To sample each species by selecting populations randomly.

Problem 2. If the list of populations is incomplete, random sampling of populations is impossible. A random sample is possible only of known populations.

Step 3. To list all places where two or more species occur together and then to sample randomly each combination of species which occur together.

Problem 3. If the list of places where different populations occur together is incomplete, random sampling of such situations is impossible.

One solution of the above problems would have been to change the scope of the study and to reduce the size of the area to be covered to proportions which might be surveyed adequately in the time available. This would have yielded less, but, for the area covered, more precise information. Since I desired to learn about *Sedum* in the whole volcanic belt, but could not explore the area thoroughly because of lack of time, my execution of step 1 was incomplete. The coverage of the area is better, however, than might first seem evident, since much information about the existence and location of populations, discovered by botanists of past or contemporary generations, is available from data on labels accompanying herbarium specimens or from the literature. If anyone in the future completely explores the volcanic belt for *Sedum*, a comparison of his results with mine should reveal what percentage of all possible populations were known to me. At present, because of the way in which I learned about populations, I do not know the percentage of completeness of my listing of populations in the part of the volcanic belt which I visited between 18° and 20° N and 97° and 104° W.

Since both steps 2 and 3 were impossible because of inability to complete step 1, the practical procedure was to learn about known populations, including those discovered by me. Accordingly, I listed problems which needed to be solved and then selected populations which seemed most pertinent to their solution. The following questions determined the selection of populations. Sometimes the questions developed in the field after discovery of previously unknown populations.

1. What are the characteristics of each of the populations from which nomenclatural types have been selected in the Trans-Mexican Volcanic Belt? This information is basic to a proper taxonomic interpretation of the species. In all, I studied eighteen type populations.

2. Does hybridization take place when two species of *Sedum* occur close together? To answer this, I studied populations at nine sites where two or more species were intimately associated.

3. What are the characteristics of populations discovered in the

course of the investigation? I studied twenty-one populations not previously reported by other botanists.

4. What are the characteristics of at least one population of each species not sampled for some other reason? I sampled three populations to answer this question.

5. Do significant differences exist among populations within each of the following species: *Sedum dendroideum, S. lucidum, S. oxypetalum, S. frutescens, S. quevae, S. bourgaei, S. griseum, S. obcordatum, S. stahlii, S. longipes, S. hemsleyanum, S. moranense,* and *S. jaliscanum?* To help to decide this, I studied forty-seven populations.

6. Are *Sedum napiferum, S. minimum,* and *S. delicatum* synonymous? For this, I studied the three type populations.

7. What should be the taxonomic status of *Sedum naviculare* and *S. syncarpum?* For this, I studied the two type populations.

Each population studied was chosen for the purpose of answering one or more of these questions. The seventy-five populations studied comprise 52 per cent of those known to me from the Trans-Mexican Volcanic Belt. Ten are the only ones known from the Trans-Mexican Volcanic Belt for the species to which they belong.

In sampling local populations, two important objectives are to find every genotype available and to obtain unbiased estimates of parameters of characteristics. To achieve the first objective with complete success, an investigator should survey the entire area of his study and collect every plant which looked different. Then he should cultivate all these plants, replicated several times, in carefully planned experiments, to eliminate from taxonomic consideration all environmental modifications. For *Sedum* of the Trans-Mexican Volcanic Belt, I collected for propagation every plant which looked different in each of the seventy-five populations which I studied. Such a method tended to maximize differences, but that was deliberate because a purpose of the study was to determine the extent of genetic variation within species.

To achieve the second objective, the ideal would be a probability sample of each local population. Depending on size of population and number of environmental conditions inhabited by each, such samples might be either simple random or stratified random. In trying to obtain probability samples of *Sedum,* certain difficulties interfere:

1. Whole strata or parts of strata are inaccessible, as vertical faces of high cliffs.

2. A method is lacking for distinguishing between different individuals (zygotes) and vegetative propagants of the same individual, with the resulting possibility of repetitive inclusion of parts of the same individual in any sample.

3. Accurate lists of plants in populations in exceedingly rough terrain are unattainable.

Of these, no. 3 may be relieved by dividing sites or parts of sites into plots of equal size and then selecting these randomly. Quadrats, as described in chapter I, if selected randomly, are excellent subdivisions in which to list plants and to obtain data on density for estimates of size of populations. The other two difficulties in obtaining random samples are perhaps impossible to resolve. For that reason, means and variances for characteristics of populations of wild plants are biased estimates. Further, these estimates include the influence of the environment.

All plants grown in experiments were from accessible situations. Individuals in inaccessible places seldom appeared in samples. The principal way that they could be obtained was by their falling from cliffs; in this case the amount of time that they were in the new site might determine the extent of their modification. Sampling of *Sedum* is difficult, but the problems are not unique.

The advantages of random samples are well known to statisticians. Although the collection of random samples takes much time, such samples yield reliable estimates of parameters. Two simple demonstrations will illustrate this, as well as the dangers inherent in results obtained from nonrandom samples. Five persons were asked to determine accurately the width of leaves of a cultivated plant of *Sedum obcordatum* from the Cofre de Perote. This plant had 192 leaves. One sampler (A) took a random sample, basing the necessary size of the sample on the variance computed from a primary sample of ten leaves. The other samplers selected leaves without using a mechanical scheme of randomization, and the size of their samples was not based on the variance. Significant differences exist among their results. When A is used as a standard, note that B, C, D, and E all overestimated the mean, with consequent upward shift of the confidence interval.

| Sampler | n | $\bar{x}$ (mm.) | s (mm.) | $s_{\bar{x}}$ (mm.) | Conf. int._.05 (mm.) |
|---|---|---|---|---|---|
| A | 25 | 10.3 | 2.3 | .21 | 9.9–10.7 |
| B | 8 | 12.6 | 2.2 | .78 | 10.8–14.5 |
| C | 10 | 10.8 | 3.3 | 1.05 | 8.4–13.2 |
| D | 13 | 12.2 | 2.3 | .63 | 10.9–13.6 |
| E | 14 | 11.4 | 1.6 | .43 | 10.5–11.4 |

Investigator A drew three additional samples, from another cultivated plant of *Sedum obcordatum* from the peak of Orizaba, and again used a table of random numbers and determined the number of observations from the variance of the first ten leaves in each drawing. This plant had 67 leaves. Although the plant was approached independently in each of the three samplings, as though it had never been studied before, the results are similar. The slight differences are of no statistical significance and may be attributed to chance.

| Sample | n | $\bar{x}$ | s | $s_{\bar{x}}$ | Conf. int._.05 |
|---|---|---|---|---|---|

12. Volcanism has not been the direct cause of the large number of species of *Sedum* present in the Trans-Mexican Volcanic Belt. Instead, it has been a secondary factor. The development of the high volcanic peaks has provided a series of diverse and disjunct environmental conditions which appear to have been of primary importance in the evolution of the present group of species.

### CONSIDERATION OF THE TEN PROPOSITIONS OF CHAPTER I

1. The obvious, natural affinity of the majority, possibly all, of the species of *Sedum* of the Trans-Mexican Volcanic Belt suggests their evolution from a common ancestor. This is the most reasonable basis for an interpretation of their relationships.

2. Subspecies, those of *Sedum dendroideum* and *S. minimum*, for example, differ in the same sorts of characters as do the species and also the genera of Crassulaceae. All are natural populations of varying magnitudes of divergence, evolving by means of similar, biological processes.

3. To distinguish among species, as *Sedum quevae*, *S. bourgaei*, and *S. griseum*, is easier and more objective than to decide whether or not *Villadia* should be interpreted as a genus separate from *Sedum*. Even the interpretation of subspecies is easier than the decision about the circumscription of genera, though problems exist at all levels in the taxonomic hierarchy.

4. Local populations of *Sedum* are remarkably distinct in the Trans-Mexican Volcanic Belt. Their boundaries usually are sharp. These are the basic units of classification and of evolution.

5. Only two species of *Sedum* of the Trans-Mexican Volcanic Belt comprise two or more subspecies within the belt. Many of the other species may just have passed the subspecific stage. The local populations of *S. jaliscanum* may be in process of attaining that stage.

6. The concept that species should differ from each other in several correlated characteristics and at the same time be effectively isolated biologically works well with *Sedum* in the Trans-Mexican Volcanic Belt. Wherever two species occur together in the same habitat, they are distinct and do not hybridize. A few border-line cases exist which are difficult to appraise, namely, the proper status of *S. aoikon* with relation to *S. dendroideum* and the stage of differentiation of *S. ebracteatum* and *S. hemsleyanum*. *Sedum*

*longipes* and *S. pentastamineum*, likewise *S. napiferum* and *S. minimum*, may also be near the threshold around which the concept of species fluctuates. If these are not species, then they are subspecies.

7. Although genetic work has not been part of this study, differences among plants of the same population, when grown in a similar environment, have been observed in thirty-two populations of twenty-one species. These differences, if genetic, are probably the products of gene mutations.

8. Among species of *Sedum* of the Trans-Mexican Volcanic Belt, differentiation has involved adjustment to different environmental conditions such as freezing, aridity, and soil low in organic matter. Such adaptations have involved physiological changes. These must have been important in the evolution of the present group of species.

9. Most of the species are effectively isolated geographically from each other. In the few places where two species occur together and flower at the same time, hybridization does not occur, suggesting that genetic isolation is effective.

10. In *Sedum* in the Trans-Mexican Volcanic Belt, interspecific hybridization appears to be of slight evolutionary importance at the present time. Two, possibly three, cases of intergeneric hybridization in nature are known. The hybrids apparently are sterile. Whether hybridization was more important in the past than at present is doubtful, but certainly plants such as the supposed intergeneric hybrids which have been found are as different from their parents as other species are from each other. The possibility that some species may have originated in this way is apparent.

### GENERAL CONCLUSIONS

1. One of the principal objectives of taxonomy is to organize in orderly fashion information about the kinds of organisms which inhabit the earth's surface. The study of *Sedum* in the Trans-Mexican Volcanic Belt is an example of an attempt to fulfill this objective.

2. Comprehensive treatments of subjects are both necessary from a practical standpoint and vital from a theoretical standpoint in order to provide perspective for details.

3. Through the use of field surveys, experimental procedures, and statistical analyses of data, the conclusions of taxonomy may become more objective and less the subject of individual opinion.

**Almoloya**—village, District of Sultepec, Mexico, 6 km. SE of Texcaltitlán; also known as Almoloya de Alquisiras.

**Alseseca**—town and glen, Puebla, 18 km. SE of Acatzingo.

**Amecameca**—city, Mexico, 19° 7′ N, 98° 46′ W.

**Angahuán**—village, Michoacán, 29 km. NW of Uruapan.

**Angostura, La**—glen, N of highway from Mexico to Toluca, Federal District, between hills of Chapultepec and Cuajimalpa, N of Turf Club and about 9 km. WSW of Chapultepec Park, city of Mexico.

**Aseseca**—cited by Hamet as in Puebla, but unknown to me. Possibly this was a mistake for Alseseca.

**Atlihuitzia**—town, Tlaxcala, about 8 km. NE of Tlaxcala; also known as Santa María Atlihuitzía.

**Atlixco**—city, alt. 1,881 m., Puebla, 18° 54′ N, 98° 26′ W.

**Atoyac River**—tributary of Mexcala River, draining large area in Puebla.

**Autlan**—city, alt. 688 m., Jalisco, 19° 46′ N, 104° 22′ W.

**Axocuapan**—town, 8 km. NW of Huatusco, Vera Cruz; also written Zacuapan.

**Balsas River**—river, S of Trans-Mexican Volcanic Belt, tributaries of which drain S slope of vast part of volcanic belt.

**Banderilla**—town, 9 km. NNW of Jalapa, Vera Cruz.

**Barranca de Alseseca**—see Alseseca.

**Barranca de Cuautilla**—see Cuautilla.

**Barranca de Guadalajara**—see Guadalajara.

**Barranca de Mala Cara**—ravine, SE slope, peak of Orizaba, E of and below Torecillas, 4 km. NE of spring at Santa Cruz.

**Barranca de Manzanilla**—see Manzanilla.

**Barranca de Tenampa**—see Tenampa.

**Barranca de Texalotengo**—see Texalatengo.

**Barranca de Tlilapa**—see Tlilapa.

**Batán**—two haciendas, one in District of Cholula and the other in District of Tecali, Puebla.

**Bejucos**—hacienda, District of Temascaltepec, Mexico.

**Boca del Monte**—station (alt. 2,416 m.) on Mexican Railroad, Puebla, 251 km. from Mexico and 174 from Vera Cruz, 6 km. SE of Esperanza.

**Borrego, Cerro**—mountain, alt. 1,570 m., W of city of Orizaba, 340 m. above city.

**Bufa, La**—mountain of Sierra de Mascota, Cantón of Mascota, Jalisco, alt. 1,630 m. according to Cubas (1896), but recorded as 2,500 m. by Mexia on labels accompanying specimens of *Sedum grandipetalum.*

**Cajones**—according to George Hinton, locality in District of Temascaltepec, Mexico.

**Campana, Sierra de la**—mountains, near Mascota, Jalisco, 20° 32' N, 104° 44' W.

**Campanario**—tall, towerlike rock on S side of Cerro Azul, Michoacán.

**Campanas, Cerro de las**—mountain, N of Querétaro, 20° 36' N, 100° 23' W.

**Campo Vello**—locality in valley of Río Los Filtros, N side of Cerro Azul, SE of Morelia.

**Cañada de Alcalican**—see Alcalican.

**Cañada de San Juan**—see San Juan.

**Cañada de Texantilia**—see Texantilia.

**Cañada Magdalena**—see Magdalena.

**Canicjuata**—volcanic cone, alt. 2,703 m., 850 m. WNW of cone of Paricutín, 9 km. NNE of Mt. Tancítaro; observation point, on NE slope of mountain, at 2,703 m.

**Capacuaro**—town, Michoacán, 17.8 km. N of Uruapan.

**Capatzun**—ridge of old lava, 3.7 km. NNE of crater of Paricutín.

**Carmen, Rincón del**—hacienda, of municipality of Tejupilco, District of Temascaltepec, Mexico.

**Casita Canicjuata**—at observation point on Canicjuata.

**Ceboruco**—volcanic mountain, alt. 2,164 m., 10 km. NW of Ahuacatlán, Nayarit.

**Centinelas**—pinnacles on N side of Cañada de Alcalican, on W slope of Iztaccihuatl, NW of La Joya.

**Cerro Azul**—mountain, 23 km. SE of Morelia.

**Cerro Borrego**—see Borrego.

**Cerro de Guadalupe**—see Guadalupe.

**Cerro de las Campanas**—see Campanas.

**Cerro del Gavilán**—see Gavilán.

**Cerro Frío**—see Frío.

**Cerro San Juan**—see San Juan.

**Cerro Tepoxuchil**—see Tepoxuchil.

**Cerro Teresona**—see Teresona.

**Chacoalco River**—river on N side of Taxco.

**Chalchicomula**—see Ciudad Serdán.

**Champs de Manoeuvres**—drill ground, vicinity of Puebla.

**Chapala**—lake, E Jalisco, 20° 15′ N, 103° W, comprising 1,685 sq. km.

**Ciudad Guzmán**—city, alt. 1,507 m., SE Jalisco, 19° 42′ N, 103° 27′ W.

**Ciudad Serdán**—city, alt. 2,540 m., E Puebla, WSW of peak of Orizaba, 18° 59′ N, 97° 27′ W; also known as Chalchicomula.

**Cofre de Perote**—mountain, alt. 4,282 m., Vera Cruz, 19° 29′ N, 97° 8′ W; also known as Nauhcampatepetl or Nauhcampatepen.

**Colima, Nevado de**—mountain, alt. 4,340 m., Jalisco, 19° 33′ N, 103° 36′ W.

**Colima, Volcán de**—see Volcán de Colima.

**Compostela**—city, Nayarit, 21° 14′ N, 104° 55′ W.

**Comunidad**—according to George Hinton, locality in District of Temascultepec, Mexico.

**Contreras**—town, Federal District, 10 km. SW of San Angel.

**Copilco**—section of city of Mexico, E of Villa Obregón and S of Coyoacán, on N side of University City.

**Córdoba**—city, alt. 924 m., Vera Cruz, 18° 53′ N, 96° 55′ W.

**Coscomatepec**—city, alt. 1,588 m., Vera Cruz, 19° 4′ N, 97° 2′ W.

**Cuajimalpa**—town, Federal District, 19° 21′ N, 99° 18′ W.

**Cuautilla**—large ravine in municipality of Axocuapan, about 10 km. NW of Huatusco.

**Cuernavaca**—capital, alt. 1,542 m., Morelos, 18° 55′ N, 99° 14′ W.

**Desierto de los Leones**—national park in W part of Federal District, on E slope of Sierra de las Cruces, 5 km. S of Cuajimalpa.

**El Alamo**—see Alamo.

**El Isote**—see Isote.

**El Parque**—see Parque.

**El Tezcal**—see Tezcal.

**El Zarco**—see Zarco.

**El Zirate**—see Zirate.

**Eslava**—hacienda, Federal District, about 12 km. SW of San Angel.

**Esperanza**—station on railroad 15 km. SSE of Ciudad Serdán.

**Espinaza del Diablo**—ridge, N slope of Mt. Ajusco, forming W side of deep canyon with origin between northernmost and central peaks.

**Fortín de las Flores**—town, Vera Cruz, 11 km. SE of Orizaba.

**Frío, Cerro**—mountain, District of Tetecala, 20 km. SW of Jojutla, S Morelos.

**Gavilán**—mountain, 15 km. S of Tlacotepec, Puebla.

**Guadalajara**—capital, alt. 1,567 m., Jalisco, 20° 40′ N, 103° 23′ W; Barranca de Guadalajara, also known as La Barranca, canyon of Santiago River about 8 km. N of city.

**Guadalupe**—city, Federal District, just N of city of Mexico, 19° 29′ N, 99° 7′ W, also known as Guadalupe Hidalgo; Sierra de Guadalupe, mountains, just N of Guadalupe Hidalgo, in both Federal District and Mexico; Cerro de Guadalupe, mountain, Puebla, cited by Hamet, exact location unknown to me.

**Hacienda Alamos**—see Alamos.

**Huatusco**—city, alt. 1,344 m., Vera Cruz, 19° 9′ N, 96° 57′ W.

**Huerta, La**—hacienda, District of Morelia, Michoacán.

**Huixquilucan**—town, alt. 2,750 m., Mexico, 23 km. W of city of Mexico, 19° 22′ N, 99° 22′ W.

**Irimbo**—town, Michoacán, 34 km. NNW of Zitácuaro.

**Isote, El**—town on N slope of Nevado de Colima, SE of Jazmín.

**Ixtapan**—town, District of Temascaltepec, Mexico, 26 km. SSW of Temascaltepec.

**Iztaccihuatl**—mountain (alt. 5,286 m.) of Sierra Nevada, SE of city of Mexico, 19° 10′ N, 98° 38′ W.

**Jalapa**—capital, alt. 1,427 m., Vera Cruz, 19° 32′ N, 96° 55′ W.

**Jazmín**—hacienda, near NW base of Nevado de Colima, 24 km. WSW of Ciudad Guzmán.

**Jesús del Monte**—town, Michoacán, 10 km. SE of Morelia.

**Jojutla**—city, Morelos, 18° 37′ N, 99° 10′ W.

**Jorullo**—volcano, alt. 1,320 m., 52 km. SE of Uruapan.

**Joya, La**—place (alt. 3,980 m.) at end of road on SW slope of Mt. Iztaccihuatl, S of Cañada de Alcalican, Mexico; town, Vera Cruz, on highway 10 km. E of Las Vigas.

**La Angostura**—see Angostura.

**La Barranca**—see Guadalajara.

**La Bufa**—see Bufa.

**La Huerta**—see Huerta.

**La Joya**—see Joya.

**Lake Chapala**—see Chapala.

**Lake Pátzcuaro**—see Pátzcuaro.

**Lake Sayula**—see Sayula.

**Lake Texcoco**—see Texcoco.

**Lake Zapotlán**—see Zapotlán.

**Las Piñas**—mountain on SE side of Ciudad Guzmán.

**Las Trojes**—locality along highway to Zitácuaro, 34 km. E of Morelia.

**Las Vigas**—see Vigas.

**Lerma River**—important river, rising in Mexico, draining N slopes of central part of Trans-Mexican Volcanic Belt and flowing into Lake Chapala.

**Los Filtros, Río**—river on N side of Cerro Azul, source of water for Morelia.

**Luvianos**—town, Mexico, 33 km. SW of Temascaltepec.

**Macho de Agua**—place along highway 18 km. E of Zitácuaro.

**Magdalena, Cañada**—glen, S of Contreras.

**Mala Cara**—see Barranca de Mala Cara.

**Malinche**—high mountain, alt. 4,461 m., 24 km. SW of Tlaxcala, 19° 13′ N, 98° 1′ W.

**Malintzin**—another name for Malinche.

**Maltrata**—town, alt. 1,700 m., Vera Cruz, 18° 48′ N, 97° 16′ W.

**Manantiales de la Concha**—spring on NE slope of Mt. Malinche, near upper part of Cañada de San Juan.

**Manzanilla, Barranca de**—glen, District of Puebla, Puebla.

**Marquesa, Sierra de la**—N part of Sierra de las Cruces, N of highway between Mexico and Toluca.

**Mascota**—city, alt. 1,270 m., Jalisco, 20° 32′ N, 104° 44′ W.

**Mesón Viejo**—town, 23 km. NE of Temascaltepec, Mexico.

**Mexican Volcanic Axis**—another name for Trans-Mexican Volcanic Belt.

**Mexico**—capital, alt. 2,300 m., United States of Mexico, 19° 26′ N, 99° 8′ W; name of broad valley in which the city of Mexico is situated; one of states of Mexico; name of country.

**Mexico** (city)—see Mexico.

**Michoacán Volcanic Region**—portion of Trans-Mexican Volcanic Belt lying between Sierra de Ozumatlán and Lake Chapala.

**Mil Cumbres**—"Thousand Peaks," seen from an overlook along highway from Zitácuaro to Morelia, in Sierra de Ozumatlán.

**Milpulco Valley**—valley of stream on SW slope of Mt. Iztaccihuatl, next one N of Cañada de Alcalican.

**Montes Las Tres Marías**—see Tres Marías.

**Morelia**—capital, alt. 1,941 m., Michoacán. 19° 42′ N, 101° 11′ W.

**Mt. Ajusco**—see Ajusco.

**Mt. Malinche**—see Malinche.

**Mt. Orizaba**—see Orizaba.

**Mt. Tancítaro**—see Tancítaro.

**Nauhcampatepetl**—see Cofre de Perote.

**Neo-Volcanic Zone**—another name for Trans-Mexican Volcanic Belt.

**Nevado de Colima**—see Colima.

**Nevado de Toluca**—see Toluca.

**Nexpayantla Canyon**—deep canyon on NW slope of Mt. Popocatepetl.

**Nexpayantla Volcano**—volcano which probably arose in late Miocene at or near present site of Popocatepetl.

**Ohuapa**—village, municipality of Axocuapan, 13 km. NW of Huatusco.

**Oriental**—town, Puebla, 48 km. NNE of Acatzingo.

**Orizaba**—highest peak (alt. 5,700 m.) in Trans-Mexican Volcanic Belt, 19° 2′ N, 97° 15′ W; industrial city, alt. 1,284 m., Vera Cruz, 18° 51′ N, 97° 6′ W.

**Ozumatlán, Sierra de**—range of mountains, Michoacán, E of Morelia, forming E portion of Michoacán Volcanic Region.

**Papaloapan River**—river, rising in Sierra Madre del Sur in Oaxaca and flowing across Gulf Coastal Plain into Bay of Campeche of Gulf of Mexico W of Tuxtla Mountains.

**Paricutín**—volcano, Michoacán, 24 km. WNW of Uruapan and 12 km. ENE of Mt. Tancítaro.

**Parque, El**—station (alt. 2,306 m.) on railroad on NW side of Sierra de Tepoztlán, 18 km. NE of Cuernavaca.

**Patambán**—mountain, alt. 3,750 m., NW Michoacán, 42 km. NNW of Mt. Tancítaro.

**Pátzcuaro**—lake, Michoacán, 19° 35′ N, 101° 40′ W.

**Peak of Orizaba**—see Orizaba.

**Tenampa**—ravine and town, about 20 km. N of Huatusco.

**Pedregal**—any area of rough and jagged lava, specifically
Pedregal de San Angel in Valley of Mexico, S of city of Mexico

**Tenancingo**—city, alt. 2,022 m., Mexico, 18° 58′ N, 99° 36′ W.

**Tenancingo River**—river, Mexico, rising in Cerro Obscuro, flowing past Tenancingo and through San Gerónimo Gorge, and, joined with other rivers, flowing into Balsas River.

**Tenango**—town, Mexico, 19° 7′ N, 99° 33′ W.

**Tenayac**—hacienda, District of Temascaltepec, Mexico.

**Tepic**—capital, alt. 915 m., Nayarit, 21° 31′ N, 104° 53′ W.

**Tepoxuchil, Cerro**—small mountain, 3 km. SE of Puebla, with elevation 165 m. above level of plateau.

**Tepoztlán**—town, Morelos, 18° 58′ N, 99° 6′ W, also written Tepoxtlán; mountains N of Tepoztlán are known as Sierra de Tepoztlán.

**Tequesquipan**—town, 12 km. NE of Temescaltepec.

**Teresona, Cerro**—mountain, NW of Toluca.

**Texalotengo**—possibly an alternate spelling of Tiscalatengo.

**Texantilia, Cañada de**—ravine tributary to Milpulco Valley, on SW slope of Mt. Iztaccihuatl.

**Texcaltitlán**—town, District of Sultepec, Mexico, 18° 53′ N, 99° 49′ W.

**Texcoco**—city, Mexico, 19° 31′ N, 98° 53′ W; lake, E of city of Mexico, 19° 28′ N, 99° W.

**Tezcal, El**—place along road about 6 km. W of Tepoztlán.

**Timbres**—hacienda, 6 km. W of Temascaltepec.

**Tiscalatengo River**—river, rising NW of Villa Guerrero and flowing into Tenancingo River SW of there.

**Tlacotepec**—town, Puebla, 18° 40′ N, 97° 39′ W.

**Tlalpam**—city (alt. 2,294 m.) in Valley of Mexico, 19° 17′ N, 99° 10′ W.

**Tlaxcala**—capital, alt. 2,252 m., Tlaxcala, 19° 19′ N, 98° 14′ W.

**Tlilapa, Barranca de**—ravine, near Ohuapa, Vera Cruz.

**Toluca**—capital, alt. 2,680 m., state of Mexico, 19° 17′ N, 99° 40′ W; Nevado de Toluca, high mountain, alt. 4,578 m., 19 km. S of Toluca, 19° 7′ N, 99° 45′ W.

**Totutla**—town, 20 km. N of Huatusco.

**Toxlaxcuoya**—hamlet along road on NE slope of Cofre de Perote, between Las Vigas and La Joya.

**Trans-Mexican Volcanic Belt**—region of volcanic activity extending transversely across Mexico from vicinity of Gulf of Mexico to Pacific Ocean; most of peaks lie between 19° and 20° N, but the

Tuxtla group is between 18° and 19° N and those near Tepic between 21° and 22° N.

**Tres Marías**—station on railroad in N Morelos, about 15 km. N of Cuernavaca; Montes Las Tres Marías, mountain nearby.

**Triguillo**—hamlet in Sierra de Ozumatlán, along highway between Morelia and Zitácuaro. at km. 287 from city of Mexico.

**Tungareo**—town, Michoacán, 81 km. NE of Morelia.

**Tuxpan River**—river, Michoacán. tributary of Balsas River.

**Tuxtla Mountains**—mountains at SE end of Trans-Mexican Volcanic Belt, SW of Bay of Campeche, Vera Cruz.

**Uruapan**—city, Michoacán, 19° 25' N, 102° 2' W.

**Valley of Mexico**—see Mexico.

**Vello**—see Campo Vello.

**Vera Cruz**—state, E Mexico, bordering Gulf of Mexico; city, alt. 14 m., Vera Cruz, 19° 12' N, 96° 8' W.

**Vigas, Las**—town, Vera Cruz, 19° 38' N, 97° 6' W.

**Villa Guerrero**—town, 5 km. WSW of Tenancingo; also known as Tecualoya.

**Volcán de Colima**—volcano, alt. 3,850 m., 5 km. S of Nevado de Colima.

**Volcanes de la Mesa Central del Sur**—another name for Trans-Mexican Volcanic Belt.

**Xitli**—small volcanic peak at S end of Valley of Mexico, NE of Mt. Ajusco.

**Ypericones**—according to George Hinton, locality in District of Temascaltepec, Mexico.

**Zacuapan**—see Axocuapan.

**Zahuapan River**—river, Tlaxcala, flowing past Atlihuitzia and San Bernabé Amaxac de Guerrero.

**Zapotlán**—lake, Jalisco, NW of Ciudad Guzmán.

**Zarco, El**—site of fish hatchery in Sierra de las Cruces, along road between city of Mexico and Toluca.

**Zirate, El**—mountain, alt. 3,340 m., Michoacán Volcanic Region, 6 km. N of Lake Pátzcuaro.

**Zitácuaro**—city, alt. 1,781 m., E Michoacán, 19° 26' N, 100° 22' W.

# Bibliography

Anderson, Edgar. 1948. Hybridization of the habitat. Evolution
2: 1–9.

Anderson, Edgar. 1949. Introgressive hybridization. New York,
John Wiley and Sons, Inc. 109 p.

Babcock, Ernest B. 1947. The genus *Crepis*. Univ. Calif. Pub.
Bot., vols. 21 and 22.

Berger, Alwin. 1930. Crassulaceae. *In* Engler, Die naturlichen
Pflanzenfamilien, ed. 2, 18a: 352–485.

Britton, Nathaniel L., and Rose, Joseph N. 1903. New or note-
worthy Crassulaceae. Bull. N.Y. Bot. Gard. 3: 1–45.

Britton, Nathaniel L., and Rose, Joseph N. 1905. Crassulaceae.
*In* North American Flora 22: 7–74.

Brown, J. R. 1955. Around San Francisco Bay. Cact. Succ.
Jour. 27: 108–114.

Candolle, Aug. P. de. 1828. Mémoire sur la Famille des Crassulacées. 47 p., 13 pl.

Clausen, Jens. 1951. Stages in the evolution of plant species.
Ithaca, N.Y., Cornell University Press. 206 p.

Clausen, Robert T. 1938. A monograph of the Ophioglossaceae.
Mem. Torrey Bot. Club 19 (2): 1–177, figs. 1–33.

Clausen, Robert T. 1942. Studies in the Crassulaceae. *Sedum*,
subgenus *Gormania*, section *Eugormania*. Bull. Torrey Bot. Club
69 (1): 27–40, figs. 1–3.

Clausen, Robert T. 1943. A new name for Rose's *Sedum nutans*.
Cact. Succ. Jour. 15: 63–64.

Clausen, Robert T. 1943. The section *Sedastrum* of *Sedum*. Bull.
Torrey Bot. Club 70 (3): 289–296, fig. 1.

Clausen, Robert T. 1945. A botanical study of the yam beans,
*Pachyrrhizus*. Cornell Univ. Agr. Exp. Sta. Mem. 264, pp. 3–38.

Clausen, Robert T. 1948. Status of *Sedum aoikon*. Cact. Succ. Jour. 20: 132–135.

Clausen, Robert T. 1949. Checklist of the vascular plants of the Cayuga Quadrangle, 42–43° N., 76–77° W. Cornell Univ. Exp. Sta. Mem. 291, pp. 3–87.

Clausen, Robert T. 1951. Description of a *Sedum* from Orizaba, Vera Cruz. Cact. Succ. Jour. 23: 125–127.

Clausen, Robert T. 1954. Ophioglossaceae of the Hawaiian Islands. Am. Jour. Bot. 41: 493–500, figs. 1 and 2.

Clausen, Robert T., and Uhl, Charles H. 1943. Revision of *Sedum Cockerellii* and related species. Brittonia 5: 33–46, figs. 1–20.

Clausen, Robert T., and Uhl, Charles H. 1944. The taxonomy and cytology of the subgenus *Gormania* of *Sedum*. Madroño 7: 161–180, fig. 1, pl. 22.

Cochran, William G. 1953. Sampling techniques. New York, John Wiley and Sons. 330 p.

Contreras Arias, Alfonso. 1942. Mapa de las Provincias Climato-lógicas de la Republica Mexicana. México, Instituto Geográfico. xxvii p., 54 tables, maps.

Cubas, Antonio García. 1896. Diccionario geográfico, histórico y biográfico de los Estados Unidos Mexicanos. México, Antigua Imprenta de las Escalerillas. 5 vols.

Darwin, Charles. 1865. The origin of species. Rev. ed. New York, D. Appleton and Company. 440 p.

Dixon, Wilfrid J., and Massey, Frank J. 1951. Introduction to statistical analysis. New York, McGraw-Hill. 370 p.

Dobzhansky, Theodosius. 1941. Genetics and the origin of species. 2d ed. New York, Columbia University Press. 446 p.

Emmart, Emily Walcott. 1940. The Badianus Manuscript. Baltimore, The Johns Hopkins Press. 341 p.

Flores, Teodoro. 1945. El Parícutin, Estado de Michoacán. México, Imprenta Universitaria. 166 p.

Foshag, William, and González, Jenaro. 1956. Birth and development of Parícutin Volcano, Mexico. Geol. Survey Bull. 965-D: 355–489, pls. 16–51.

Fröderström, Harald. 1930–1935. The genus *Sedum* L. Act. Hort. Goth. 5, 6, 7, and 10 (App.).

Garfias, Valentin, and Chapin, Theodore. 1949. Geología de México. México, Editorial Jus. 202 p.

Goldschmidt, Richard. 1940. The material basis of evolution. New Haven, Yale University. 436 p.

Goode, J. Paul. 1943. Goode's School Atlas. Rev. ed. New York, Rand McNally and Company. xvi, 286 p.

Heilprin, Angelo. 1892. The temperate and alpine floras of the great volcanoes of Mexico. Proc. Am. Phil. Soc. 30 (137): 4–22.

Hemsley, William. 1879–1888. Botany. *In* Godman and Salvin, Biologia Centrali-Americana, vols. 1–5.

Huxley, Julian. 1942. Evolution, the modern synthesis. New York, Harper and Brothers. 645 p.

Lanjouw, J., and Stafleu, F. A. 1954. Index Herbariorum. Part 1. The herbaria of the world. Reg. Veg. 2: 1–179.

Léon, Nicolás. 1895. Biblioteca Botánico-Mexicana. México, Oficina Tip. de la Secretaría de Fomento. 372 p.

Liebmann, Fr. 1844. Eine pflanzengeographische Schilderung des Vulkans Orizaba. Bot. Zeit. 1844: 668–672, 684–688, 699–702, 717–719, 734–736, 750–752, 767–768, 781–784, and 797–800.

Martin, Paul S., and Harrell, Byron E. 1957. The Pleistocene history of temperate biotas in Mexico and eastern United States. Ecology 38: 468–480.

Martínez, Maximino. 1944. Las plantas medicinales de México. 3d ed. Ediciones Botas, México. 630 p.

Mason, D. D., and Obenshain, S. S. 1938. A comparison of methods for the determination of soil reaction. Proc. Soil. Sci. Soc. Am. 3: 129–137.

Mayr, Ernst. 1942. Systematics and the origin of species. New York, Columbia University Press. 334 p.

Mendel, Gregor. 1865. Experiments in plant-hybridization. Trans. by Royal Horticultural Society of London and reprinted in 1933 by Harvard University Press, Cambridge, Mass., pp. 313–353.

Mooser, Federico. 1956. Consideraciones geológicas acerca de la formacíon del lago de Texcoco. Instituto Nacional de Antropología e Historia, Dirección de Prehistoria, Publicaciones 2: 9–18.

Ordóñez, Ezequiel. 1902. Le Xinantecatl ou Volcán Nevado de Toluca. Memorias de la Sociedad Científica "Antonio Alzate" 18: 83–112.

Ordóñez, Ezequiel. 1904. Las rocas arcaicas de México. Memorias de la Sociedad Científica "Antonio Alzate" 22: 315–331.

Ordóñez, Ezequiel. 1905. El Nauhcampatépetl o Cofre de Perote. Boletin de la Sociedad Geológica Mexicana 1: 151–168.

Ordóñez, Ezequiel. 1946. Principales provincias geográficas y geológicas de la Republica Mexicana. *In* Guía Explorador Minero. México, Instituto de Geología. Pp. 103–142.

Ordóñez, Ezequiel. 1947. El Volcán de Parícutin. México, Editorial "Fantasia." 181 p.

Palarea, Edgar. 1954. A nonsurgical treatment of opacities of the lens and of the cornea. Ohio Jour. Sci. 54: 114–116.

Praeger, R. Lloyd. 1921. An account of the genus *Sedum* as found in cultivation. Jour. Roy. Hort. Soc. 46: 1–314, figs. 1–185.

Quimby, Maynard Ward. 1939. The floral morphology of the Crassulaceae. Ph.D. thesis, Cornell University. 42 p., 11 pl. (typewritten).

Reko, B. 1947. Nombres botánicos del Manuscrito Badiano. Bol. Soc. Bot. México 5: 23–43.

Rush, Ethel. 1941. *Sedum confusum* Hemsley, rediscovered. Cact. Succ. Jour. 13: 146–148.

Segerstrom, Kenneth. 1950. Erosion studies at Parícutin, state of Michoacán, Mexico. Geol. Survey Bull. 965-A: 1–164.

Snedecor, George W. 1956. Statistical methods applied to experiments in agriculture and biology. 5th ed. Ames, The Iowa State College Press. xiii, 534 p.

Standley, Paul C. 1922. Trees and shrubs of Mexico (Fagaceae-Fabaceae). Cont. U.S. Nat. Herb. 23 (2): 171–515.

Standley, Paul C., and Steyermark, Julian A. 1946. Flora of Guatemala. Part IV. Fieldiana: Botany 24 (4): 1–493.

Stebbins, G. 1950. Variation and evolution in plants. New York, Columbia University Press. 643 p.

Stein, Charles. 1945. A two-sample test for a linear hypothesis whose power is independent of the variance. Ann. Math. Statistics 16 (3): 243–258.

Thomas, M., and Ranson, S. L. 1954. Physiological studies on acid metabolism in green plants. III. Further evidence of $CO_2$-fixation during dark acidification of plants showing Crassulacean acid metabolism. New Phytologist 53: 1–30.

Toscano, Ricardo, ed. 1954. Anuario del Observatorio Astronomico Nacional de Tacubaya para el año de 1955. México,

Universidad Nacional Autónoma de México.  258 p.

Vivo, Jorge.  1949.  Geografía de México.  2d ed.  México, Fondo de Cultura Económico.  325 p.

Waitz, Paul.  1910.  Observaciones geológicas acerca del Pico de Orizaba.  Bol. Soc. Geol. Mex. 7: 67–76.

Walther, Eric.  1935.  Collecting succulents in Mexico.  Cact. Succ. Jour. 6: 137–140, 149–151, 163–165, 185–189.

Walther, Eric.  1936.  Phylogeny of *Echeveria*.  Cact. Succ. Jour. 8: 82–88.

Walther, Eric.  1953.  *Sedeveria*, a new bigeneric hybrid.  Cact. Succ. Jour. 25: 20–21.

White, Sidney.  1951.  A geologic investigation of the late Pleistocene history of the volcano Popocatépetl, Mexico.  Abstract of dissertation, Syracuse University.  7 p.

White, Sidney E.  1956.  Probable substages of glaciation on Iztaccíhuatl, Mexico.  Jour. Geol. 64: 289–295.

Wilcox, Ray E.  1954.  Petrology of Parícutin Volcano, Mexico.  Geol. Survey Bull. 965-C: 1–353.

Williams, Howel.  1950.  Volcanoes of the Parícutin Region, Mexico.  Geol. Survey Bull. 965-B: 165–279.

Ximénez, Francisco.  1888.  Cuatro libros de la naturaleza y virtudes medicinales de las plantas y animales de la Nueva España.  Morelia, Imp. y Lit. en la Escuela de Artes.  300 p.

# Abbreviations and Symbols

| | |
|---|---|
| * | denotes a significant difference, the probability of difference between samples being $<.05 >.01$ |
| ** | denotes a highly significant difference, the probability of difference between samples being $<.01$ |
| $b$ | regression coefficient of one dimension per unit of another |
| cf. | cold frame |
| cult. | cultivated |
| gh. | greenhouse |
| h. | herbarium specimen |
| $n$ | number of plants studied |
| $n\text{-}obs.$ | number of observations of the characteristic in the whole sample |
| pH | logarithm of the reciprocal of the hydrogen ion concentration |
| pr. | preserved in alcohol |
| $s$ | standard deviation of the sample; unless indicated otherwise, the standard deviation among plants of the sample |
| $s_{\bar{x}}$ | standard error of the mean $(\bar{x})$ |
| $w$ | observed range of variation of the sample, the absolute extreme dimensions being cited |
| $\bar{x}$ | arithmetical mean (average) of the sample |

(See page 5 for abbreviations of names of herbaria.)

# Index

Principal entries for species and subspecies are indicated by numerals in italic type. New names of plants appear in boldface type.